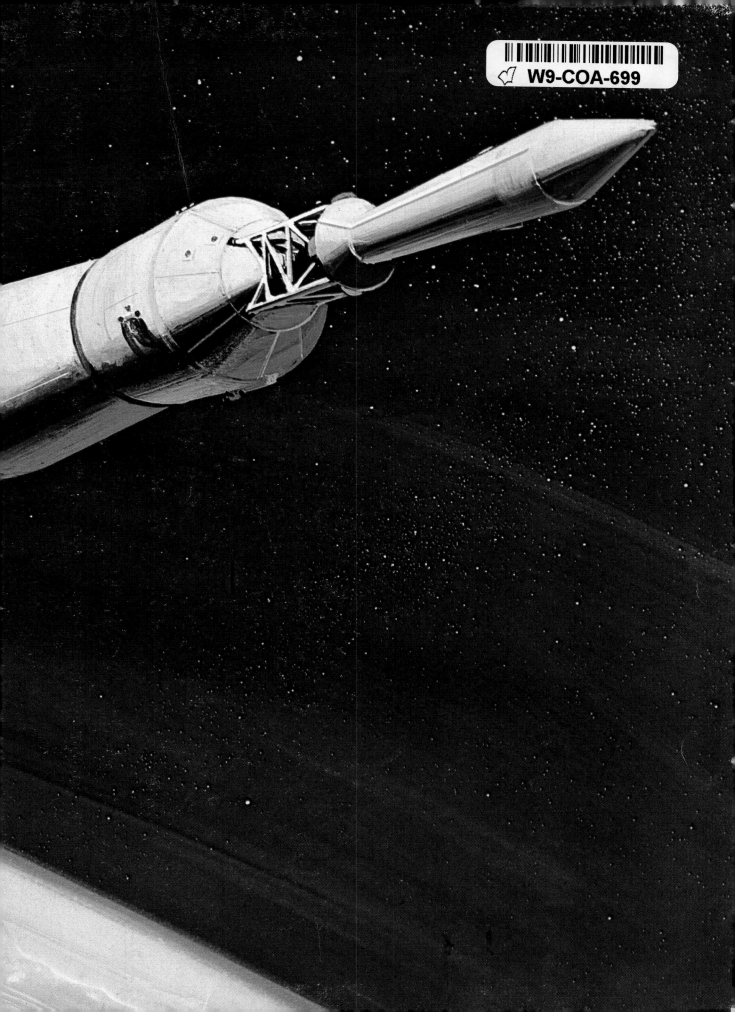

SPACE

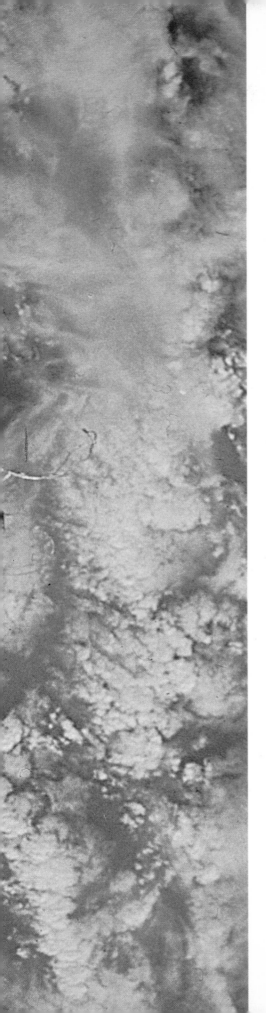

SPACE

PATRICK MOORE

with illustrations by David A. Hardy

Published for

The American Museum of Natural History

THE NATURAL HISTORY PRESS

Garden City, New York

1969

SPACE: The Story of Man's Greatest Feat of Exploration was
originally published in England by Lutterworth Press in 1968. The
Natural History Press edition is published by arrangement with
Lutterworth Press.

14

Printed in Great Britain
by Fleming & Humphreys (Baylis) Limited, Leicester
First Edition in the United States of America

Contents

Chapter   1   WORLDS IN SPACE   9

2   EARTH AND SKY   16

3   INTO SPACE?   18

4   THE DREAMERS   22

5   SPACE-GUNS AND ANTI-GRAVITY   33

6   THE UPPER AIR   39

7   THE ROCKET   52

8   THE ROCKETS RED GLARE   56

9   PIONEERS OF SPACE   60

10   THE FIRST OF THE NEW ROCKETS   65

11   THE ROCKET FLYING FIELD   71

12   PEENEMÜNDE   77

13   FROM EUROPE TO WHITE SANDS   82

14   OPERATION VANGUARD   86

15   4 OCTOBER, 1957   93

16   TRACKING THE SATELLITES   98

17   THE VAN ALLEN ZONES   103

18   SATELLITES OF MANY KINDS   110

19   MAN IN SPACE   124

20   SPACE MEETINGS AND SPACE WALKS   136

21   ROCKETS TOWARDS THE MOON   145

22   ROUND THE MOON   154

23   TOUCH DOWN ON THE MOON   163

24   MARINER TO VENUS   180

25   THE CRATERS OF MARS   189

26   EXPLORING THE SOLAR SYSTEM   198

27   INTERSTELLAR FLIGHT   204

CONCLUSION   208

Appendices   1   THE FIRST 25 EARTH SATELLITES   208

2   SOME IMPORTANT DATES IN THE HISTORY OF ROCKETRY AND SPACE RESEARCH   209

The Natural History Press, publisher for The American Museum of Natural History, is a division of Doubleday and Company, Inc. Directed by a joint editorial board made up of members of the staff of both the Museum and Doubleday, the Natural History Press publishes books and periodicals in all branches of the life and earth sciences, including anthropology and astronomy. The Natural History Press has its editorial offices at The American Museum of Natural History, Central Park West at 79th Street, New York, New York 10024, and its business offices at 501 Franklin Avenue, Garden City, New York 11530.

Acknowledgements

I have had a great deal of help in the preparation of this book. The following are among those who assisted me greatly in obtaining illustrations: F. J. Acfield, A. D. Andrews, W. M. Baxter, Henry Brinton, J. Carson, Arthur C. Clarke, P. E. Cleator, Bill Dunn, Peter Gill, Cdr. H. R. Hatfield, R.N., Dr. G. J. H. McCall, Prof. Hermann Oberth, James Paton and H. B. Ridley. I must make special mention of H. G. Miles, who read through the whole manuscript in its original form and made useful comments. I also have great pleasure in expressing my thanks to the publishers, and in particular to Michael Foxell, and to Cedric Bush and Maxine Reilly who designed the book, for all they have done.

PATRICK MOORE

SPACE RENDEZVOUS. A meeting in space between two orbiting craft. The space-ship shown here is Gemini 7; the photograph was taken by the crew of Gemini 6. This was one of several successful rendezvous operations undertaken during the U.S. Gemini programme; the programme itself was an essential stage in the larger project of sending a man to the Moon.

Worlds in Space

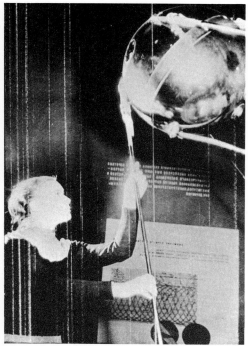

MODEL OF SPUTNIK 1. This is a life-size replica of Sputnik 1, the first artificial satellite, which was launched on 4 October 1957 and remained in orbit until January 1958. The model is shown here in the space-exhibition presented in Moscow in late 1957.

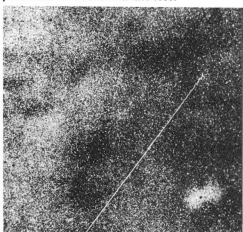

TRAIL OF SPUTNIK 1, photographed by K. Gottlieb from Australia on 8 October 1957—four days after the launching. The trail of the Sputnik is shown as a line across the photograph; the star-field is a rich area in the southern sky, and the large starry patch is the Large Magellanic Cloud, an independent galaxy well beyond the boundaries of our own system.

On the morning of 12 April 1961, the first true space-flight was made.

Few people knew much about it until later in the day. Then the official Moscow news agency announced that Major Yuri Gagarin, of the Soviet Air Force, had been sent up in a space-craft and had made a complete circuit of the Earth, landing safely in the pre-arranged spot after a total journey lasting 108 minutes. Gagarin had not been seared by radiation or battered to death by meteorites; he had remained in full control of himself; apparently he had even enjoyed the trip, nerve-racking though it must have been. And he had shown, without the shadow of a doubt, that inter-planetary flight was possible.

Scientists all over the world were not amazed or sceptical, as they had been on 4 October 1957—the day on which the Russians had launched their artificial satellite Sputnik 1, which sped round the Earth sending back its plaintive 'Bleep! bleep!' signals which were re-broadcast over every radio station in every continent. In 1957, the whole idea of space-flight was still regarded as little more than science fiction, and various eminent astonomers required some persuasion before they could bring themselves to believe that Sputnik 1 was fact instead of fancy. By Gagarin's flight of 1961, matters were very different. Indeed, most people would have been surprised if the Russians had delayed their first space-trip for very much longer.

Some time afterwards, I asked Gagarin whether he hoped to go to the Moon. He replied that if he were chosen, there would be no difficulty—and there is every reason to suppose that he might have been right but for the tragic air-crash in which he lost his life seven years later. People in general have accepted the space-travel idea, and the launching of a new artificial satellite or lunar probe has little chance of reaching the headlines of the daily newspapers; it is more likely to be found in small print somewhere beneath the latest pronouncements of dreary politicians or explosive strike-leaders.

Yet the whole picture is becoming more and more fascinating as time goes by. We no longer doubt that men will go to the Moon, and beyond; the only question is—When? On the other hand, it is also important to remember that the manned space-flight pro-gramme is only one of the many branches of space research.

We must bear in mind, too, that the range of rocket exploration is very limited indeed. So far as the twentieth century is concerned, only three worlds—the Moon, Mars and Venus—are within reasonable range; voyages to more remote planets, either by manned or unmanned vehicles, may have to wait for much longer. Also, the Solar System in which we live is a tiny part of the universe as a whole. It is difficult to improve upon the old statement that the Earth is less important in the universe, relatively speaking, than a single sand-grain in the whole Sahara Desert.

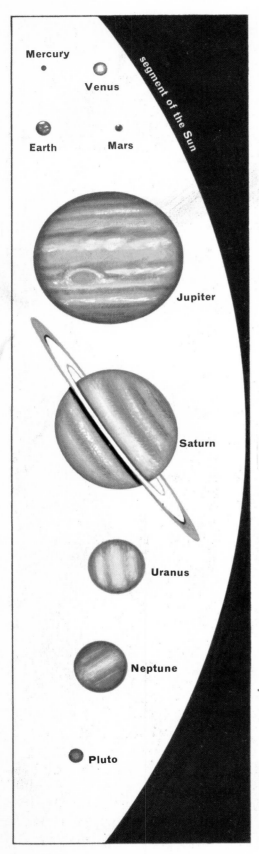

Mercury

Venus

Earth

Mars

segment of the Sun

Jupiter

Saturn

Uranus

Neptune

Pluto

RELATIVE SIZES OF THE SUN AND PLANETS. A segment of the Sun is shown, together with the nine planets; even Jupiter, the largest of the planetary family, is very small compared with the Sun.

Before tracing the history of space research, then, something must be said about the various worlds which we can see in the sky.

From our point of view, the most important of them is the Sun. Without the Sun, life on Earth could never have started, and indeed the Earth itself would not exist. If the Sun became slightly more luminous or slightly more feeble, *homo sapiens* would perish either by scorching heat or icy cold. Yet though the Sun is a globe 865,000 miles in diameter, so that it could hold more than a million bodies the size of the Earth, it is nothing more than a normal star. Many of the stars visible on any clear night are much larger, hotter and more brilliant than the Sun; they appear as tiny twinkling points only because they are so far away from us. No doubt many of them have inhabited worlds circling round them.

The distance between the Earth and the Sun is 93,000,000 miles. This may sound a long way, but on the astronomer's scale it is negligible. In fact, the newcomer to astronomy must become used to talking about vast distances and immense periods of time; we may be confident that the figures given are correct, but the human brain is too limited to appreciate what is really meant. It is all the more surprising, then, to find that our measures are so exact. There is no chance that our estimate of the Sun's distance is in error by more than a fraction of one per cent., though admittedly the accuracy is much lower when we turn to bodies beyond our own particular region of space.

The Earth is a planet—that is to say, a non-luminous body circling around the Sun. The period of revolution, or year (more scientifically termed the 'sidereal period') amounts to $365\frac{1}{4}$ days, and the velocity of motion is about $18\frac{1}{2}$ miles per second, or 66,000 m.p.h. We are not conscious of this movement, but we are in fact being whirled through space at a tremendous rate. The Earth keeps moving in a stable path, or 'orbit', simply because there is nothing to stop it.

There are eight other planets, two of them closer to the Sun than we are, while the others are further out. The diagram shows a plan of the Solar System, but it is not easy to draw all the orbits to the same scale, because the System covers a vast area. Mercury, the innermost of the planets, moves at a mean distance of only 36,000,000 miles from the Sun; Neptune, the outermost of the main planets, lies at a distance of over 2,790,000,000 miles, while Pluto, a peculiar little world on the fringe of the System, has an orbit which carries it out even further. But even a casual glance shows that the Solar System is divided into two parts. There are four inner planets: Mercury, Venus, the Earth and Mars, all of which are relatively small and all of which are solid, though in other respects they are totally unlike each other. Then comes a wide gap, populated by a swarm of miniature worlds known as the asteroids or minor planets, followed by the four widely-spaced giants Jupiter, Saturn, Uranus and Neptune.

On this scale, incidentally, the orbits have to be shown as circles. To be accurate, they are not circles, but ellipses. The conventional way to draw an ellipse is to fasten two pins into a board and stretch a thread between them, leaving a certain amount of slack, after which a pencil is put into the loop and a curve traced out. The curve will be an ellipse, with the two pins representing

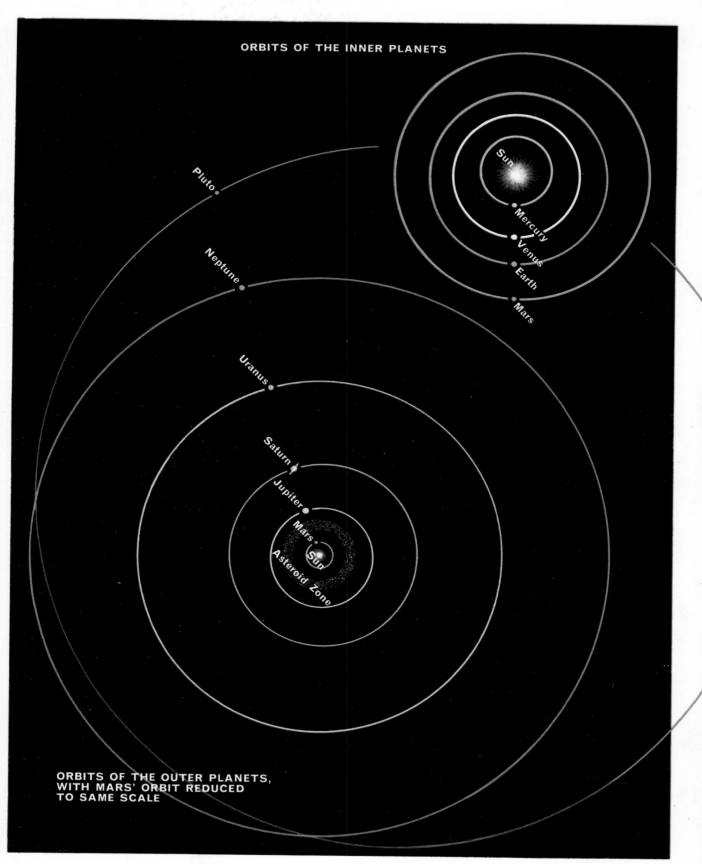

ORBITS OF THE INNER PLANETS

Sun

Mercury
Venus
Earth
Mars

Pluto

Neptune

Uranus

Saturn

Jupiter

Mars
Sun
Asteroid Zone

ORBITS OF THE OUTER PLANETS,
WITH MARS' ORBIT REDUCED
TO SAME SCALE

PLAN VIEW OF THE SOLAR SYSTEM.

the 'foci'. If the foci are wide apart, the ellipse will be of high eccentricity (long and narrow), while if the foci are close together the ellipse will be almost circular. A perfect circle is produced if the two pins coincide; but no celestial body is likely to have an exactly circular orbit, though those of the planets, apart from Pluto, are not very different from circles.

Any space-journey is bound to be dangerous, and if it takes a long time there are various so-called minor problems, such as air and water supply, which turn out to be anything but minor. This means that in the foreseeable future, we must confine our attention to the nearest of the planets. It may be useful to give a table, showing some useful facts which will have to be borne in mind:

Planet	Minimum distance from Earth, in millions of miles	Sidereal period	Diameter in miles
Mercury	48	88 days	2,900
Venus	24	225 days	7,700
Earth	—	365 days	7,926
Mars	34	687 days	4,200
Jupiter	364	$11\frac{3}{4}$ years	88,700
Saturn	740	$29\frac{1}{2}$ years	75,100
Uranus	1,604	84 years	29,300
Neptune	2,674	$164\frac{3}{4}$ years	27,700
Pluto	2,671	$247\frac{3}{4}$ years	8,000 ?

These values have been 'rounded off', and, in passing, the distance of Pluto as given here is not a misprint; when at its closest it really can approach nearer to us than Neptune, though for most of its orbit it is much more remote. In any case, it is much too early for us to talk about space-voyages of more than a 100,000,000 miles at most. This leaves us with only three planets, and in fact only Venus and Mars are within reasonable range. Actually, the situation is even more difficult than might appear from the table, because the planets, like the Earth, go round the Sun—and it is not often that they are at their minimum distances. Even Venus may recede to more than 160,000,000 miles from the Earth when it is on the far side of the Sun.

However, there is one body which is much closer to us, and which automatically becomes our first target. This is the Moon, which is officially regarded as the Earth's satellite, though in many ways it would be better to think of the Earth–Moon system as a double planet. The Moon accompanies us in our never-ending journey round the Sun and its distance from us is a mere 239,000 miles, which is equivalent to nearly ten times round the Earth's equator. A modern rocket can reach the Moon in a few days, whereas a voyage to Venus or Mars is bound to take several months.

Other planets have satellites of their own; Mars has two (both very small), Jupiter twelve, Saturn ten, Uranus five and Neptune two, while Mercury, Venus and Pluto do not seem to have any.

Some of these satellites may be reached eventually, though it seems most unlikely that a rocket will ever be able to land upon any of the giant planets themselves. Jupiter, Saturn, Uranus and Neptune are totally unlike the Earth, and are made up of gas, so that they have no visible solid surfaces. Moreover, they are so far from the Sun that they are intensely cold.

Of the junior members of the Solar System, particular mention should be made of the comets and meteors. A comet is not a solid, rocky body; it is made up of large numbers of tiny particles surrounded by an envelope of thin gas, sometimes with a long tail. It moves round the Sun, but usually in a very eccentric orbit. Brilliant comets have immensely long periods, so that they come into view for only a few weeks or months every few thousands of years, and obviously they cannot be predicted. Smaller comets, too faint to be seen with the naked eye, may have much shorter periods, so that they are seen regularly; one old friend, Encke's Comet, completes its journey every $3\frac{1}{3}$ years, and has now been seen at almost fifty different returns. The only bright comet with a period of less than a century is Halley's, which was last bright in 1910, and which will be back once more in 1986.

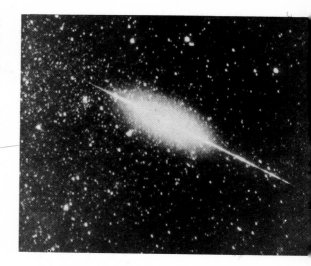

EXPLODING METEOR, photographed by H. B. Ridley. The meteor itself can have been no larger than a grain of rice.

Meteors are extremely small bodies, usually no larger than grains of sand, moving round the Sun. In the ordinary way they are too faint to be seen, but if a meteor enters the Earth's upper atmosphere it rubs against the air-particles and becomes heated by friction, destroying itself in the streak of luminosity which we call a shooting-star. (Note that a meteor flashes across the sky and is gone in a second or two, whereas a comet does not shift obviously.) Because meteors are very plentiful, it used to be thought that a space-ship incautious enough to venture above the dense part of the Earth's atmosphere would be destroyed by a sort of cosmical bombardment. Like various other bogeys, this danger has proved to be much less than had been feared, though the meteor hazard cannot be neglected completely. Larger bodies or meteorites, which can survive the complete drop to the ground and may even produce craters, would certainly be able to destroy a space-craft, but the risks of a fatal collision do not appear to be high. It is thought that there is no essential difference between a large meteorite and a small asteroid.

All these bodies—the planets, satellites, asteroids, comets and meteors—belong to the Sun's family, or Solar System. Since the Solar System is our home, we naturally tend to regard it as important, but appearances are deceptive. When we look further out into space, it does not take long for us to realize how insignificant we really are.

The stars are suns. Like our Sun, they are huge globes of hot gas, and they shine by their own light, whereas the Moon and planets depend entirely upon light reflected from the Sun. They are, of course, very remote; even the nearest of them lies at a distance of more than 24,000,000,000,000 miles, so that no telescopes yet built can show them as anything more than points of light.

When measuring distances of this kind, the ordinary miles becomes too short to be a convenient unit, just as it would be clumsy to measure the distance between London and New York in inches or centimetres. Luckily, there is a better unit to hand. Light moves at a velocity of 186,000 miles per second, so that in a year it covers

COMET IKEYA-SEKI OF 1965, photographed by A. D. Andrews from the Boyden Observatory in Africa. This was a relatively bright comet, and was very spectacular for a few evenings as seen from some parts of the world, though from Europe it was badly placed in the sky, and never became visible to the naked eye.

about 5,880,000,000,000 or almost six million million miles—a distance which is known as the light-year. On this reckoning, the nearest star beyond the Sun is 4.2 light-years away.

It is painfully clear that there are no imminent prospects of interstellar travel. Whether it will ever be achieved is a matter for debate; personally, I doubt it. Even if it were possible to make a rocket move at the velocity of light, a journey to the nearest star and back would still take over eight years. Moving at speeds which we may regard as practicable, the voyage would take millions of years. This may be labouring the obvious, but it does seem important to stress that our rocket range is confined to the Solar System. If we are to go further, then we must develop means of travel about which we know nothing at the present time.

The star-system or Galaxy contains about 100,000 million stars, arranged in a form which may be described scientifically as resembling a double-convex lens, or unscientifically as being rather like two fried eggs clapped together back to back. It is also known that the Galaxy has a spiral structure, reminding one of a Catherine-wheel. Since the Solar System lies inside the Galaxy, the actual arrangement of the stars is difficult to study, because we cannot obtain an overall view; but far away in space we can see other galaxies, many of which have the same spiral form.

The nearest of these galaxies visible to the naked eye from Britain

THE ROSSE 72-INCH REFLECTOR, photographed by the author in 1968. This great telescope, completed in 1845, was once the largest in the world. It fell into disuse after the first decade of the 20th century; the tube, shown here, is at Birr Castle. The mirror is at the Science Museum, London.

(below) OBSERVING WITH THE ROSSE REFLECTOR. This painting, from the original hanging in Birr Castle, shows the method of using the Rosse reflector. The mounting was difficult to adjust, and the observer was forced to do some rather hazardous climbing up ladders!

or North America is the Great Spiral in Andromeda, which shows up as a dim, misty patch. Photographs of it taken with giant telescopes show it to be a spiral system even larger than our own, and its distance has been measured, fairly accurately, as a little over 2,000,000 light-years. This means that the light now reaching us started on its journey more than 2,000,000 years ago, before men appeared on Earth. Yet this is only the beginning; we know of galaxies whose light has been thousands of millions of years on its way. To make the situation even more fantastic, the galaxies are racing away from us at high speeds, amounting in some cases to well over 100,000 miles every second. The whole universe seems to be in a state of expansion.

Ideas of this kind are not easy to appreciate. One has to emulate Lewis Carroll's White Queen, who made a habit of believing at least six impossible things before breakfast every day. But though many errors may remain, it does look as though modern astronomy is on the right track—and certainly we know much too much to think that the Earth is a genuinely important body.

Until a few years ago, professional astronomers paid very little attention to our nearest neighbours, the Moon and planets. Their main concern was with the remote stars and star-systems, which are so much more significant. The world's great telescopes were used to study objects far beyond the Solar System, and less important matters, such as mapping the surface of the Moon, were left mainly to amateurs, who rose nobly to the challenge. But when the rockets started to fly, there was a change of view. By now there is no hard and sharp boundary between the ancient science of astronomy and the new science of astronautics or space research; it is impossible to decide where the one leaves off and the other begins.

Yet we must never forget that no man-made rocket can venture far on the astronomical scale. Perhaps a single comparison will drive the point home. Suppose that we represent the distance between the Sun and the nearest star as four miles; then how far from the Sun must we put the Earth? The answer is—one inch; and no manned rocket has yet travelled further than a distance which on this scale would be represented by a tiny fraction of a millimetre. In the future we may do better, but for the moment it is enough to say that we have made a reasonably good start.

COMET AREND-ROLAND, 1957. This was one of the brighter comets of modern times, and was clearly visible with the naked eye. It was notable for its unique "spike", or reverse tail. This is probably the best photograph of it, taken on 25 April 1957 by E. M. Lindsay with the 12/18in. Schmidt telescope at Armagh Observatory.

THE SHAPE OF THE GALAXY. The Galaxy is a flattened system; along the main plane there is considerable dark obscuring matter. Outside the main system are small numbers of stars together with the globular clusters.

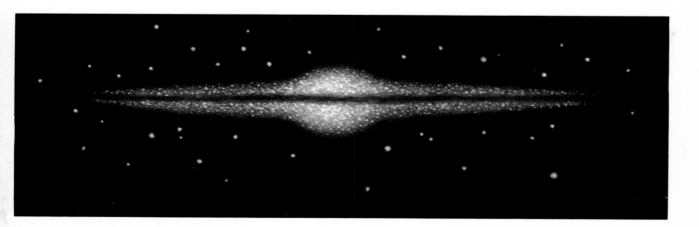

Chapter 2

Earth and Sky

Five hundred years before the time of Christ, the Greek philosopher Heraclitus was teaching that the Sun and Moon must each have a diameter of about one foot. Since it would be difficult to achieve a landing upon a remote body no larger than a tea-tray, Heraclitus can have had no inward dream of a lunar voyage; but he was one of the leading thinkers of his time. Man's ideas about the nature of the universe were still in a very primitive state.

Astronomy is generally regarded as the oldest of all the sciences, but at first it was purely observational. As civilizations developed, the skies were studied and the stars charted; but originally the Earth was thought to be flat, and to lie at rest in the centre of the universe. This was natural enough, and the ancients could not possibly tell that the so-called 'fixed stars' are really moving through space at all sorts of speeds in all sorts of directions; after all, the constellation patterns seem to all intents and purposes unchanging, and the Great Bear that we see today is virtually the same as the pattern which must have been seen by the builders of the Pyramids. It was only later that men came to realize that the stars appear more or less stationary, in respect to each other, simply because they are so far away from us.

Astronomy entered a new phase with the rise of Greek philosophy. It became clear that the Earth is a globe, and Eratosthenes of Cyrene, whose dates are given as 276 to 196 B.C., measured the size of the world with surprising accuracy. Moreover, the Greeks were well aware that the planets are quite different in nature from the stars.

The five naked-eye planets (Mercury, Venus, Mars, Jupiter and Saturn) were given special attention. The Greeks reasoned, quite correctly, that they must be a great deal nearer than the stars, which is why they wander about the sky instead of being fixed; some of the Greek philosophers may even have supposed that the planets are worlds of considerable size, in which case they might presumably be inhabited. The Sun and Moon, too, were of special interest, and gradually it became known that the Sun at least is much larger than the Earth. Hipparchus of Nicæa, who was a particularly accurate observer and who drew up an excellent star-catalogue about 150 B.C., believed that the Sun's diameter was about twelve times that of the Earth, and its distance was given as at least 8,000,000 miles. Both these estimates are much too low, but Hipparchus' values for the size and distance of the Moon were much closer to the truth. At least he knew that the universe is an extremely large place.

The great mistake, of course, was in supposing that the Earth must lie in the centre of the universe, with all other bodies moving round it. This idea had not passed unchallenged, and one or two of the Greek philosophers had been bold enough to suggest that the Earth travels round the Sun; but unorthodox views of this sort were not popular, and never took root. (Later, during the Christian

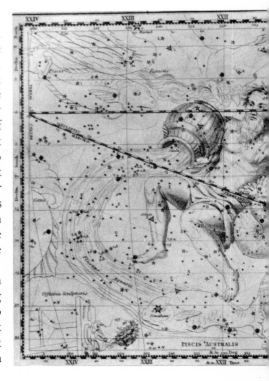

16

**MEDIÆVAL REPRE-
SENTATION OF THE
UNIVERSE, from an old
woodcut.**

**THE FIGURE OF
AQUARIUS, THE
WATER-BEARER, from an
old star map.** The constellation figures are pictur-
esque, even if few of the
groups bear any resem-
blance to the objects they
are meant to represent!
Aquarius is in fact a faint
and ill-defined constellation; it lies in the Zodiac,
and is one of the original 48
constellations listed by
Ptolemy about A.D. 150.
Other groups shown here
include Capricornus, the
Sea-Goat, and Piscis Aust-
rinus, the Southern Fish.
Note the constellation of
the Balloon, which has
been dropped from modern
star-maps.

era, the Church showed itself bitterly opposed to the idea of a
moving Earth, and it was only during the seventeenth century that
the matter was finally settled.)

Moreover, there were other factors to be taken into account.
Originally the Sun and Moon had been regarded as gods, and even
when astronomy had become a real science it was still thought that
signs in the sky must indicate divine displeasure. Comets were particularly feared, and it is worth quoting Pliny, the Roman writer
who lost his life during the disastrous eruption of Mount Vesuvius
in A.D. 79. Pliny wrote: 'We have in the war between Cæsar and
Pompey an example of the terrible effects which follow the
apparition of a comet . . . that fearful star which overthrows the
powers of the Earth, showing its terrible locks.' It is amusing,
though hardly profitable, to speculate as to what Pliny would have
said had he been told that scientists of the twentieth century would
be making serious plans to send a space-probe toward a comet in
order to find out what materials are present there.

By Pliny's time the political greatness of Greece had decayed,
but Greek science still flourished, and it reached its peak with the
work of Ptolemy—or, to give him his proper name, Claudius
Ptolemæus. We know nothing about Ptolemy's life or personality,
but we do know that he lived and worked in Alexandria between
about A.D. 120 and 180. He may have been of Egyptian blood, but
in outlook he was purely Greek, and he wrote a major book which
is an invaluable summary of the state of science at the time. The
original has been lost, but the book has come down to us by way
of its Arab translation, the *Almagest*.

To Ptolemy, the Earth was a central globe. Round it moved the
Moon, Sun and planets, with the star-sphere at a much greater
distance. Since the circle was regarded as the perfect form, and
nothing short of perfection could be allowed in the sky, Ptolemy
had to suppose that the orbits of the planets were circular; since
this did not fit in with the observations, he adopted a system
according to which each planet moved in a small circle or epicycle,
the centre of which itself moved round the Earth in a perfect
circle. The theory—always known as the Ptolemaic, though
Ptolemy himself did not invent it—was hopelessly clumsy and
artificial, but it did agree with the facts as they were then known,
and it remained almost unchallenged for the next fourteen
centuries.

This book is not a history of astronomy, but I have felt justified
in saying something about Greek ideas, because it was at this
period that the first serious thoughts about space-travel were
written down. They could not have been produced earlier, because
primitive peoples had no idea about the nature or scale of the
universe; yet as soon as men became aware that there are other
worlds, dreams of reaching them were bound to follow. It is
significant that Lucian of Samosata, author of what may be
termed the first science-fiction novel, was contemporary with
Ptolemy.

Of course the first space-travel writings were fanciful, but they
marked the beginnings of what we now call astronautics. More
than 3,000 years separated Ptolemy from the star-gazers of
Ancient Egypt; but now, less than 2,000 years after Ptolemy's
death, man-made rockets have already started to fly to the Moon.

Chapter 3

Into Space?

Any would-be space-traveller must start by making up his mind where he wants to go. So far as the Greeks were concerned, there could be only one logical choice: the Moon, which they knew to be the nearest body in the sky. Their reasoning was sound enough, and it is still valid today. The Moon must be our first target. It has virtually no atmosphere, and is unfriendly in every way; but it is the Earth's companion in space, and always stays close to us.

The Greeks realized that the Moon is very close on the astronomical distance-scale, but at first they knew nothing about its nature. Heraclitus, as we have seen, taught that it is only one foot in diameter. At about the same time, Xenophanes of Colophon wrote that 'there are many suns and moons according to the regions, divisions and zones of the earth, and at certain times the disk falls on some division of the earth not inhabited by us, and thus when, as it were, stepping where there is void, exhibits eclipse'. (It may be added that Xenophanes also thought the Earth to be flat, with the upper side touching the air and the lower side extending without limit.) Yet not so very long afterwards, Anaxagoras of Clazomenæ, whose life extended from about 500 to 428 B.C., was claiming that the Moon has plains, mountains and ravines upon its surface. Gradually, the idea of the Moon as a sort of second Earth took root; and when its size and distance were measured with reasonable accuracy, the scene was set for the first discussion of a lunar voyage.

One of the early books dealing solely with the Moon was a long, rambling and apparently incomplete essay by Plutarch, the most famous of Greek biographical writers, who lived during the first century A.D.—that is to say, after the time of Hipparchus but before that of Ptolemy. His essay, *De Facie in Orbe Lunæ* (On the Face in the Orb of the Moon) seems to have been completed about A.D. 70, and has since been translated into almost every language. Yet Plutarch was not primarily a scientist; his fame rests mainly upon his biographical works, and he may not have taken his Moon essay very seriously. Part of it seems to be an attempt to sum up what was then known about the Moon, while the rest is pure fantasy. The essay is in dialogue form, and consists of an imaginary conversation between eight friends.

The markings on the Moon's surface can be seen with the naked eye, and it has always been said that they give the vague impression of a human face; who has not heard of the Man in the Moon? Plutarch's dialogue begins with two suggestions – first that the lunar markings are due to defects in our own eyes, and secondly that they are nothing more than reflections from Earth. Having disposed of both these ideas, Plutarch goes on to more scientific theories. The Moon, he says, contains 'deep places and ravines'; and 'just as our Earth has great depressions, so she [the Moon] is opened up by great depths and clefts containing water or dark air, which the light of the Sun does not penetrate or touch'.

THE FULL MOON. It has been said that the outlines of the bright and dark areas recall 'the Man in the Moon', and even Plutarch wrote about 'the face' there, but with any optical aid the Old Man vanishes in a mass of detail.

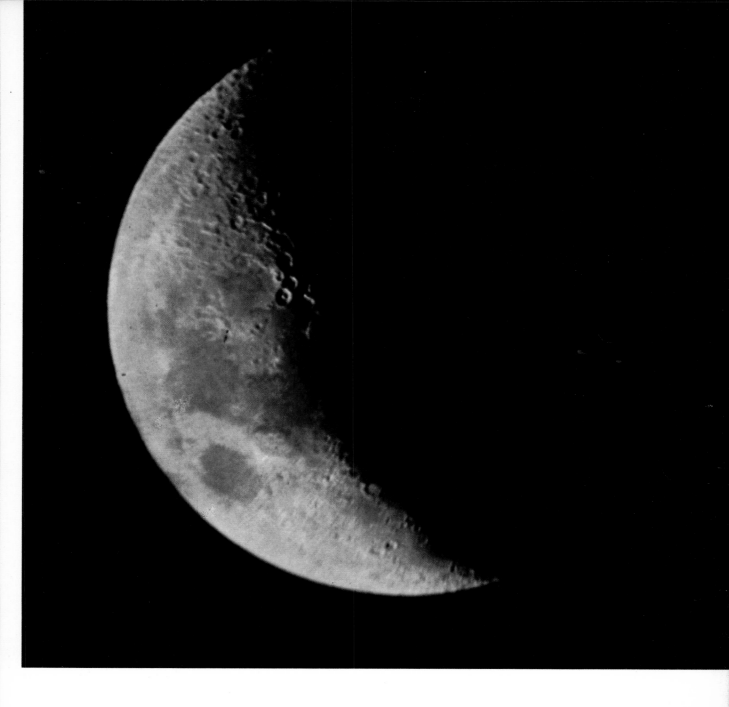

COLOUR PHOTOGRAPH OF THE MOON, taken in 1964 by Henry Brinton with his 12in. reflector at Selsey. The well-defined 'sea' of the Mare Crisium, or Sea of Crises, is seen toward the limb, rather below centre. Note also the great Theophilus group of craters, on the terminator slightly above centre; Theophilus, which has a prominent central mountain, is 64 miles in diameter.

In fact, Plutarch regarded the Moon as an earthy body. Since he accepted Hipparchus' figures for its size and distance, his views were not so very far removed from those of today, except that we now know the Moon to be airless and waterless and we can hardly accept Plutarch's speculation that the lunar world may be a dwelling-place for 'spirits'. Whether Plutarch really believed in Moon-spirits, or whether he simply used his essay as a means of putting forward his personal philosophy, need not concern us at the moment, but one of his conclusions is certainly worth quoting.

During the dialogue, one of his characters states that 'the Moon has a security against falling in her very motion and the swing of her revolution, just as objects put in slings are prevented from falling by the circular whirl; for everything is carried along by the motion natural to it if it is not deflected by anything else. The Moon is not carried down by her weight, because her natural tendency is frustrated by her revolution.' In other words, the Moon does not fall upon the Earth for the simple reason that it is moving round us—and this, after all, is what Newton proved mathematically more than fifteen centuries later.

Consider a stone being whirled round on the end of a string. If the movement stops, the stone will fall; but if the string is kept taut, and the circular movement continues, the stone will remain in a stable path. This is precisely what happens with the Moon, but there is no need to give any regular 'push', any more than we need give power to the Earth in order to make it keep on travelling round the Sun. More will be said about this later on, when we come to discuss the problems of weightlessness. For the moment, it is enough to say that Plutarch evidently had some very sound ideas about the force of gravity, even if he were reasoning mainly by instinct.

Less than a hundred years after Plutarch came Lucian of Samosata, who is usually regarded as the first of all science-fiction writers. He was born in Asia Minor about or shortly before A.D. 120, and became one of the most brilliant satirists of the ancient world; he combined a cool brain with a gift for fluent, easy writing and a strong sense of humour. Nowadays he is best remembered for his *True History*, which, as he takes care to point out, is so named because it is made up of nothing but lies from beginning to end.

In the story, Lucian and fifty companions set out upon a voyage toward the then-unknown Western Ocean. Passing through the Pillars of Hercules, now known to us as the Straits of Gibraltar, the ship was caught up in a whirlwind, which 'spun the boat about, raised her into the air about 300 furlongs and did not let her down into the sea again; but while she was hung up aloft a wind struck her sails and drove her ahead with bellying canvas. For seven days and seven nights we sailed in the air, and on the eighth day we saw a great country in it, resembling an island, bright and round and shining with a great light.' The airborne sailors had reached the Moon.

Their arrival caused something of a stir. Almost at once they came upon some warriors mounted upon huge birds; each bird had three heads, and was of immense size. The bewildered Earthmen were arrested and brought before Endymion, the King of the Moon, who told him that he was about to give battle to the King of the Sun. There had been a dispute over the colonization of the planet Venus, and a full-scale war was inevitable. Endymion's colonists had been halted by an army of Ant Dragoons, 'large beasts with wings' at least 200 feet long, and the lunar forces were being made ready for attack. Lucian and his sailors promised their support, and were allotted 'horse vultures' for their own use.

The ensuing battle, described in considerable detail, seems to be the first account of an interplanetary war. Endymion's army included 60,000,000 men, 80,000 horse-vulture troops, and 20,000 soldiers mounted upon birds with grass-like plumage and wings like lettuce-leaves, to say nothing of 30,000 men riding fleas as large as elephants. On the enemy side there were the Ant Dragoons together with 'stalk-mushroom' troops, using mushrooms for shields

and stalks of asparagus for spears, together with dog-faced men who had been sent by the inhabitants of the Dog-Star, Sirius. At first the Moon-forces were successful, but eventually they were routed by the arrival of 'Cloud-Centaurs', half-horse and half-men, who fell upon Endymion's armies and scattered them. Peace was concluded, and the sailors from Earth were free to study the strange world in which they had arrived.

There was much to see, wrote Lucian. The Moon-men lived on roast frogs; every man had a small beard below his knee, and his eyes were removable, so that they could be taken out and stored in a safe place when necessary. Anything impure or unclean was abhorrent, and when a Moon-man died he simply dissolved into smoke. There were even some intelligent beings who were hatched from acorns, and grew like trees . . .

After seven days the sailors decided that it was time to return home, and Endymion agreed, though with reluctance. Lucian departed, laden with presents and with an escort of horse-vultures; on the way back he paid a flying visit to the colony on Venus, which had just been started. Eventually the ship landed back on Earth, coming down in the ocean and being swallowed by an immense sea-serpent over a hundred miles long. After some amazing adventures in the creature's belly, the sailors came out by way of its teeth—and so on; the story ends rather suddenly, and though Lucian promised a sequel he apparently never wrote it.

There is no science in the *True History*. Obviously the tale was intended to be nothing more than a satirical frolic, and Lucian made no attempt to keep to the astronomical facts even as he knew them. The same is true of his other lunar story, *Icaromenippus*, in which the hero makes himself artificial wings and flies into space, only to be struck down by the gods on Olympus who resent his attempt to invade their dominions. One is reminded both of the old legend of Icarus, who flew sunward with the aid of wax wings but fell to his death when the wax melted, and of the myth of Bellerophon, who flew heavenward on the back of the winged horse Pegasus and was unceremoniously struck down with a thunderbolt.

The importance of Lucian's stories is that they show, quite unmistakably, that the idea of flying to the Moon had taken hold of men's imagination. So long as the Earth was taken to be the centre of the universe, however, no properly scientific plan could be put forward—even if Lucian had had any wish to do so, which in point of fact he had not.

For the moment, this was more or less the end of speculation of any kind. When Lucian died, about A.D. 180 (the same time as Ptolemy), the ancient world was almost at an end. The glory of Greece lay in the past, and the immense Roman Empire was showing signs of cracking; indeed, the last great emperor, Marcus Aurelius, also died in A.D. 180. Science came to a virtual halt, and the Dark Ages descended upon Europe. For century after century, men could do no more than concern themselves with their own immediate problems, and the Moon shone down unheeded.

In Lucian's *True History*, the mariners were hurled on to the Moon by the action of a huge waterspout.

Chapter 4

The Dreamers

The Dark Ages lasted for a surprisingly long time. From an intellectual point of view Europe, at least, was asleep, and science was at a complete standstill. It was particularly unfortunate that many of the old Greek books had been lost. There had been a great library at Alexandria, once in the care of Eratosthenes—the first man to measure the size of the Earth—but after the general decline, the Alexandrian Library was scattered. Even Hipparchus' original star-catalogue was lost. Yet by a lucky chance, the most important of all the books survived, and a copy of it found its way to Baghdad during the eighth century. This was Ptolemy's great work, which (as referred to above) was translated into Arabic and is always known to us as the *Almagest*.

It was the Arabs who took the lead in the re-birth of astronomy. True, there was no real distinction between genuine astronomy and the naïve pseudo-science of astrology, which may be called the superstition of the sky, and which tries to link the positions of the planets with human characters and destinies. In mediæval times astrology was taken very seriously indeed, and there are still people who believe in it (just as there are still people who believe the Earth to be flat). Yet the Arab observers were extremely skilful, and they drew up star-catalogues which were better than

THE TWO 'SYSTEMS OF THE WORLD', by the Ptolemaic and the Copernicus' system.

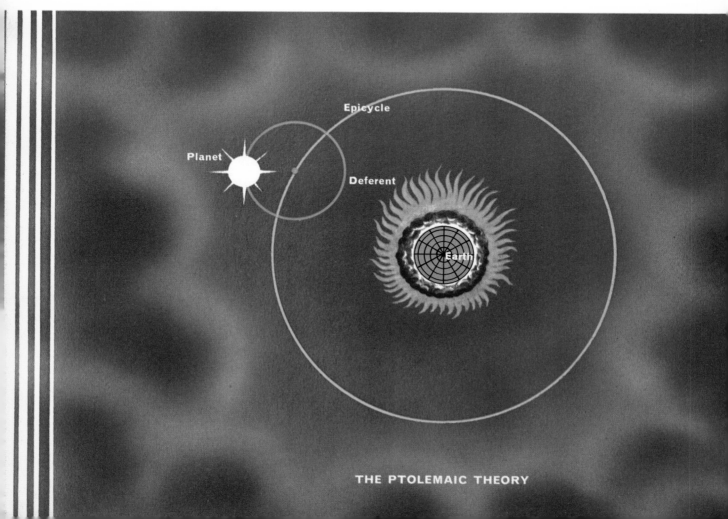

Epicycle

Planet

Deferent

Earth

THE PTOLEMAIC THEORY

Ptolemy's. For several centuries following A.D. 800, Baghdad was the main astronomical centre of the world.

Arab astronomy does not concern us here, but one of their ideas must certainly be mentioned. They believed that the Earth's atmosphere thins out with increasing height above the ground, and ends at an altitude of about 1,000 miles, instead of filling the whole of the universe. Of course there was no proof, but the estimate was reasonably good, and was certainly on the right lines. We now know that though most of the atmosphere is concentrated within a layer less than ten miles above the ground, definite traces linger on up to well over 1,000 miles.

After the Arabs, scientific interest was revived in Europe. The awakening was slow to come, but after the sixteenth century there were striking developments, and many of the old theories were first challenged and then destroyed. The most important of these theories was the Ptolemaic System, according to which the Sun and all other bodies move round the Earth. In 1543 a Polish canon, Copernicus, published his famous book *De Revolutionibus Orbium Cœlestium* ("Concerning the Revolutions of the Celestial Orbs"), in which he took the bold step of removing the Earth from its proud central position and putting the Sun there instead. In fact, he went back to an ancient theory put forward in Greek times by the enlightened philosopher Aristarchus. However, Copernicus was wise enough to withhold publication until the last weeks of his life, simply because he knew that the Church would be bitterly hostile. To suggest that our world might not be the supreme body of the universe was obvious heresy, and would strike at the heart of the Catholic doctrine.

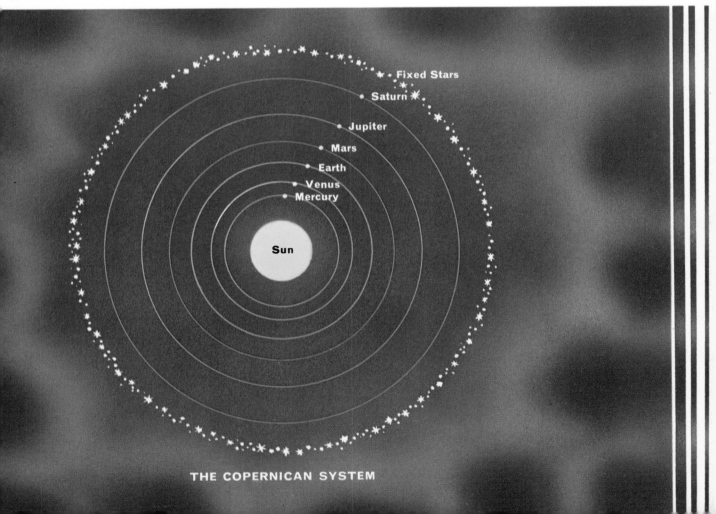

THE COPERNICAN SYSTEM

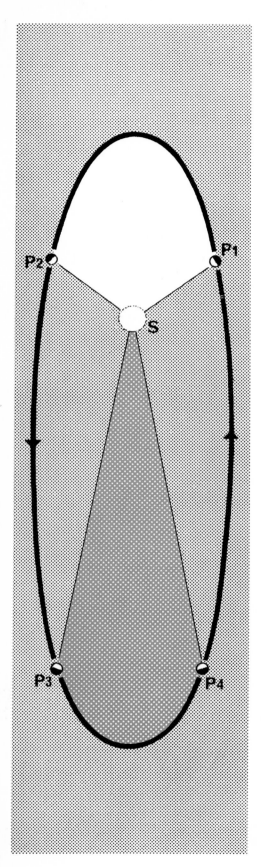

Copernicus' fears were well-founded, and some of his followers were savagely persecuted (one, Giordano Bruno, was burned at the stake in Rome in 1600, though his defence of the Copernican theory was only one of his many sins in the eyes of the Church). The change-over to the new system took something like a hundred years, and was not completed until the work of Newton during the last part of the seventeenth century. However, by that time telescopic astronomy had begun. Telescopes were invented about 1608, and the great Italian scientist Galileo was one of the first to apply them to the sky. What he saw there made him convinced that Copernicus had been right and Ptolemy wrong, and he never changed his opinion, though he too was called before the Roman Inquisition and made to give a public recantation of his 'heresy'.

The original difficulty with the Ptolemaic system had been that the planets obstinately refused to move as they ought to have done. Copernicus still believed in perfectly circular orbits, and he was even reduced to bringing back the clumsy 'small circles' or epicycles, so that his plan for the Solar System was still very wide of the mark even though he had taken the essential first step. The problem was finally solved by a German mathematician, Johannes Kepler, who was one of the greatest theoretical astronomers of his age, and who is of special interest to us here because he also produced a story about a Moon-voyage.

Kepler was born in 1571, and became a university lecturer. In 1600 – the same year that Bruno met his death – Kepler went to Prague, in what is now Czechoslovakia, to act as assistant to the Danish astronomer Tycho Brahe, who had left his native country after a quarrel with the Court authorities and had become Imperial Mathematician to the Holy Roman Emperor, a curious, moody ruler named Rudolph II. During the twenty years that Tycho had spent at his observatory in Denmark, he had made many thousands of accurate observations of the positions of the planets, particularly Mars. When he died, in 1601, the observations came into Kepler's hands, and Kepler used them well.

From the outset Kepler had complete faith in the accuracy of the measures made by Tycho, and, try as he might, he could not make the observations of Mars agree with a perfectly circular orbit. After years of work, he found the answer. Mars does indeed move round the Sun, but it travels in an ellipse instead of a circle, with the Sun occupying one of the foci of the ellipse. Kepler was satisfied, and realized that the same must also be true of the other planets, including the Earth. He was then able to draw up the three famous Laws of Planetary Motion which are still known by his name. The first two were published in 1609, and the third appeared ten years later.

Kepler's Laws are of vital importance in any discussion of astronautics, ancient or modern, so that it is worth giving them in full. They state that:

1. A planet moves round the Sun in an ellipse, with the Sun occupying one of the foci of the ellipse; the other focus is empty.
2. The radius vector sweeps out equal areas in equal times.
3. The square of the sidereal period is proportional to the cube of the planet's mean distance from the Sun.

KEPLER'S SECOND LAW. For the sake of clarity, the orbit given here is shown as much more eccentric than that of any planet, and is much more like the orbit of a comet.

The First Law is quite straightforward. In the Second Law, the term 'radius vector' means 'the imaginary line joining the centre of the planet to the centre of the Sun', and the effect of the Law is that a planet moves at its fastest when it is closest-in. The diagram will make the situation clear. The planet is assumed to move from P1 to P2 in the same time that it takes to move from P3 to P4, with S representing the Sun; then the sector P1SP2 must be equal in area to P3SP4. When the planet is approaching its perihelion, or closest point to the Sun, it speeds up; as it nears its furthest point, or aphelion, it slows down.

The Third Law is just as significant, since it provides a link between the planet's mean distance from the Sun and the period which is taken for the planet to complete one journey. Therefore, when the revolution period is known, the mean distance from the Sun, compared with that of the Earth, can be worked out.

This particular problem can also be approached 'the wrong way round', so to speak. Find the actual distance of a planet in miles, and it becomes possible to work out the Earth–Sun distance, or astronomical unit. Modern space-research methods have given a very precise result. Kepler was not so successful, but at least he believed that the Sun is some 14,000,000 miles from us, which was a marked improvement on the older estimates. In 1672 an Italian astronomer, Cassini, used the same method with better results, and arrived at an Earth–Sun distance of 86,000,000 miles, which is within ten per cent. of the correct figure.

Incidentally, it is obvious that a close-in planet will move faster than a planet which is further from the Sun. Mercury, the innermost of the planets, will have the greatest velocity in its orbit; Venus, Earth, Mars and the rest will be progressively slower. I shall have much more to say about this when we come to consider transfer orbits in space-flight, which may be said to be based entirely upon Kepler's principles.

Science owes a great debt to Kepler. The Ptolemaic theory was largely discredited after the Laws were published, even though it took some time to die. On the other hand, Kepler had some strange views of his own. He practised astrology (though it is doubtful whether he believed in it; he had to eke out his meagre salary as Imperial Mathematician, a position he had inherited from Tycho Brahe), and he was certainly a mystic. He also wrote a science-fiction story, the *Somnium* or Dream. It was published posthumously in 1634, four years after his death.

The *Somnium* is a mixture of science and fantasy. Basically, it is a defence of the theory that the Earth goes round the Sun, though by 1634 this question had been more or less settled in the eyes of most astronomers even though the Church continued to support Ptolemy. In the story, it is Kepler's suggested mode of travel which is so much removed from any semblance of credibility. Instead of using waterspouts or wings, the hero is taken to the Moon by 'demons'.

The story is related by Duracotus, a young Icelander whose mother, Fiolxhilda, proves to be a witch. When Duracotus has grown into a young man, his mother tells him that a Moon-voyage can be accomplished during a lunar eclipse, when the shadow of the Earth falls on to the Moon and provides a 'bridge' across which the demons can pass. Reaching the Moon—or

THEORY OF AN ECLIPSE OF THE MOON. When the Moon passes into the main umbra, or shadow of the Earth (black cone), its supply of sunlight is cut off, apart from a certain amount refracted on to the Moon by way of the Earth's atmosphere. To either side of the umbra is the penumbra, or area of partial shadow, due to the fact that the Sun is a disk instead of a point source of light.

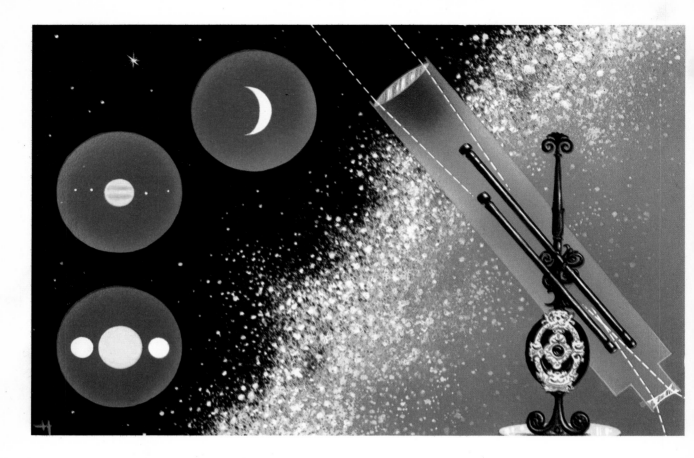

Levania, as it is called in the story – is not easy, and is 'made at grave risk to life'. As Fiolxhilda says: 'No inactive persons are accepted into our company; no fat ones; no pleasure-loving ones; we choose only those who have spent their lives on horseback, or have shipped often to the Indies and are accustomed to subsisting on hard tack, garlic, dried fish and such unpalatable fare.' It is added that no Germans are suitable, but that lean, strong Spaniards are not to be despised!

Duracotus, naturally, wants to make the journey for himself, but his mother goes on to stress that it will not be a comfortable experience. A man making the voyage will be 'twisted and turned just as if, shot from a cannon, he were sailing across mountains and seas. Therefore, he must be put to sleep beforehand . . . and he must be arranged, limb by limb, so that the shock will be distributed over the individual members'. As the voyage continues. there will be intense cold, and the traveller will find it hard to breathe, so that he will have to apply wet sponges to his nostrils.

Fanciful though it is, there are some remarkably modern ideas here, and Kepler seems to have had a good idea about gravity even though he lived more than half a century before the publication of Newton's Laws. Kepler also knew that the atmosphere does not stretch all the way from the Earth to the Moon, and his wet-sponge suggestion is interesting even though Kepler can hardly have meant it to be taken seriously.

Once Duracotus has arrived on the Moon, the story takes a genuinely scientific turn. At that time, it was thought that the

GALILEO'S FIRST TELESCOPES, feeble by modern standards, but powerful enough for him to make many spectacular discoveries. He saw, for instance, the phases of Venus, the four bright satellites of Jupiter, and the many stars of the Milky Way; Saturn he thought to be a triple planet, because his telescope was not strong enough to show the ring-system clearly. Galileo may not have been the first telescopic astronomer, but he was certainly one of the earliest, and his observational skill and patience placed him in a class of his own.

BISHOP GODWIN'S GANSAS. In the famous story, Domingo Gonzales is carried aloft on a raft towed by gansas, or wild geese —who hibernate on the Moon, and proceed to fly there, taking Gonzales with them!

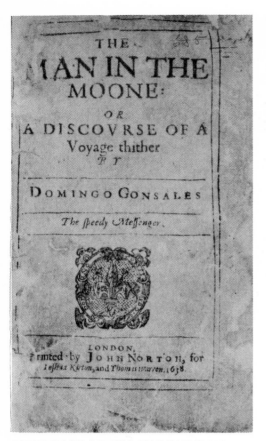

TITLE-PAGE OF *THE MAN IN THE MOONE*, **by Bishop Godwin, published posthumously in 1638. This is one of the most famous of 'historical' lunar-voyage stories.**

JOHANNES KEPLER, the great mathematician who drew up the Laws of Planetary Motion, and who also wrote a science-fiction work, the *Somnium.* **It must be said, however, that this book is mainly a defence of the Copernican theory, rather thinly disguised as a story.**

Moon might well have air and water; there was no reason to think otherwise, and it was also known that the same hemisphere is kept turned toward the Earth permanently. Therefore, Kepler divided his Moon into two parts, Subvolva and Privolva; from Subvolva the Earth was always visible, while from Privolva it could never be seen.

The Moon goes round the Earth in 27.3 days. It also spins on its axis in 27.3 days, so that there is a part of it which we can never see, and which remained unexamined until Russian rockets obtained photographs of it as recently as 1959. The best analogy is to consider a man walking round a chair, turning so as to keep his head turned chairward. Anyone sitting on the chair will never see the back of the walker's head; similarly, we on Earth never see the far side of the Moon. There is no mystery about this behaviour; tidal friction over thousands of millions of years has 'captured' the Moon's rotation. More will be said about this in Chapter 22. Meanwhile, it is enough to note that Kepler was wrong in supposing that his Subvolva and Privolva would have different climates. So far as sunrise and sunset are concerned, conditions over the two hemispheres of the Moon are exactly the same.

In the *Somnium*, Kepler's footnotes are considerably longer than the actual text, emphasizing that the story is meant to be a thinly-disguised scientific treatise. In the last section, admittedly, there is a description of the lunar inhabitants which takes us out into the realm of pure fantasy; some of the creatures are winged, while others have furry bodies, and a 'race of serpents predominates in general'. In Subvolva, all plants and creatures are of huge size, and live for only a few lunar days. If caught in the open near mid-day, a Moon-being's fur will be singed by the intense heat, so that the creature drops as though dead; at nightfall it revives, and the singed parts of its fur drop away.

All in all, it may be said that much of Kepler's venture into science fiction is an interesting forecast of things to come. He used demons for his mode of travel because he knew of nothing better; but once his extraordinary Moon-creatures have been removed, his description of the lunar world fits in very well with the state of astronomical knowledge at the time. Incidentally, the title of the 'Dream' is explained in the very last sentence. Duracotus suddenly comes to himself, to find that he has been asleep and that his lunar voyage never really happened; he awakes with his 'head covered by a cushion, and his body tangled in a rug'.

By a coincidence, Lucian's *True History* appeared in its first English translation in the same year that Kepler's *Somnium* was published. Four years later, in 1638, came the famous *Man in the Moone* of Francis Godwin, son of the Bishop of Bath and Wells. Godwin was a distinguished scholar, and himself became Bishop of Hereford; he was the author of a number of theological works, to say nothing of an immense catalogue of English bishops. Yet he would hardly be remembered now but for his venture into science fiction.

He was not a scientist in any sense of the word, and he never accepted the heretical view that the Earth moves round the Sun. Unlike Kepler, he was not trying to prove a point; his aim was to produce an amusing, witty tale, and he succeeded very well. The book proved extremely popular, and ran to six impressions during

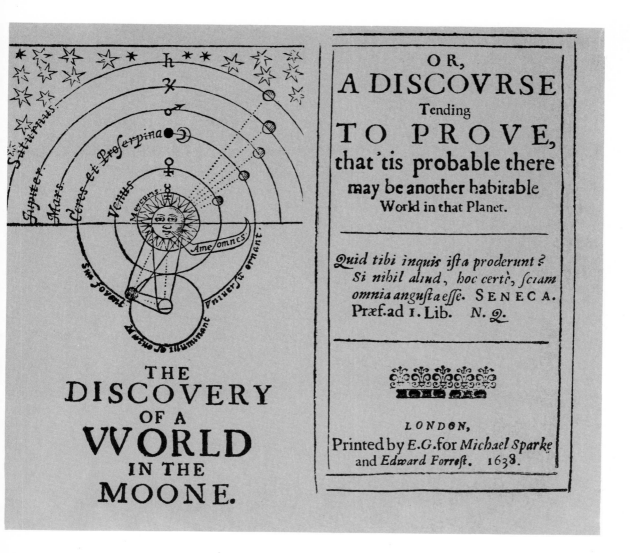

THE
DISCOVERY
OF A
WORLD
IN THE
MOONE.

OR,
A DISCOVRSE
Tending
TO PROVE,
that 'tis probable there
may be another habitable
World in that Planet.

Quid tibi inquis ista proderunt?
Si nihil aliud, hoc certè, sciam
omnia angusta esse. SENECA.
Præf.ad I.Lib.   N. 2.

LONDON,
Printed by *E.G.* for *Michael Sparke*
and *Edward Forrest*. 1638.

the following half-century. Actually, the *Man in the Moone*, like Kepler's *Somnium*, was posthumous; Bishop Godwin died in 1633.

The central figure in the story was Domingo Gonzales, a young Spaniard of noble but impoverished family. The early adventures need not concern us; suffice to say that Godwin and his Negro servant were marooned on a remote island, and decided to escape by training gansas. or wild geese, to tow them through the air on a raft. This was all very well, but Gonzales had not realized that these particular gansas hibernated on the Moon. By the time he had become aware of his danger, he was already well on his way.

Gonzales' journey was much more pleasant than Duracotus'. The worthy Bishop Godwin paid no attention to trifles such as the lack of air, and the only calculations which he gave were wildly in error. All attempts at an authentic background are abandoned when Gonzales sets foot upon the Moon; he finds a true Utopia, peopled by a race whose language is so musical that it can be written down only in note form, and some of whom are thirty feet tall. Any Moon-child showing signs of latent wickedness is at once dispatched to Earth, where, presumably, there is so much evil already that a little more will not matter. The usual landing-place

TITLE-PAGE OF CYRANO DE BERGERAC'S BOOK OF 1687. This was not intended to be taken seriously; Cyrano set out to write an entertaining story, but his book is no more 'unscientific' than other works of the period.

JOURNEYING MOONWARD BY DEW. In Cyrano's first story, his pioneer attempt is made by fastening dew-bottles to his body, the theory being that the Sun will suck up the dew and thus carry the wearer upward toward the Moon. Even in the story, this attempt at a lunar flight was unsuccessful!

for such children, writes Godwin, is 'a certain high hill in the North of America, whose people I can easily believe to be wholly descended of them'.

The only real scientific idea is given when Gonzales leaves the Moon, and orders his gansas to take him back to Earth. The outward trip has taken twelve days; the return takes only nine, because the Earth has a greater attractive power. At one stage the gansas are swooping down so quickly that disaster seems imminent. Gonzales solves the re-entry problem easily, by using a magic jewel that has been given to him by the Prince of the Moon; nowadays, rocket braking would be considered rather more reliable!

Almost simultaneously with Godwin's story came *The Discovery of a World in the Moone*, by John Wilkins. He, too, was a bishop; he too was a man of great learning. He firmly believed the Moon to be inhabited, and urged the British Government to consider acquiring it for the nation. So far as the actual voyage was concerned, he suggested either flight by means of wings attached to the traveller's body; bird-power, clearly borrowed from Godwin; or else a 'Flying Chariot', powered in some way that he did not attempt to describe. Wilkins' book, let it be said at once, was not meant to be fiction. It was a serious essay, and was intended to be taken as such. Of course he was laughed at, but after three and a half centuries we are bound to admit that his Flying Chariot, at least, does not sound particularly far-fetched.

Wilkins' book is important because it was one of the first, if not the very first, of all space-travel books written by a competent scientist in all seriousness. In addition to being Bishop of Chester, Wilkins was also—later—the first Secretary of the Royal Society, which was to become the most famous scientific society in the world. Yet at the time, nothing could be done except to make vague speculations, so that the story-tellers could be given full rein.

It would be too much of a digression to describe all the various methods suggested for carrying out a trip to the Moon. Cyrano de Bergerac, in 1657, even proposed to use dew. He reasoned that since dew on a grass lawn disappears when the Sun has risen, it must have been sucked up; therefore, the would-be space-traveller has only to collect a number of bottles, fill them with dew, fasten them to his body, stand outside on a fine morning, and let the Sun do the rest. Actually, Cyrano wrote a second part to his story in which he unconsciously came quite close to the idea of rocket propulsion, but he, like Lucian so long before, was trying to do no more than tell a good story.

As the years passed by, striking advances were made in all branches of science, particularly in astronomy. Telescopes were developed into powerful instruments, very different from the feeble 'optic tubes' used by Galileo; Newton's Laws of Gravitation laid the foundations of what we now call celestial mechanics, and during the eighteenth century astronomy entered what might be regarded as its modern phase. Moreover, manned flight began in 1783—not with aircraft, but with balloons. And though powered flight in the atmosphere was still a long way away, it no longer seemed impossible.

Even so, strange ideas still lingered on. Sir William Herschel, perhaps the greatest astronomical observer of all time, believed that there were intelligent beings on the Moon and planets, and even inside the Sun, he thought that below the brilliant solar surface there might well be a cool, temperate region able to support life. Not many of his contemporaries agreed with him, but he never wavered in his views, and he continued to support the idea of a habitable Sun until he died in 1822. Then, in 1835, came the famous Moon Hoax, which is worth describing here because it was significant as well as frankly funny.

Sir William Herschel had discovered a new planet (Uranus), and, more important, he had drawn up the first reasonably accurate picture of the way in which the stars of our Galaxy are arranged. He had carried out careful measurements of the stars in the northern part of the sky, but he had spent almost all his life in England, where the brilliant constellations of the far south never rise above the horizon. His son John—afterwards Sir John—Herschel extended the survey to the southern hemisphere. He went to the Cape of Good Hope, taking with him a powerful telescope, and he stayed there for several years, collecting a mass of observations that took more than a decade to sort and publish. He was not concerned with the Moon, which can be seen just as well from England as from South Africa. However, an enterprising reporter on a New York paper, the *Sun*, saw that there was the chance of a good story—and he took it.

Richard Locke, an English journalist who had emigrated to America and joined the *Sun* staff, was a plausible writer with a lively imagination. He reasoned that Herschel was on the other side of the world; communications in those days were slow and uncertain; who was there to issue a prompt denial of anything that might be printed? And so, on 25 August 1835, the *Sun* came out

PHOTOGRAPH OF SIR JOHN HERSCHEL, who died in 1871 at the age of 79. Herschel, son of the discoverer of Uranus, was a great astronomer in his own right. It was also he who first coined the word 'photography'.

SIR JOHN HERSCHEL'S TELESCOPE, taken to the Cape of Good Hope in order to be used in carrying out studies of the southern stars. It was while Herschel was busy at the Cape that Richard Locke, in New York, perpetrated his famous 'Moon Hoax'. The telescope is now on display at the Science Museum in London, where it was photographed by the author in 1966.

with a headline: 'Great Astronomical Discoveries Lately Made by Sir John Herschel, LL.D., F.R.S., &c., at the Cape of Good Hope.' After a convincing description of a new type of telescope that Herschel was supposed to have invented, Locke promised that startling revelations would follow. They did . . .

During the following week, the *Sun* printed a series of articles about extraordinary inhabitants seen on the Moon with the aid of Herschel's new telescope. There was, for instance, 'a strange amphibious creature, of a spherical form, rolling with great velocity along a pebbly beach'. There was, too, a creature 'of a bluish lead colour, about the size of a goat, with a head and beard like him, and a single horn, slightly inclined from the perpendicular . . . This beautiful creature afforded us the most exquisite enjoyment'. Finally, on 28 August, came the lunar bat-men. 'Certainly they were like human beings . . . They averaged four feet in height, were covered, except on the face, with short glossy copper-coloured hair, and had wings composed of a thin membrane, without hair, lying snugly on their backs. . . . The face, which was of a yellowish flesh colour, was a slight improvement upon that of a large orang-ou-tang, being much more open and intelligent in its expression, and having a much greater expansion of forehead. The mouth, however, was very prominent, though somewhat relieved by a thick beard upon the lower jaw.'

Locke was clever enough to force his readers back to 'science' every now and then. Sometimes conditions were unsuitable for observing; sometimes the telescope gave trouble, and the series was brought to an end by an account of how the astronomers forgot to cover up the main mirror of the instrument, so that it acted as a huge burning-glass when it caught the rays of the Sun and set light to the equipment.

The series met with a mixed reception, but many people accepted the stories whole-heartedly. The *New York Times* described the discoveries as 'both possible and probable', and an earnest message was received from a women's club in Massachusetts, asking Herschel his opinion of the best way to get in touch with the bat-men and convert them to Christianity. Admittedly, the hoax was soon exposed by a rival New York paper, and the *Sun* itself confessed on 16 September, but not for some time was the whole absurd episode finally dismissed as a joke.

Short-lived though it may have been the Moon Hoax showed that even some scientists could be taken in by incredible stories about lunar life. But in 1837 two Germans, Wilhelm Beer and Johann von Mädler, published the first good map of the Moon, drawn up with the aid of the telescope at Beer's observatory in Berlin, and also produced a complete description of the lunar surface. Beer and Mädler knew that the Moon has practically no atmosphere, and that conditions there are hopelessly hostile to any form of life. The great hoax came only just in time; after 1837, it would never have sounded convincing. (All the same, there is a distinct parallel with the flying saucer stories of the nineteen-fifties, which, after all, are just as ridiculous as Locke's bat-men.)

Then, in 1865, came the classic novel *From the Earth to the Moon*, by Jules Verne. This was a story, not a scientific text, but it had a tremendous influence upon thoughts about space-travel. The age of serious planning was about to begin.

THE MOON HOAX OF 1835. This is a reproduction of part of the New York *Sun* series, which deceived a great many people—even if for only a short time. It is significant that people were quite ready to believe in fantastic lunar life; but within a few years the patient work of Beer and Mädler, who produced the first good map of the Moon, had led to a radical change in outlook.

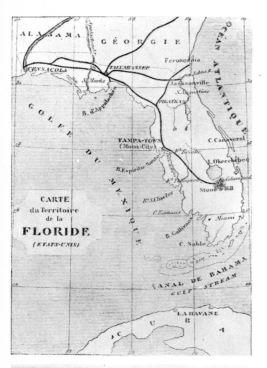

L'arrivée du projectile à Stone's-Hill (p. 139).

FLORIDA, showing Stone's Hill, where Jules Verne situated his fictional space-gun. This is a woodcut from the original edition of Verne's book *From the Earth to the Moon.* **It is interesting that he has marked in Cape Canaveral—now known as Cape Kennedy, the American rocket launching site from which the first U.S. space-voyages were made.**

THE ARRIVAL OF THE PROJECTILE AT STONE'S HILL. A woodcut from the original edition of Verne's novel; the projectile has been safely transported, and is ready to be hurled Moonward from the mouth of the huge Columbiad cannon.

Chapter 5

Space-Guns and Anti-Gravity

In 1865 Jules Verne, already becoming known as one of the world's master story-tellers, produced his novel *From the Earth to the Moon.* In it, he described how a party of United States artillerymen, left with nothing much to do following the end of the American Civil War, built a vast cannon and used it to send a projectile toward the Moon. Inside the projectile were the three heroes of the story, together with two dogs and various pieces of scientific equipment. Five years later came the sequel, *Round the Moon*, in which the actual voyage was described, ending with the return to Earth and a splash-down in the ocean. Since the two books are part of the same novel, there is no point is discussing them separately; they have been translated into almost every language (they are particularly popular in Britain and in Russia), and they are usually published together.

Jules Verne was not a scientist. On the other hand, he believed in making his facts as correct as possible; he was certainly not prepared to use demon power or to invent weird and wonderful Moon-Men. As so often in his books, he gave exact calculations and descriptions, and in 1865 the result was very credible indeed. Also, the story was of scientific importance even though the basic idea—that of a space-gun—is faulty. So let us say something about Verne's plot, and then see which parts of it are right and which are technically wrong.

In the book, the original idea of the voyage comes from members of the Baltimore Gun Club, headed by their President, Impey Barbicane. With them worked a brilliant mathematician, J. T. Maston, who, like so many artillerymen, had a steel hook instead of one of his arms. At a special meeting of the Gun Club, Barbicane pointed out that 'the resisting power of cannon and the explosive force of gunpowder are practically unlimited', and he suggested that it might be possible to fire a shot to the Moon. Amid tremendous applause, he continued: 'I have looked at the question in all its bearings, I have resolutely attacked it, and . . . I find that a projectile endowed with an initial force of 7 miles per second[1], and directed at the Moon, must necessarily reach it. I have therefore the honour of proposing to you, my worthy colleagues, the attempting of this little experiment.'

Enthusiasm was unbounded, and the great cannon, the Columbiad, was soon designed. The explosive was to be guncotton, with the projectile itself made of aluminium, then a very rare and costly metal. But before the plans were far advanced, there came a dramatic development. Michel Ardan, a young Frenchman, not only volunteered to go to the Moon inside the projectile, but reconciled Barbicane to his mortal enemy, Captain Nicholl, and persuaded them both to accompany him. The form of the projectile was altered. It became cylindro-conical, and was fitted with hydraulic shock-absorbers, an air-conditioning plant, padded

---

[1] The original book naturally uses the Metric system.

walls, deeply set windows, and—gas lighting.

The launching site was Stony Hill, in Florida; not so very far from the modern Cape Kennedy, from which rockets have been sent to the Moon and beyond. At last all was ready. The travellers were inside their projectile, and the controlling engineer pressed the switch which would complete the circuit, firing the 400,000 pounds of gun-cotton. 'An appalling, unearthly report followed instantly . . . An immense spout of fire shot up from the bowels of

CAPTAIN NICHOLL. From the original edition of Verne's novel.

INSIDE THE PROJECTILE. Michel Ardan arranges his belongings ready for the Moon voyage. From the original edition of Verne's novel.

FIRE! The Columbiad cannon is fired, and the projectile carrying Barbicane, Nicholl, Ardan and the animals is on its way to the Moon. From the original edition of Verne's novel.

the earth as from a crater. The ground heaved, and with great difficulty a few spectators gained a brief glimpse of the projectile cleaving the air in the midst of the fiery vapours.' Barbicane, Nicholl and Michel Ardan were on their way.

They had no thought of return. Their trip to the Moon would be a one-way journey only, but why should they not find air, water and food awaiting them on the lunar world? Almost at once however, the space-travellers met with danger, in the shape of

'. . . an enormous disk, the colossal dimensions of which could not be estimated. . . . It looked like a small moon reflecting the light of the large one. It advanced at a prodigious speed, and seemed to describe round the Earth an orbit right across the passage of the projectile . . . The asteroid passed within a distance of a few hundred yards and then disappeared, . . . because its side opposite to the Moon was suddenly confronted with the absolute darkness of space.'

Barbicane and his friends had almost collided with a dwarf moon, moving round the Earth above the top of the atmosphere. Small though the intruder might be, its pull was enough to upset the careful calculations of J. T. Maston, the one-armed mathematician. The orbit of the projectile was changed, and it entered an orbit round the Moon, passing over the side which is always turned away from Earth. At that time, it was lunar night over the far hemisphere, but suddenly a meteor burst into flame nearby, and for a few seconds the travellers saw 'long bands across the disk, veritable clouds formed in a thin atmosphere . . . Veritable seas, oceans which reflected in their liquid mirror all the fires of space'. Then the meteor died away, and everything was dark once more.

Barbicane had thoughtfully brought with him the lunar map drawn by Beer and Mädler in 1837, much the best of its time, and the travellers were able to follow their progress over the Moon's sunlit face. They had no wish to remain circling for ever, but a means of escape occurred to them. Between the Earth and the Moon, they supposed, was a 'neutral point', at which the Earth's pull of gravity exactly balanced that of the Moon; on reaching it, the space-men would lose all feeling of weight, and would float in their cabin. When they reached this neutral point, and felt their weight vanish, Michel Ardan fired the small recoil rockets fixed to the projectile. There was a distinct shock, and then the vehicle started to fall—not on to the Moon, but back on to the Earth. At last it landed in the ocean with a tremendous splash, and floated there until an American corvette on patrol located it, and discovered Barbicane, Nicholl and Michel Ardan quietly awaiting rescue, and whiling away the hours by playing dominoes. J. T. Maston was overjoyed to see them; his iron hook had made it impossible for him to attempt the voyage in person, but he had been doing his best to track the projectile, using the 192-inch reflecting telescope built specially for the purpose and set up on the summit of a high mountain, Long's Peak.

Such is the story as Verne told it. Now let us see just how much is scientifically correct.

The great weakness, of course, is the idea of the space-gun itself. Apart from the fact that no return from the Moon would be possible (except by a convenient chance, such as Verne intro-

APPROACHING THE MOON, from the original Verne novel. The projectile is seen against the stars, while the lunar craters lie below. The largest crater shown is Tycho. For his lunar topography, Verne depended upon the map drawn by Beer and Mädler.

THE PROJECTILE BETWEEN EARTH AND MOON. Here Verne almost hit upon the correct theory of rocket propulsion, even though he had used the space-gun idea for his main theme.

duced), there are two fatal objections which Verne either forgot or else chose to ignore.

First, air causes resistance, and a solid body moving at a sufficiently high speed will become extremely hot. This is shown by the fate of a meteor which enters the upper air at tremendous velocity and destroys itself as a shooting-star. It is true that a meteor may move at anything up to 45 miles per second relative to the Earth, which is very different from Verne's proposed 7 miles per second, but the principle holds good, and the projectile would have been destroyed even before it had left the barrel of the cannon. The density of the air would have prevented it from even beginning its flight toward the Moon.

Secondly, there is the question of initial shock. If sent up with a sudden acceleration of 7 miles per second, nothing could have prevented Barbicane, Nicholl and Michel Ardan from being killed instantly; it has been said that even if the air-resistance problem is ignored, a traveller starting in such a way will be turned into fine jelly spread against the walls of his craft. Similarly, the projectile's hydraulic shock-absorbers would have been of no use whatsoever. If a manned vehicle is to land safely upon a world as massive as the Earth or the Moon, it must be slowed down before arrival. Should it hit the ground with full velocity, it is certain to be destroyed, as many of the early lunar probes of the late nineteen-fifties and early nineteen-sixties actually were.

Ironically, Verne very nearly hit upon a more accurate solution. In his story, the recoil of the rockets fired upon arrival at the neutral point between Earth and Moon proved sufficient to accelerate the projectile back toward the Earth. This is logical enough, but it leads us to another serious error, concerning the neutral point itself.

The Earth is eighty-one times as massive as the Moon, and it is quite true that there must be a point where the gravitational pulls of the two worlds balance; since the Moon is the lighter member of the pair, the point will be closer to it than to the Earth. But we must remember that both Earth and Moon are moving, and, moreover, there is the Sun to be taken into account. When these factors are included, it becomes clear that the so-called neutral point, on the lines supposed by Verne, is a myth.

Then, too, Verne thought that his travellers would become weightless only upon arrival at the critical point. This is another error, and perhaps the most serious of all. Actually, the three men would have been weightless from the moment of blast-off, because they would have been moving under conditions of what is termed free fall.

If I take a coin and put it on top of a book, the coin will press down on the book; with reference to the book, it is 'heavy'. If I drop the book, both it and the coin will fall to the ground. During the few brief seconds of descent, the coin will cease to press upon the book; certainly it will be falling, but the book will be falling away from underneath it, so that there will be no pressure. With reference to the book, the coin has become weightless, simply because it is moving in the same direction at the same speed. The same would be true if the two bodies were moving upward at the same direction at the same rate.

In the projectile, the travellers can be compared to the coins,

QUEL SPECTACLE! The brilliant bolide explodes, giving Barbicane, Nicholl and Ardan a fleeting view of the mysterious 'other side of the Moon' below. This is another woodcut from the Verne original.

SEA-RESCUE—according to Jules Verne. The projectile has landed in the ocean; it floats, as J. T. Maston has at last realized; and Barbicane, Nicholl and Ardan are safely inside. It is interesting to compare this picture, of more than a century ago, with a modern 'pick-up' of an astronaut from much the same part of the sea.

and the vehicle itself will represent the book. While moving in identical paths, the travellers will stop pressing against their surroundings, so that they will be weightless—or, in other words, under conditions of zero gravity; so-called neutral points have nothing whatever to do with it. Neither, for that matter, has the presence of the Earth. When a space-traveller becomes weightless inside his vehicle, he has not 'got out of gravity', as has been suggested in so many popular books and articles. Strictly speaking, one cannot 'get out of gravity', though a space-traveller moving in free fall will not feel any downward force even when he is still close to the Earth.

On the other hand, Verne's calculated velocity of 7 miles per second is accurate enough, because this is the value of the Earth's escape velocity. If I throw a stone upward, it will rise to a certain height, stop, and fall back. If I give it a greater starting-speed, it will rise higher; and if I could send it up at 7 miles per second it would never come back at all, because the Earth's gravity would be too weak to hold it. Therefore, any projectile sent up with an initial speed of less than 7 miles per second will fall back, while a vehicle dispatched at the full escape velocity will not. This is sound science, and still holds good today, but there are any number of reasons why the full velocity cannot be given at once; a modern rocket starts slowly, and accelerates to its maximum power only when beyond the atmosphere of appreciable density. This is practicable for a rocket, but not, of course, for a projectile shot out of a cannon.

All in all, the Columbiad space-gun idea simply cannot work. Yet there is a chance that in the future, something of the sort may be used to launch unmanned vehicles from airless worlds such as the Moon. This lies far ahead, but it may not be entirely out of the question.

With regard to the hidden side of the Moon, Verne was using his literary licence, much as he had done in the first of his great novels, *Journey to the Centre of the Earth*. At that period there was a theory, due to the Danish astronomer Hansen, that all the Moon's air and water had been drawn round to the hidden side. Few scientists took the idea seriously, but it had been proposed by an eminent astronomer, and Verne evidently saw no reason why he should not make use of it.

On the credit side, Verne produced some remarkably interesting and convincing arguments all the way through his book. The 192-inch reflecting telescope built by the Gun Club is a forecast of the 200-inch reflector which now operates from Palomar Mountain; the launching site of the Columbiad was not far from the modern Kennedy, and Verne's travellers splashed down in the ocean just as the present-day American astronauts do, though admittedly Verne took no account of the need for slowing-down before impact.

For a pleasant few hours' reading, I would wholeheartedly recommend the two Moon-voyage books. Of course they are period pieces; the rather quaint, stilted language takes us back into the past, but surprisingly little is lost in translation, and one can well picture the scene as the Columbiad erúpted in fire and smoke, sending two Americans and a Frenchman on their long journey toward the Moon.

Jules Verne died in 1905, mourned throughout the world. Four years earlier, another literary genius had produced a space-fiction story of quite different type. This was *The First Men in the Moon*, by H. G. Wells, which is much more modern in its style and approach, but which is, one must confess, less scientific. Unlike Verne, Wells was a story-teller first and foremost, at least in the earlier stages of his career, and he was prepared to distort the known facts to an extent which Verne would have considered unforgivable.

In his book, Wells creates a sphere which travels to the Moon because it is coated with a special substance which has the power of screening gravity. By opening various blinds, the sphere can be made to travel in any required direction.

The material is called Cavorite, after its inventor—Cavor, probably the first of all the absent-minded professors of science fiction. As soon as the manufacture is complete, the Cavorite becomes a total shield, so that everything above it becomes weightless. Early in the story there is a delightful account of Cavor's first experiments, which nearly end in disaster. He completes a sheet of the marvellous substance, but at once the column of air overhead becomes weightless, and rushes off into space. Surrounding air fills the vacuum, only to become weightless in its turn; and had not the Cavorite sheet itself flown upward, the experiment might have ended by removing the Earth's atmosphere altogether . . .

If it were possible to believe in anti-gravity material, Wells' story would be credible enough, but unfortunately his Cavorite is purely imaginary, and it is impossible to manufacture. The whole idea goes against everything we have learned about nature. Gravity is a property which belongs to every particle of matter, and, so far as we know, it can never be screened.

Yet it is always dangerous to be too positive, and we must admit that so far we have no idea of what gravity really is. Until we know more, we cannot say that Cavorite is out of the question. On the other hand, our ignorance is so complete that it is rather pointless to speculate; and we may be reasonably sure that however the first space-ships manoeuvre, it will not be by anti-gravity blinds.

The Moon-world as described by Wells is very different from the crater-scarred vista seen by Jules Verne's voyagers. In many ways it is more like Kepler's Subvolva; there are masses of vegetation, a breathable air, and an underground civilization of Selenites with insect-like bodies. I shall have more to say about Selenites when discussing alien life in general, and commenting upon what are usually termed B.E.M.'s or 'bug-eyed monsters'. Meanwhile, we must regard *The First Men in the Moon* as a brilliant novel, but hardly a forecast of space-travel in our time.

There have been many other schemes for reaching the Moon; huge coiled-spring launchers, magnetic devices of all kinds, and various other ideas, but no interplanetary stories can really stand up to comparison with these two. Both will continue to be read long after the Moon has been reached and explored, and in centuries to come they may still be remembered. In any case, their authors cannot be forgotten. On the Moon's far side, never to be seen from Earth, are two craters which the Russians have aptly named in honour of Jules Verne and H. G. Wells.

CAVOR'S SPACE-SHIP. In his novel *The First Men in the Moon*, **H. G. Wells made use of a gravity-shielding substance developed by the eccentric inventor Cavor. In this illustration, from the original edition of Wells' book, Cavor and his travelling-companion, Bedford, are examining the interior of the space-craft which Cavor has built for his journey to the Moon.**

Chapter 6

The Upper Air

The Earth has a reasonably dense atmosphere. This is a result of several circumstances which, from our point of view, are extremely fortunate. Our distance from the Sun gives a climate favourable for our sort of life; if the Earth were much closer-in it would be unbearably hot, while if it were a great deal further out the surface of the world would be permanently frozen. Moreover, it is this equable temperature which has helped in the development of the Earth's oxygen-rich atmosphere which we breathe every moment of our lives.

The Earth has an escape velocity of 7 miles per second. Air, of course, is made up of countless millions of atoms and molecules, all flying about at high speeds; if one of these particles were able to travel outward at escape velocity, it would depart permanently, and the Earth would lose it. If the process kept on being repeated, there would eventually come a time when the atmosphere would have become too thin to support life. This has happened in the case of the Moon, which has a mass of only 1/81 of that of the Earth, and where the escape velocity is a mere 1½ miles per second. In the remote past it is possible (though by no means certain) that the Moon had a thick atmosphere, but by now almost all of it has escaped into space, so that the popular description of the Moon as 'an airless world' is not very far wrong.

The velocity of an atmospheric particle depends partly upon the kind of particle it is, and to some extent upon its temperature; the higher the temperature, the greater the speed. Therefore, if the Earth were very much closer to the Sun, the particles in its atmos-

RUSSIAN EQUIPMENT FOR EXPLORING THE UPPER ATMOSPHERE, current in the late 1950s. Many Soviet rockets were sent up to study the extreme upper part of the Earth's layer of air, and often enough the instruments were separated and brought down by parachute. This photograph shows the containers carrying the geophysical instruments, after descent from an altitude of 212 kilometres.

phere would be speeded up until they could move at escape velocity, and would leak away. Heavier gases, such as carbon dioxide, might be retained — but a carbon-dioxide atmosphere would be unbreathable.

Nobody is sure how the Earth and other planets came into being. The old idea, according to which they were torn off the Sun by the action of a passing star, has been reluctantly given up, because there are fatal mathematical objections to it; on the modern view, the planets were produced from material collected by the Sun during its journey through a cloud of gas and dust in space. In any case, it seems that the Earth must originally have had an atmosphere made up largely of hydrogen, the lightest of all gases. Hydrogen particles move about very rapidly, and the Earth could not hold them down, so that they escaped. There may have been a period when the Earth was without atmosphere, but then a new or 'secondary' atmosphere was formed from gases sent out from inside the globe, mainly by volcanic eruptions. This new atmosphere was composed largely of carbon dioxide, together with a great quantity of water vapour. Such was the situation about 600,000,000 years ago; if we could go on board a time-machine and send ourselves back to that remote period, we should promptly choke.

Originally there was no life on Earth. The first living things appeared in the sea, and it was only later that plants spread on to the continents. When they did so, they caused a dramatic change in the make-up of the atmosphere, because plants have the ability to remove carbon dioxide and replace it with oxygen—so cancelling out the harm done by animals (including men), which breathe in oxygen and sent out carbon dioxide. Over the millions of years, the plants produced a vast amount of oxygen, and the end result was the atmosphere we now know. At the moment there is a complete balance, and the air is not changing to any marked extent.

Actually, the most plentiful of the gases in our atmosphere is nitrogen, which accounts for 77.6 per cent of the whole. Oxygen makes up 20.7 per cent, and carbon dioxide only 0.03 per cent, which is not very much. There is 0.9 per cent of the inert gas argon, and a varying amount of water vapour, together with traces of other rare gases which need not concern us at the moment.

No other planet in the Solar System has an atmosphere of this kind. The giant worlds (Jupiter, Saturn, Uranus and Neptune) are so massive that they were able to hold on to all their original hydrogen, and the result is atmosphere which is poisonous from our point of view; unpleasant hydrogen compounds, such as

HISTORIC PHOTOGRAPH OF THE EARTH AS SEEN FROM 232,000 MILES. This picture was taken on 23 August 1966 by Orbiter. The Moon is shown in the foreground; in the background we see the crescent Earth. At the time, Orbiter was moving away from the Earth at about 3,000 m.p.h. The picture was developed and printed inside the Orbiter, and then scanned for relaying back to the Earth.

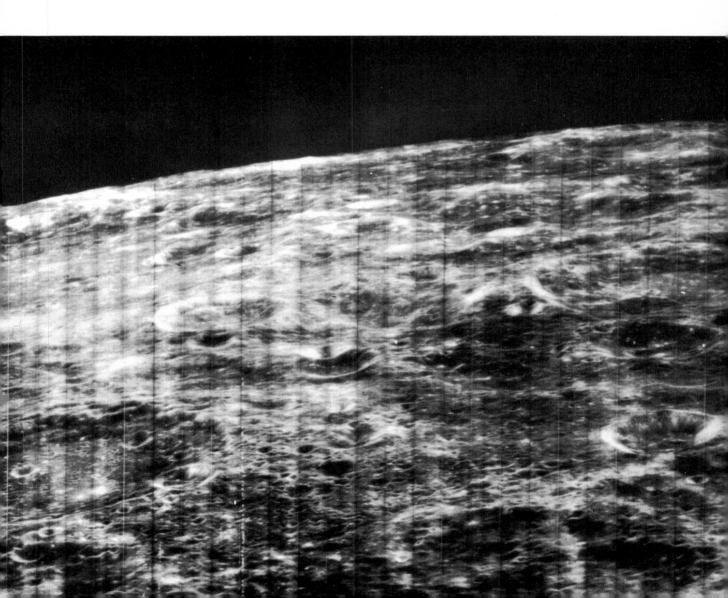

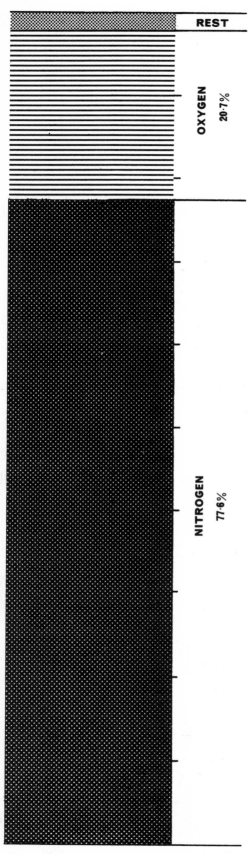

COMPOSITION OF THE ATMOSPHERE.
Nitrogen makes up 77.6%, oxygen 20.7%, and
other gases account for the remainder.

ammonia and methane or marsh gas, are much in evidence. Venus seems to have an atmosphere relatively rich in carbon dioxide, so that plant life may not have developed there, while smaller bodies such as Mercury and the Moon have lost practically the whole of any atmosphere they may once have had. Mars has given us a surprise recently, but in any case the atmosphere is extremely thin, and will be of little use to Earth-travellers of the future.

As we have noted, early men thought that the atmosphere must extend upward for ever, filling all space. The Arabs of a thousand years ago knew better, but their estimates were based on little more than inspired guesswork, and it was not until the invention of the barometer, during the seventeenth century, that any real progress could be made. The barometer, of course, is an instrument used for measuring the pressure of the air above it. A climber who goes up a high mountain and takes a barometer with him will find that the pressure drops, and, moreover, the temperature will fall; the lapse-rate, or drop in temperature with height, amounts to about 3° Fahrenheit every 1,000 feet, though this figure is only an average and is subject to considerable fluctuations.

Above 15,000 feet or so, breathing becomes difficult, because a man's lungs are not able to draw in enough oxygen from the thin air around him. By less than 30,000 feet, breathing-masks are essential, as any airman knows (and I may add that I have personal experience here; once, during the war, my oxygen supply became disconnected when I was flying at high altitude, and it was very fortunate for me that my wireless operator re-connected it quickly). With still greater height, the air becomes excessively tenuous, and above 100 miles there is so little left that for most practical purposes, though not all, it may be neglected.

This is why no ordinary flying-machines are of the slightest use for space-travel. Aircraft, of either old or new design, cannot operate except when they have air around them. Balloons can rise rather higher, but they too are limited. Yet it was with balloons that the first practical studies of the Earth's upper air were carried out.

The first hot-air balloons which actually flew seem to have been made by a Portuguese, Gusmão, in the early eighteenth century. They were only models, but they were certainly effective. In 1783 the 'balloon age' started in earnest; the hot-air vehicles designed by the Montgolfier brothers in France proved to be very successful, and the first aviators in history made a trouble-free flight. The aviators in question were a sheep, a cock and a duck. All landed in excellent condition apart from the duck, which was looking somewhat dejected; it was later found to have been trodden on by the sheep.

Shortly afterwards, manned balloon ascents became quite common, and within three years of the Montgolfiers' success two flyers, Blanchard and Jeffries, managed to cross the Channel by air. (Some Soviet historians state that a Russian, Kryakutny, made a balloon flight as early as 1731, but the evidence seems rather uncertain.)

Naturally, the manned balloons were limited to low altitudes, but from 1898 another Frenchman, Teisserenc de Bort, began to use unpiloted balloons carrying scientific instruments. Some of these balloons reached heights of 9 to 10 miles, and the information

THE FIRST BALLOON VOYAGE, by the
hot-air balloon developed by the Montgolfier **Brothers** in 1783. Before long these
simple hot-air balloons were superseded,
but at least they paved the way for manned
flight inside the atmosphere.

sent back was remarkably interesting. In particular, there was the question of temperature.

It had long been known that temperature falls with increasing height; as we have noted, the lapse-rate is about 3° Fahrenheit per 1,000 feet. To his surprise, De Bort found that above a height of approximately 7 miles, this fall in temperature stopped. At greater altitudes, the value remained constant at roughly —67° Fahrenheit. It seemed as though the air must be made up of two distinct layers, and De Bort's names for them—'troposphere' for the lower region, 'stratosphere' for the upper—have become part of our language. De Bort naturally supposed that the temperature would remain steady right to the top of the atmosphere.

In this he was wrong. More modern work has shown that at heights well above balloon range, the temperature starts to rise again, and there is a 'high-temperature' belt centred around 30 miles above the ground. Then, after another 'cold layer', the temperature shoots up to amazing values, reaching well over 2,500° at a height of 200 miles. Also, the stratosphere does not extend upward for more than a few tens of miles. Above it comes a completely different region, the ionosphere, above which in turn is the outer part of the atmosphere, known as the exosphere. There is no sharp boundary to the exosphere; it simply thins out until its density is no greater than that of the material spread between the planets.

In fact, the structure of the atmosphere is extremely complex. I have given the simplest system; many other terms are in use, but they need not concern us here, and the diagram will suffice for our present needs. All our normal weather is confined to the troposphere, and no ordinary aircraft can reach upward as far as the ionosphere.

Before going any further, it will be wise to say something about temperature. It has been suggested that space-craft passing through the 'hot zones' on their way to the Moon will be melted, and that any passengers inside will meet with an unpleasant death. Fortunately, there is no fear of anything of the sort, because the scientific meaning of 'temperature' is not the same as our everyday use of the word 'heat'.

Matter is made up of atoms and molecules, all of which are moving around at high speeds. Temperature depends upon speed; the greater the speeds, the higher the temperature. In the Earth's upper air, the various atoms and molecules are moving very rapidly, and so that they are at a high temperature. However, the air at such altitudes is very thin; at 60 miles above sea-level, for instance, the atmospheric density is only a millionth of the ground value, and it is clear that almost all the mass of the atmosphere is concentrated in the bottom few miles. This means that although the upper air is at a high temperature, it contains very little 'heat', because there are relatively few atoms and molecules there.

A useful comparison, though not a very accurate one, is to consider a firework sparkler. Each spark is white-hot, but the firework may safely be held in the hand because, the sparks contain so little mass or heat that they are quite harmless. Each individual spark is hotter than the end of a glowing poker, but to grasp the poker would not be really advisable!

THE FIRST CHANNEL CROSSING BY BALLOON, made in 1785—only two years after the pioneer 'Montgolfier' balloons.

In short, the high-temperature regions in the upper air are not 'hot', and on this score they present no hazard to a space-craft passing through them.

The height of the top of the troposphere is not constant, but 7 miles is a good average. Above it comes a boundary layer, the tropopause, and then follows De Bort's stratosphere. Here we find some ozone, which is a special form of oxygen. There is not much of it, but without it we could not survive, because the ozone layer absorbs many of the harmful short-wave radiations sent out by the Sun, and so provides us with a perfect screen. Incidentally, it is this ozone which is responsible for the high-temperature layer. It absorbs about one-twentieth of all the radiation from the Sun, so that its temperature is increased.

The matter of radiations in general is all-important in space research, and I shall have much more to say about it later. For the moment, it may be enough to note that light may be regarded as a wave-motion, the distance between two successive crests being known as the wavelength; the standard unit is the Ångström, equal to one hundred-millionth part of a centimetre. Red light has a wavelength of about 7,500 Ångströms, while violet goes down to about 3,900 Ångströms. It is hardly necessary to stress, then, that the wavelength of visible light is remarkably short. (The name for the unit of measurement has been given in honour of the last-century Swedish physicist Anders Ångström, who carried out pioneerresearch into the whole problem.)

Light shorter in wavelength than 3,900 Ångströms cannot be seen; this is the ultra-violet radiation, much of which is dangerous, but most of which is blocked by the convenient ozone layer. On the longer-wave end of the visible band we have infra-red and radio waves, whose wavelengths may amount to many metres. A radio wave need not be artificial, and during the past thirty years it has been found that many bodies in the sky—the Sun, the planet Jupiter, and objects in our Galaxy and beyond—are radio sources.

Radio waves travel in straight lines. If, then, a wireless operator at position A (diagram p.49) tries to call up a colleague at position B, one may think that he will be unable to do so; the Earth, after all, has a curved surface. Yet we all know that long-distance wireless communication is easy with modern instruments, and most household radio sets can pick up programmes from far afield. The reason is that in the ionosphere, the region lying between roughly 40 and 350 miles above sea-level, there are various layers which reflect some of the radio waves and bounce them back to the ground. The first-discovered of these layers was tracked down early in the present century, independently by Kenelly in America and Oliver Heaviside in England.

We also know that the composition of the atmosphere is not the same for all levels. The lower eighty miles is made up of the familiar mixture of oxygen and nitrogen, together with smaller amounts of other gases; but higher up, things are different, because the air is so thin that 'mixing' cannot counteract the effects of gravity. Oxygen is the main gas up to 350 miles, and above this come layers first of helium, then of hydrogen. These last two are the lightest of all the gases, so that—other factors being equal—they will tend to rise to the top of the atmosphere.

THE PRINCIPLE OF WAVELENGTH. The idea of wavelength can be shown by looking at ripples in a pond; the distance between successive crests is the wavelength. Light also may be regarded as a wave-motion, though the wavelength of visible light is extremely short by everyday standards. Radio waves have longer wavelengths, up to several metres.

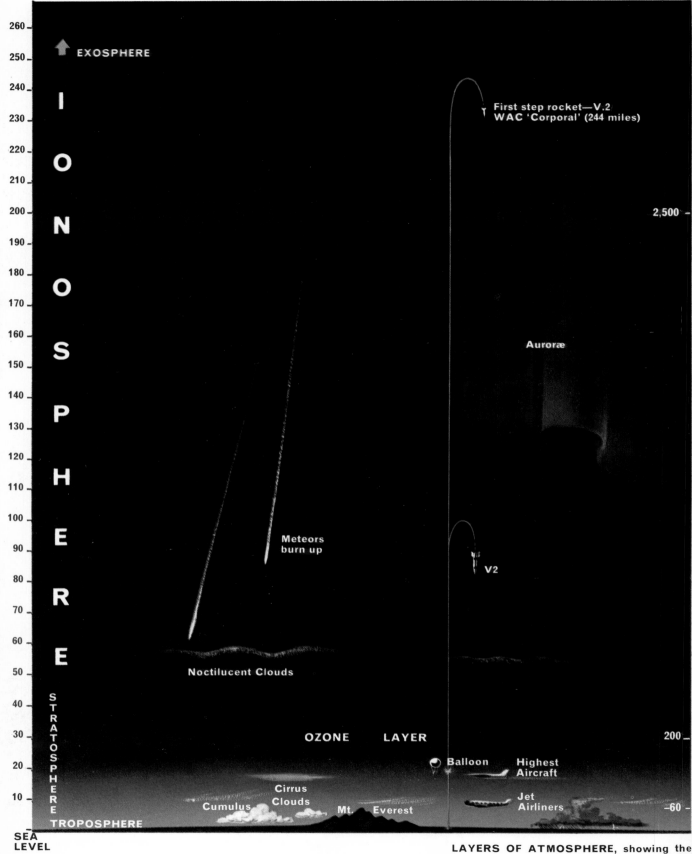

LAYERS OF ATMOSPHERE, showing the troposphere, ozone layer, noctilucent clouds, the regions of meteors and auroræ, and the maximum height of the V2 and the first step-rocket.

In passing, it may be added that although all our normal clouds are confined to the troposphere, there are some strange, luminous clouds to be seen at about 50 miles above the ground. These are the noctilucent clouds, which are thought to be due to ice-coated particles coming from space, though not all authorities accept this explanation. They shine because they catch the Sun's light while the lower atmosphere is still in darkness, and they are extremely beautiful, though from places such as Britain and the United States they are not common. Apparently they were first described in detail by a German scientist, O. Jesse, in 1896.

In the ionosphere we have the brilliant glows known as auroræ, but these are so closely linked with the Earth's magnetic field that they are best left until Chapter 17. It is only since the start of rocket exploration that we have begun to understand the precise way in which they are caused. Also, meteors become visible when passing through the ionosphere, before it has plunged down to the bottom of the ionospheric layer, the average meteor has destroyed itself by friction against the air-particles.

The outermost region, the exosphere, begins at roughly 350 miles. We cannot decide just where the Earth's air comes to an end, but at 1,500 miles the density is only a million million millionth of the value at sea-level. At a sufficiently great distance from the Earth, the exosphere merges with what is usually, though inaccurately, called 'empty space'. In point of fact, it seems dubious whether there is truly empty space everywhere in the universe; even in the immense areas between the stars there are always considerable numbers of particles, and the amount of thinly-spread material in our own local region, the Solar System, has been found to be surprisingly great. On the other hand, this tenuous interplanetary material is quite unable to affect the motion of any vehicle, and the rocket designer can afford to neglect it completely —even though the theoretical astronomer regards it as both interesting and significant.

THE ELECTROMAGNETIC SPECTRUM. The atmosphere is transparent only to visible light (coloured band) and the so-called radio window (white). All other wavelengths are blocked before reaching the surface of the Earth. To study these wavelengths, therefore, it is essential to rise above the shielding layers of atmosphere—which means, in effect, using space research methods, since only rockets will rise to the heights required (though in some fields of research, balloons have their uses also).

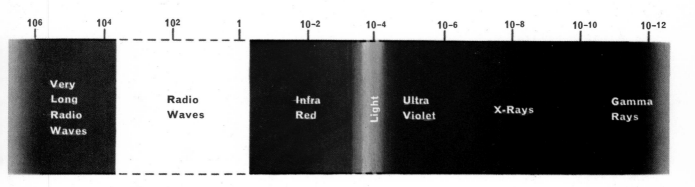

| 10^6 | 10^4 | 10^2 | 1 | 10^{-2} | 10^{-4} | 10^{-6} | 10^{-8} | 10^{-10} | 10^{-12} |

Very Long Radio Waves

Radio Waves

Infra Red

Light

Ultra Violet

X-Rays

Gamma Rays

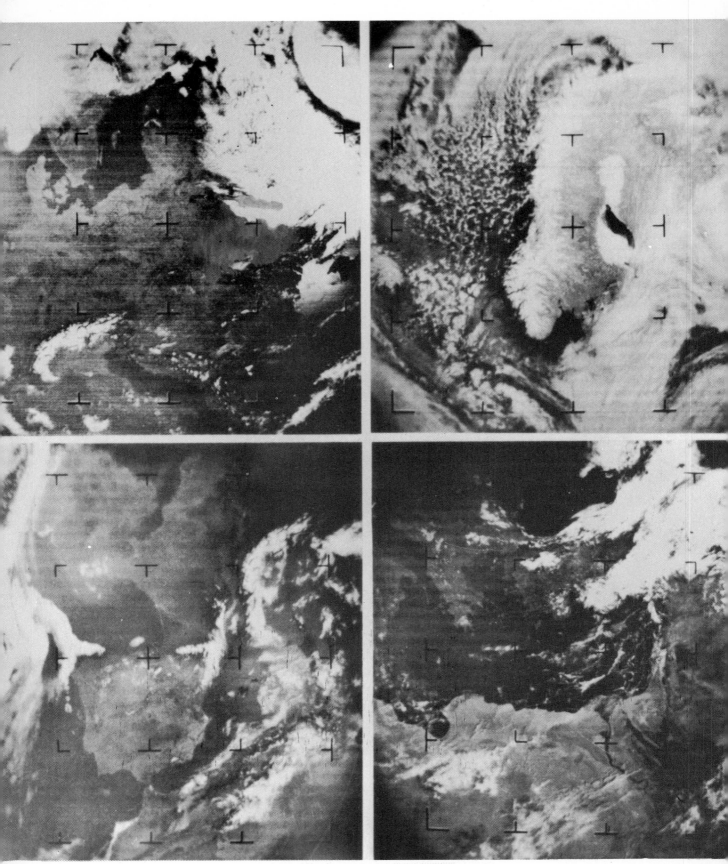

48

THE EARTH FROM ABOVE. These four photographs, showing central and northern Europe (above) and the eastern and western Mediterranean (below) were sent back from the ESSA-2 orbiting weather satellite. The cloud systems are well shown, and photographs of this sort, with whole weather systems displayed, are immensely valuable to meteorologists.

The meteorologist can study the atmosphere which is within a few miles of ground-level; he can take its pressure and its temperature, he can work out the weather systems, and he can send up the radio-sonde balloons which transmit information from many thousands of feet up (and which, in passing, give rise to so many of the flying saucer reports). Eventually he will appear on your television screen and show various charts, smiling grimly as he warns us of icy roads, approaching fog, and deep depressions advancing from Iceland. But to understand the atmosphere fully, we must consider the whole of it, and not only the bottom part. Only then can we hope that weather forecasting will become really reliable.

To the astronomer, it must be admitted that in some ways the atmosphere is a thorough nuisance. It blocks out most of the radiations coming from space; and if these radiations are to be studied, the only course is to send instruments above the screening layers. All sorts of methods have been tried, with varying degrees of success. Until the development of rocketry, the balloon was the most valuable aid, but no balloon can rise to more than a relatively few miles.

If we are to venture into space, we must certainly start by exploring the upper part of our own atmosphere. The only practicable method is to use the rocket, which will work excellently even when there is no air surrounding it. Rockets alone can help us, soaring first into the lofty atmosphere and then far beyond.

RADIO WAVE RECEPTION. Radio waves travel in straight lines, but some wavelengths are 'bounced back' by layers in the Earth's air; thus the transmitter at A, on the Earth's curved surface, is able to send a radio signal to a receiver at B. On an airless world, radio reception would be limited to the distance of the horizon.

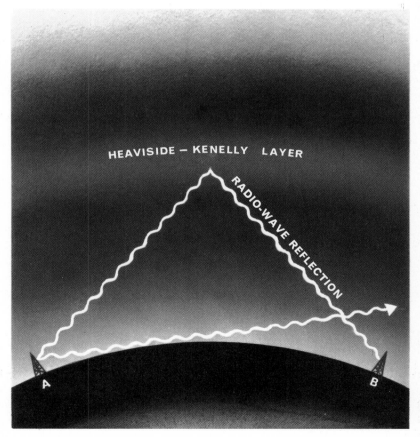

HEAVISIDE — KENELLY LAYER

RADIO-WAVE REFLECTION

A

B

49

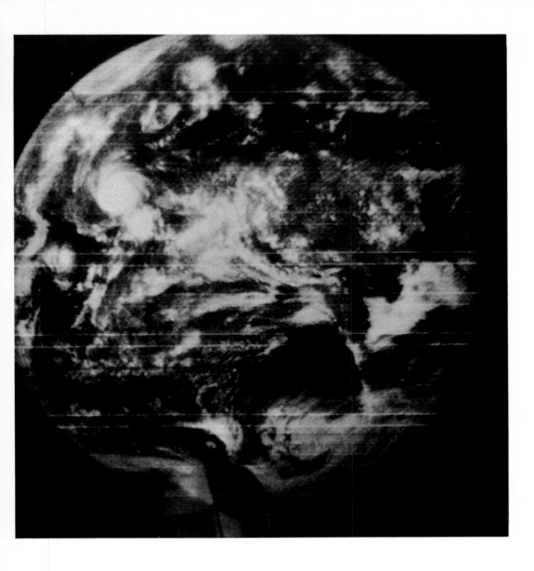

AFRICA AND WEST-ERN EUROPE, photo-graphed in colour on 25 July 1967 from an American artificial sat-ellite. Again the weather systems are excellently shown.

NOCTILUCENT CLOUDS. These strange clouds are seen at great altitudes, and are not the same as normal clouds; they may be associated with meteoric debris. They are best seen from countries such as Nor-way, and are never visible from low lati-tudes.

◀**THE AURORA. A** display of the Northern Lights, seen over the Arctic.

Chapter 7

The Rocket

"Nose cone"
(Payload)

Propellant

Hot
Gases

Direction
of
Thrust

Constriction

Nozzle

Exhaust
Gases

PRINCIPLE OF THE ROCKET. A rocket—whether a firework toy, or a space-craft launcher—works according to the principle of reaction. Gases are expelled from the exhaust, and the rocket itself moves in the opposite direction.

Rockets are much the most spectacular of all display fireworks. Almost every country has its national holidays, when fireworks are set off in their thousands, and the sky is red with the light of bonfires; rockets rise high into the air, bursting and showering out multi-coloured sparks and stars.

There would seem to be little in common between a firework rocket fired from a bottle, and a huge, costly space-probe bound for the Moon or Mars. Yet in point of fact the principles involved are exactly the same, and before going into the history of rockets we must pause to say something about the way in which they work.

To recapitulate: the Earth's atmosphere does not extend upward for very far on the astronomical scale. The dense part of it ends at a few tens of miles, and no ordinary aircraft can rise higher than this. The propeller aeroplane cannot function except when it is surrounded by air dense enough for its propellers to grip; the jet has to draw in oxygen to make its engines work, and the balloon depends upon being lighter than the air around it. This point is too obvious to be laboured. In fact, conventional aircraft are limited to much less than 100 miles—and it is well over 200,000 miles to the Moon.

There are only two possibilities. Either the space-vehicle must be given a starting velocity great enough for it to complete its journey without using any extra power, or else it must be given the means of extra acceleration once it is out in space. This was fully realized by Jules Verne, who foresaw the development of the heavier-than-air craft even though nothing of the kind could be built at the time when he was writing his novels.[1] Verne solved the problem by means of the space-gun, but, as we have seen, there are fatal objections to anything of this sort.

Similarly, there is no point in trying to develop other non-rocket methods of providing a launching-speed of 7 miles per second. Long acceleration ramps have been suggested from time to time, but these would be of no help in solving the air-resistance problem even if they were practicable—which they are not. Neither does it help to build a space-gun on the top of a mountain. Admittedly, the air is thinner at high altitude, but one would need to go up for many miles to gain any real advantage. All in all, it is essential to find some means of propulsion which will function in vacuum, and the rocket is the only answer.

Let us go back to our display firework. It is made up of a hollow tube, filled with gunpowder or some such explosive, and with a stick added to give stability. When you 'light the blue touch-paper and retire immediately', the gunpowder starts to burn, and gives off hot gas. This gas tries to escape from the rocket, but can do so in only one direction: through the exhaust, where the touch-paper has been burned away. A stream of gas rushes out, and

[1] In his book *The Clipper of the Clouds*, Verne demonstrated the superiority of the heavier-than-air machine over the airship type. Incidentally, he also forecast the submarine; and I shall have something to say about his artificial satellite in Chapter 14. He was indeed a remarkable prophet.

Charles
Simmons

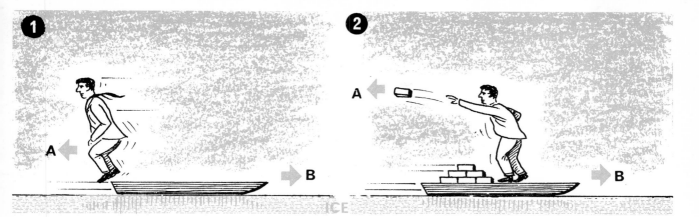

THE REACTION PRINCIPLE. If a sleigh rests on very smooth ice, a man jumping off one end in direction **A** will make the sleigh move toward direction **B** (Fig. 1); this illustrates Newton's reaction principle. A more sensitive test is shown in Fig. 2, where the man throws a brick off toward **A** and so causes the sleigh to move toward direction **B**.

paper has been burned away. A stream of gas rushes out, and propels the rocket in the opposite direction. This is why the rocket flies; and so long as the gas keeps streaming out of the exhaust, the flight will continue.

Surrounding atmosphere, let it be noted, is not concerned at all. In fact it is actually a hindrance, because it sets up air-resistance and tends to slow the rocket down. The rocket is working on the principle of Newton's Third Law: 'Every action has an equal and opposite reaction'. It is quite untrue to suppose, as many people do, that the rocket is thrusting against the atmosphere. On the contrary, it is thrusting against itself.

A simple though rather far-fetched comparison should make the situation clearer. Consider a man who is standing on a sleigh resting on a sheet of ice, as shown in the diagram. If the man jumps in direction A, then the sleigh will move off in direction B; the harder the jump, the greater the motion. If the experiment could be carried out in vacuum, it would work just as well. Very broadly, it may be said that the man represents the stream of gas, while the sleigh stands for the rocket body.

More accurately, we can picture our demonstrator standing on the edge of the sleigh and throwing bricks toward A, which will propel the sleigh—and himself—towards B. Here, of course, we would have to suppose that the ice is virtually frictionless, but the principle is valid enough.

There is a much more down-to-earth experiment, which may be carried out indoors. Blow up a toy balloon, and then suddenly let go of the 'exhaust'. The gas inside will stream out, and the balloon will shoot across the room. It will corkscrew around, because it is hopelessly unstable and because it is being braked by the surrounding air; the thrust given by the outrush of gas is feeble by any standards. Yet again, the principle holds good, and the experiment would work just as well even if there were no air in the room.

I may well be making too much of this point, but I am anxious to clarify the situation at the outset rather than to have return to it

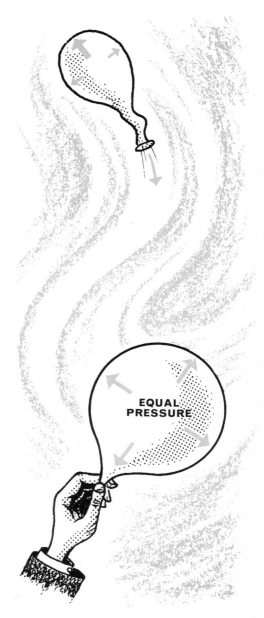

REACTION PRINCIPLE SHOWN BY A TOY BALLOON. If a toy balloon is inflated, and the exhaust is suddenly released, air will stream out and the balloon will spin off across the room. It will twist and turn only because it is having to combat the resistance of the atmosphere, and the 'thrust' is naturally very feeble indeed.

later. To sum up: the rocket works by reaction, and does not need to have anything to 'push' against other than itself. This means that it is not limited in scope, and it is actually at its best in vacuum, because there is no surrounding atmosphere to set up resistance.

The implications of this are far-reaching. Certainly a modern space-probe has to accelerate to escape velocity, but it can do so gradually. When a rocket is launched, it begins its journey very gradually, and does not accelerate to full power until it is beyond the limits of the dense atmosphere and so is in no danger of being burned away in the manner of a meteor—or, more accurately, becoming so heated that its scientific equipment would be destroyed and any human occupants would meet with a hot and extremely unpleasant death. This acceleration can be achieved simply by turning on the rocket motors. With a space-gun, there would be no possible means of providing extra power after the initial bang.

In theory, there is no need for a space-probe to reach escape velocity at all. If kept moving at a constant speed of, say, 30 m.p.h., and suitably controlled, it would be able to reach the Moon or even Mars. It would take some time; about 11 months for the lunar journey, assuming that it went by the quickest route, and something like 140 years to arrive on Mars—but it could be done. However, providing acceleration all though a long space-journey would mean using up more fuel than could possibly be carried, and so it is essential to reach escape velocity and 'coast' for much of the way. I shall return to this later, but the point seemed to be worth making here.

Also, it is hardly necessary to add that no gunpowder rocket would be of any use for space research. Solid fuels in general are not particularly powerful, and they are difficult to control; when they have started to burn, they continue to do so, and after they are exhausted the rocket is powerless. Modern vehicles use liquid fuels, and the simple powder tube is replaced by an immensely complicated rocket motor. In the future, no doubt it will become possible to make use of atomic power, which will lead to higher velocities and much more fuel reserve. Yet the principle will still be the same, and the vehicle will still be classified as a rocket.

Forty years ago, the idea of using rockets as space-vehicles was regarded as very much of a joke, and it is only recently that the practical exploration of space has begun. On the other hand, the rocket principle had been known for centuries, even if it had not been properly understood. The fireworks made by the Chinese were, in their way, the ancestors of the massive vehicles which in our own time will take men to the Moon.

AUSTRALIA, from Perth to Port Darwin, photographed from a height of 740 miles from an American satellite on 14 August 1966. Part of the satellite itself is also shown, and the curvature of the Earth is brought out in spectacular manner.

LAUNCHING OF THE FIRST LUNAR ORBITER, from Cape Kennedy, on 10 August 1966. This was the first American vehicle to orbit the Moon and send back detailed photographs of the lunar surface; the experiment was a complete success, and magnificent pictures were obtained.

Chapter 8

The Rockets' Red Glare

Nobody can be sure when the rocket was invented. Stories of Chinese rockets used thousands of years ago, when China boasted of the most advanced civilization in the world, seem to rest on very uncertain evidence, and in fact we cannot trace the story back any further than A.D. 1232. However, the Chinese do appear to have priority, and probably they made firework rockets much earlier than the thirteenth century.

The reaction principle itself can be followed back to Greek times. About 360 B.C., an inventor named Archytas produced what is always known as a flying pigeon. Archytas had a wide reputation, and was a friend of the great philosopher Plato; he was a military general as well as a scientist, and lived until 347 B.C., when he was drowned during a voyage across the Adriatic Sea.

Actually, Archytas' pigeon did not fly. According to a description of it given by a later Roman writer, it simply moved round in a circle, so that it was supported in some way—probably by a cord. Evidently it moved because of steam coming out of holes in it, so that at least it depended upon the reaction principle.

Then, in the third century B.C. (though the date is uncertain), Heron of Alexandria is said to have built a device called an aeolipile. Here, the spherical body contained water, and was heated from below; steam escaped from two narrow tubes, each bent backwards, so that there was a reaction effect strong enough to make the sphere rotate. Exactly the same principle is used today in the rotating lawn-sprinkler. Almost nothing is known about Heron or his aeolipile, but it must have been interesting mechanically even though it can hardly have been put to any practical use.

But a chance application of the reaction principle is very different from the building of a rocket, and nothing of the sort was ever achieved by the Greeks, It was not for more than 1,000 years after the end of the Greek period that the first proper rockets were described, though let us repeat that the Chinese probably made them well before the thirteenth century.

In A.D. 1232, the Mongols besieged the city of Kai-fung-fu. The cause and result of the war is of interest only to students of Oriental history, but this particular battle was of importance in the story of rocket research. The Chinese defenders made use of what have been called 'arrows of flying fire', and these seem certainly to have been primitive rockets, no doubt adapted from the fireworks used for ceremonial display. Explosive powder was already known, and then crude rockets carrying burning material would be unpleasant weapons to face. Apparently they were at least reasonably successful on this occasion, and it is not surprising that military rockets were revived now and then all through mediæval times; but they were confined mainly to Europe, and it seems that the Chinese made no attempt to develop them further.

This book is not a history of war-rockets, but brief mention must

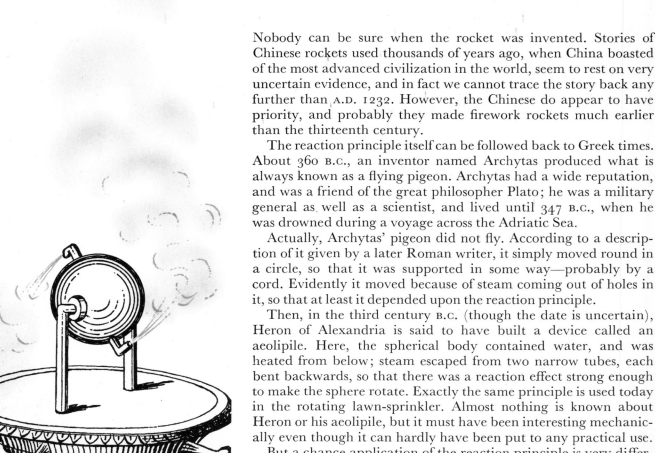

HERON'S ÆOLIPILE; a reconstruction of how the device apparently worked. It can have been of no practical value, but at least it demonstrated how motion can be obtained by means of the reaction principle. Needless to say, the device itself has not survived, but written descriptions of it have come down to us, and seem to be authentic.

be made of Konrad von Eichstädt, a German military engineer who described rocket weapons in 1405, and Joanes de Fontana, an Italian, who worked out a whole series of projects some 15 years later. The Fontana rockets were to be disguised as flying birds, floating fishes and running hares. The hare, designed to run on rollers, was planned to be dispatched toward enemy defences and set them on fire. It was an intriguing idea, but one rather doubts whether it would have worked, and in any case it seems to have developed no further than Fontana's sketch-book.

Then, in 1591, came a book by Johann Schmidlap of Nuremberg. It was devoted to display fireworks, but it contained two new suggestions. The rockets were to be stabilized with sticks, as modern toy fireworks actually are; and Schmidlap planned to mount small rockets on top of larger ones, so forecasting the step-vehicles of today. Much later, in 1668, Colonel Christoph von Geissler carried out some practical military experiments near Berlin, and apparently came to the conclusion that the rocket was a potentially useful weapon, though whether he ever tried to put his ideas into practice is not known.

Until the latter part of the eighteenth century, nobody in Britain had paid much attention to rockets except as fireworks, but then the possibilities of rocket weapons were brought home in a very unwelcome fashion. At that time there was persistent trouble in India, and the most able and warlike of the Indian rulers, Hyder Ali, formed a corps of rocket gunners. The weapons were made of heavy iron tubes, and they were guided by long bamboo poles. They were not accurate, but they had a range of at least a mile, and they were good enough to cause a great deal of damage. Hyder Ali's son, Tippoo Sahib, increased the rocket corps to some 5,000 men, and the British forces were roughly handled on more than one occasion.

The reports from India took some time to filter through, but at least one Briton saw that the idea of military rocket warfare was practicable enough to be developed. He was William (afterwards Sir William) Congreve, whose father had been a distinguished soldier, and who had grown up in a thoroughly military atmosphere.

Congreve bought numbers of skyrockets, and started experimenting. He wanted to make the rockets more accurate, and he wanted to give them a longer range, which meant improving their design; the Indian weapons, after all, had been no more than iron tubes which 'spat flame', as one eye-witness had put it. (Congreve himself never went to India, so that he had to rely upon second-hand accounts of what had happened there.) He interested the military authorities, and at Woolwich Arsenal some larger rockets were built according to his specifications; some of them were over 3 inches in diameter and 3½ feet in length. The device was slid into a thin-walled copper tube, and set off by lighting a fuse projecting from the nozzle.

The results were encouraging, and Congreve went to the Prime Minister, Pitt, with a plan to bombard the French port of Boulogne. Britain had been at war with France for many years— this, of course, was the period when Napoleon was menacing the whole of Europe—and Pitt was prepared to listen to any new ideas; besides, Congreve was a friend of the Prince of Wales, the future

SIR WILLIAM CONGREVE, who was born in 1772 and died in 1828. This is a portrait painted by J. Lonsdale. Congreve was a pioneer of military rockets, and was mainly responsible for the rocket barrages used by British forces during the Napoleonic Wars. Indeed, rockets of this sort were always known as 'Congreve rockets', and for a time they were quite successful.

King George IV, which gave him considerable influence.

In 1805 the bombardment was tried. Accounts of it are not clear, but what seems to have happened is that the wind changed at the wrong moment, ruining the whole plan. Yet oddly enough the rocket idea was not dropped, and in 1806 Boulogne was attacked again. This time the results were spectacular, and huge fires were caused in the port. The rockets soared over their main targets, the ships of the French fleet, but at least they showed their power, and with a little more accuracy they could be highly devastating.

The next target was Copenhagen, in 1807. Denmark had been drawn into the war on the French side, and was therefore officially an ally of Napoleon's. The full story is somewhat involved, and the Danes had been forced into a very difficult position, but at any rate the British fleet was ordered to attack the capital, and Congreve and his rockets played a major role. More than 25,000 rockets were sent against Copenhagen, and at least half the city was burned down, while the Danish Navy was to all intents and purposes put out of action. Danzig was similarly attacked in 1813. Not all the authorities approved; Lord Gambier, for instance, described the rockets as 'infernal machines', and the Duke of Wellington was similarly unimpressed.

Land-launched rockets were coming to the fore, too. In 1813 a Rocket Brigade was formed within the British Army, and it went into action before the Battle of Leipzig in 1813—the battle which shattered Napoleon's power. Meanwhile, war had broken out with the United States. In 1812 a small British force fired rockets against American troops at Bladensburg, and the immediate result was dramatic; Washington was taken, and the White House burned down. And in 1814, rockets were fired against Fort McHenry. The bombardment was not a success, but at least it was noisy, and it was then that one of the defenders, Francis Scott Key, wrote the famous line about 'the rockets' red glare' which is part of the modern American anthem.

That, for the moment, was the end of the first period of the military rocket. After Napoleon was finally beaten and banished, an uneasy peace settled over Europe, and the Congreve weapons were no longer needed, though they were kept in reserve. Congreve himself went on experimenting; in 1826, for instance, he proposed a twin rocket, with the head of one touching the base of the next to give an extra burst of power—an idea based on Schmidlap's book of well over a century earlier. Congreve died two years later, firmly convinced that the rocket would prove to be the most deadly of all war machines.

He was right—but not in the way that he expected.

For a time, his ideas were still followed. Many European nations organized rocket corps, and on various occasions full-scale barrages were used (by the Dutch, for example, against the Celebes natives during a campaign in the East Indies in 1825). Another Briton, William Hale, developed a stickless rocket which was probably more accurate than anything that Congreve had produced. But by then, the whole situation had changed.

The rocket, in its old form, had almost reached its peak. By methods available at the time it could not be developed much further, but it was still inaccurate and unreliable, so that its main

CONGREVE ROCKET, fired from a ship in 1812. Rocket bombardments from the sea were carried out on several occasions during the Napoleonic Wars, and on the whole they proved to be quite effective.

strength lay in sending over heavy barrages for a long period. On the other hand, conventional weapons, which had been primitive during the Napoleonic wars, were improved out of all recognition during the next few decades. They soon far outstripped the rocket in performance, in accuracy and even in range. This being the case, why bother about a method which could never be relied upon? The Austrians had been particularly enthusiastic about rockets, but when their corps was faced by Prussian artillery in 1866 it was completely routed, and was disbanded a year later. So far as is known, the last nation to use the old-fashioned war rocket was Russia. This was in 1881, during a long and tedious campaign in Turkestan. After that, the rocket as a weapon was more or less forgotten; it had been superseded.

Of course, rocket manufacture continued. Firework displays were fashionable everywhere, and there was a more useful application too; rockets had been designed to act as life-lines between the shore and ships in distress, and proved able to save many lives. Indeed, the marine rocket is still in use today. All in all, the rocket had lost its sinister reputation well before the end of the nineteenth century. It had reverted to its former role of a harmless and amusing toy, capable of being put to good use in certain restricted ways.

Under the circumstances, it is not surprising that when suggestions were made about sending rockets toward the Moon, few people were impressed. Even at the very end of the nineteenth century, such ideas sounded hopelessly far-fetched.

THE STORMING OF CIUDAD RODERIGO, during the Peninsular War of 1812. Note the rocket barrage, which was used on this occasion and which was an important if not a decisive factor in the operation.

Chapter 9

Pioneers of Space

ORVILLE WRIGHT, the first 'man in the air', who made the pioneer hop in the primitive *Flyer* **in 1903.**

YURI GAGARIN, the world's first space-man, who went round the Earth in *Vostok I* **on 12 April, 1961. Gagarin will always be remembered as the greatest of the space pioneers. He died tragically in an air crash on 27 March 1968.**

Around the turn of the century, flying-machines were becoming a real possibility. Men such as Otto Lilienthal had built excellent gliders, and were well on the way to complete success. When the first true flight was made, in 1903, it was by Orville Wright, a bicycle mechanic who—with his brother Wilbur—had worked out the theory of the problem and then put it into practice. The Wright brothers had no official backing, and, amazingly, few people took the slightest notice of them for some years after their triumph. Neither had they any scientific training; they had to work everything out for themselves.

The development of space-flight followed very different lines. The pioneer trip was not made until 1961, and when Yuri Gagarin of Soviet Russia became the first astronaut in history he was certainly not an independent pioneer. The full resources of a great nation, and the results of more than half a century's theoretical work, were needed before he could make his journey round the Earth. Yet the interval of 58 years between the two achievements does not seem much, all things considered. I have met both Orville Wright and Yuri Gagarin, and I can see how they belong to two different ages; but they were contemporaries, and it would have been perfectly possible for them to meet, though in fact they never did.

There has never been any chance of a brilliant amateur inventor building a space-ship and launching himself toward the Moon. The absent-minded professor of the story-books, who constructs a rocket in his back garden and then sets off for distant worlds, has no place in science; he is entertaining in fiction, but he can never exist. But although this is so very clear nowadays, it was not so obvious 70 years ago. And it was during the nineteenth century that the first scientific plans for space-travel were worked out, though at that stage there was no possible means of putting them into practice.

Before discussing these ideas, however, we must spare a thought for a Chinese gentleman with the rather improbable name of Wan-Hoo. According to reports, Wan-Hoo became interested in rockets as early as A.D. 1500, and decided to carry out an experiment. He built a framework of bamboo, with a chair in the middle, and attached forty-seven rockets to it. When all was ready, he sat in the chair and ordered his retainers to light all forty-seven rockets at once, the idea being that he would be lifted into the air and would land gently by means of a kind of primitive parachute. Unfortunately, all that happened was a tremendous bang, accompanied by clouds of black smoke. When the smoke cleared away, Wan-Hoo was no longer to be seen . . .

I have no idea whether this report is reliable; I have an inner feeling that it is not. I am also dubious about the story that an early nineteenth-century Italian inventor, Ruggieri, sent up small animals such as mice in cages attached to rockets, and rescued them alive after parachute descents.

In 1865 an otherwise obscure French writer, Achille Eyraud, published a novel called *Voyage à Vénus*, in which he proposed to make his space-ship function by the reaction principle. The book caused no real interest; for one thing it was poorly written, and moreover it was completely overshadowed by Jules Verne's lunar novel, which appeared at about the same time. So far as I know, Eyraud's book has never been translated into English.

Meanwhile the first of the great theoretical pioneers, Konstantin Tsiolkovskii, was already growing up; but perhaps the story really begins with a most unusual inventor—Nikolai Ivanovitch Kibaltchitch. Kibaltchitch was an engineer, and an expert in explosives. His most unwise exploit was to make the bomb which was used by a group of revolutionaries to kill the Czar of Russia, Alexander II, in 1881. Not unnaturally, Kibaltchitch was arrested, thrown into prison and condemned to death. While awaiting execution, he worked out what he called a 'preliminary design of a rocket aircraft', and he spent his last days working busily upon mathematical formulae. He was too interested even to make a real attempt to defend himself in court—though one must admit that the authorities had every reason for arresting him; one cannot assist in murdering the ruler of one's country, and then expect to be treated as an honoured scientist. Kibaltchitch did grasp some of the fundamental principles, but his design was quite impracticable, and he was given no opportunity to revise it.

In the strict historical sequence, we come next to Hermann Ganswindt, a German who was as full of ideas as the White Knight in Lewis Carroll's *Through the Looking-glass*. He was born in 1856, in Prussia, and originally meant to become a lawyer, but he soon decided that his talents would be wasted in the legal profession. For 30 years he produced invention after invention, some of which were basically sound while others were frankly weird.

It is not easy to sum up Ganswindt's ability. He, of all people, really did resemble the eccentric inventor of the story-books, and it was a pity that his crazy ideas tended to overshadow his occasional flashes of real insight. At an early stage he worked out plans for an airship—not a small one, let it be noted; Ganswindt never did things by halves, and he said that to be successful an airship would have to be really large. He bombarded the German War Ministry with his papers and pamphlets, and he even managed to interest the Crown Prince, though his airship never progressed further than the drawing-board. Later, during the First World War, the Germans did use airships of the kind developed by Count von Zeppelin—and Ganswindt accused Zeppelin, the Ministry, and almost everyone else of stealing his ideas.

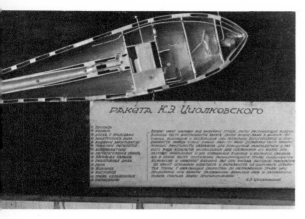

MODEL OF A ROCKET DESIGNED BY K. E. TSIOLKOVSKII. This is one of Tsiolkovskii's many designs; the model is on display at the museum in Kaluga in the U.S.S.R.

THE TSIOLKOVSKII MEDAL, awarded in honour of Konstantin Tsiolkovskii's outstanding contributions to the pioneer theory of space research. For many years Tsiolkovskii's work remained largely unknown even in Russia, but by the time of his death he had become something of a national hero, and he is still so regarded to-day.

Much more successful was his invention of the free-wheeling mechanism for bicycles. He also developed what he called a 'tretmotor', worked by a man shifting his weight from one leg to the other and so operating the mechanism; it was fitted to a boat with mild success, and it was also used on a wheeled vehicle on the road. When Ganswindt rode about in his 'horseless carriage', as early as 1894, the police became somewhat alarmed, and asked him to notify the local headquarters whenever he felt like making a trial run. He adapted the principle to work a fire-engine, but then wanted so large a sum of money for the device that the City authorities refused to buy it. Next he designed a helicopter, but since he was unable to provide it with an engine it was of little practical use, though it did include some sound ideas.

Like many eccentrics, Ganswindt became infuriated because more conventional scientists refused to take him seriously. Much of his later life was spent in bringing lawsuits against those who were alleged to have copied his inventions without permission, and it came as something of a surprise to him when he was at last given a small award by the Nazi Government for his pioneer work.

The award was not, however, for his free-wheeling device, his fire-engine or his helicopter. The German authorities were thinking about his original theories concerning space-travel, which had been expressed in a public lecture as long ago as 1891.

Ganswindt had grasped the idea that reaction, and reaction alone, can send a vehicle into space. He could never work out the full details, and in any case he made some basic errors; he thought that the rocket would have to 'push' against some outside mass. Accordingly, he designed an extraordinary system in which the power was to be given by cartridges, fired from below so as to knock the top off the craft and propel it upward in a series of jerks. One is entitled to doubt whether any sane astronaut would have risked his life in a Ganswindt machine even if it could have been built; but at any rate, Ganswindt did realize that a spaceman moving in free fall would be weightless, and he suggested rotating the craft so as to create 'artificial gravity'.

Ganswindt continued to work on his theories, but he lacked the patience (and probably the ability) to make much further progress. Certainly he cannot be classed with his contemporary Tsiolkovskii, who was working on the same problems at about the same time.

Konstantin Eduardovitch Tsiolkovskii[1] was born at Ijevsk, in Russia—a village some way southwest of Moscow—in 1857, so that he was a year younger than Ganswindt. His father was a forester, and young Konstantin's education was by no means extensive; to make matter more difficult, he caught scarlet fever when he was ten years old, and he was left permanently deaf, so that he did not find school life easy. Yet he showed that he had great ability in all scientific subjects, and it is a great tribute to him that by the age of 19 he had learned enough for him to teach others. He became a schoolmaster, and remained so until he retired in 1921.

Tsiolkovskii's first official contact with the scientific world was

[1] Willy Ley, the leading historian of astronautics, spells the name phonetically—Ziolkovsky. This is much more sensible, and I am tempted to follow it, but the version 'Tsiolkovskii' has come into general use, and I suppose it must be accepted.

most unusual. When he was 23, he sent in some papers to the Academy of Sciences in the city then known as St. Petersburg, now called Leningrad. The papers dealt with the theory of gases, and some research into the nature and behaviour of light. The learned scientists at St. Petersburg read them with amazement, and for some time they were badly puzzled. Everything that Tsiolkovskii said was correct—but all the results had been published at least twenty years before.

Inquiries were made, and the truth was found. Tsiolkovskii, with his limited educational facilities, was unable to consult the books in large libraries, and he had simply not heard about the earlier work; he had found it out for himself without any prior knowledge whatsoever. At least it showed that he had a lively, original mind, and it was typical of him that he was not discouraged.

He became interested in flying machines. During his early researches he built a device known as a wind tunnel, certainly the first ever to be constructed in Russia, and he worked away on various designs. Some of them were quite sound, but he never tried to obtain official support, as Ganswindt had done; he was always disinclined to push himself forward, and this may have been one of the reasons why he remained unknown for so long.

Slightly later than Ganswindt, he began thinking seriously about the design of a space-craft. He too grasped the idea of reaction, but much more clearly than Ganswindt had been capable of doing, and he also realized that solid fuels were of no use for practical research. The only solution that occurred to him was to use liquids instead.

In a liquid-fuel arrangement there are two liquids, one the actual 'fuel' and the other known as the 'oxidant'. These propellants are forced into a combustion chamber by a pumping mechanism, and are ignited. They react together, and produce hot gas; this gas is sent out of the exhaust, and the rocket flies. The advantages of this arrangement are many. For one thing, much more power can be gained; also, the whole vehicle can be controlled, by regulating the flow of the liquids into the combustion chamber.

Tsiolkovskii was undoubtedly the first serious scientist to consider using liquid propellants. Yet he went even further. He knew that even liquids are limited in their power, and so he suggested mounting one rocket on top of another in the now famous step-principle.

The general theory is shown in the diagram. When the vehicle takes off, the larger lower engine provides all the power, and lifts the craft high into the atmosphere. When it has exhausted its propellants, the whole lower stage breaks away and falls back to the ground. Meantime the second motor has been started, and the upper part of the space-ship continues the journey with a double advantage; it has been taken above the densest part of the air, and it has been given what may be called a 'running start'. If need be, a third stage can be fixed on to the second, and so on. All modern space-probes are launched by step vehicles, just as Tsiolkovskii foresaw.

Tsiolkovskii's ideas about weightlessness, or zero gravity, were perfectly correct. He was also well aware of the many problems involved in long space-journeys, and he suggested taking various

THE PRINCIPLE OF THE STEP-ROCKET. On launching, the power is provided by the lower stage (4). After this has exhausted its fuel, the next stage (3) starts its motors, and the journey is continued. The succeeding stage (2) takes over in turn, and the payload (1) is finally injected into orbit.

types of green plants to remove the excess carbon dioxide from the cabin's atmosphere and replace it with free oxygen.

All this sounds very up to date—and in fact it is. But when first put forward by a shy, deaf Russian schoolmaster in an article submitted to an obscure journal in 1895 (though not published immediately), it sounded quite fantastic, and it attracted no attention. Three years later Tsiolkovskii developed his ideas about liquid-propelled rockets, and sent them in to the editor of a small Russian periodical, *Na-ootchnoye Obozreniya* (Science Survey). Apparently the editor was distinctly unenthusiastic, and it was not until 1903 that the article finally came out in print. Like its predecessor, it passed virtually unnoticed. Moreover it was in Russian, which few scientists of other countries could read, and it was not translated into any other language until many years later.

Incidentally, Tsiolkovskii had also written a novel. It seems to have been finished in 1895, though its publication was delayed until 1920 and its English translation did not appear until 1960. The English title is *Beyond the Planet Earth*, and the book is well worth reading, because it contains so many ideas which are universally accepted now but which were quite new then. As a story, and as a literary effort, it can only be described as atrocious, but as a forecast it was half a century ahead of its time.

After his original articles came out, Tsiolkovskii continued working away at his plans. Some articles which he wrote during and after 1911 attracted some attention, and he was given a certain amount of support and encouragement by the Bolshevik government which came into power after the Russian revolution of 1916, but it was only after 1924, when the space-travel idea became 'headline news', that he achieved fame.

The developments of the immediate post-war period are best left until Chapter 10. For the moment, it is enough to say that a book by a Roumanian mathematician, Hermann Oberth, became something of a best-seller, and scientists began to realize that the idea of reaching other worlds was not so far-fetched as had been thought. Then, too, there was a paper by an American, Goddard, which discussed the possibilities of exploring the upper atmosphere by means of rockets. Tsiolkovskii, now retired from teaching, was remembered – and thrust into the limelight. His earlier works were reprinted, and he became something of a national hero. His 75th birthday, in 1932, was marked by official celebrations, and the old pioneer even received a telegram of congratulations from Josef Stalin, then the supreme ruler of Soviet Russia.

Though Tsiolkovskii was not a man to seek honours, he must surely have been satisfied that he had made a real contribution to human knowledge. And though he never actually fired a rocket in his life, and though some of his ideas were very wide of the mark, nobody can deny that he must be regarded as 'the father of space-travel'.

Tsiolkovskii died in 1935. There are many people still living who remember him, and not long ago, when I was in Moscow, I met a man who recalled having read the original article published in 1903. 'I didn't pay much attention to it,' I was told. 'It sounded like science fiction then.' Science fiction it may have been—in 1903; but before 2003, many of Tsiolkovskii's dreams may well have come true.

KONSTANTIN EDUARDOVICH TSIOLKOVSKII, the great Russian pioneer of theoretical space research. This is one of the few surviving photographs of him; it shows him in his study together with one of his rocket models. The photograph was taken about 1930, a few years before his death.

Chapter 10

The First of the
New Rockets

On 12 January 1920, a startling headline appeared on the front page of one of America's leading daily papers, the *New York Times*. It read, baldly; BELIEVES ROCKET CAN REACH MOON, and it was followed by a long article in which some remarkable forecasts were made.

The article caused something of a sensation. Of course, there had been many 'moon-voyage' suggestions before, but none of then had been backed by professional scientists; at that time, remember, Tsiolkovskii was still to all intents and purposes unknown (even if he could be regarded as a professional scientist, which was dubious), while Hermann Ganswindt was more generally associated with engineless helicopters, pedalled fire-engines, and never-ending lawsuits. But the new work came from Professor Robert Hutchings Goddard, of Clark University. Goddard was known to be working on rocket problems, and he had been busy in developing new-type weapons at the direct request of the United States Government.

Goddard himself was not responsible for the *Times* article. In

ROBERT HUTCHINGS GODDARD, the American rocket pioneer. Goddard was above all a practical experimenter; he not only designed rockets, but he also built them and launched them. This picture shows him at the blackboard at Clark University.

fact, he was far from pleased when he read it. He had written a slim booklet called *A Method of Reaching Extreme Altitudes*, which he had prepared for the benefit of technical experimenters, and in which he had dealt mainly with the possibilities of sending up rockets to study the upper atmosphere. To his later regret, he had also said that it might eventually be practicable to send a rocket to the Moon, perhaps carrying a charge of flash-powder so that it would make a visible spark when crash-landing upon the lunar surface. It was this last idea which had caught the attention of the New York columnist, and the sensational *Times* headline was the result.

To make matters worse, the next day's *Times* published an editorial comment headed 'A Severe Strain on Credulity', in which Goddard's ideas were to some extent ridiculed. Reading the article today, one can see only too well that the author had no idea of the principles of rocketry, and that he made mistakes of which no Fifth Form schoolboy of the present time would be guilty. Goddard could certainly have made an ample reply; instead, he merely pointed out that too much emphasis had been placed on the Moon-rocket idea, and too little on the importance of studying the Earth's upper air. In fact, he said as little as possible, and after a while the whole episode was more or less forgotten.

Goddard was born at Worcester, in Massachusetts, in 1882. He took his first scientific degree in 1908, and was awarded a doctorate from Clark University three years later. By then he had already begun to experiment with rockets, and on more than one occasion his fellow students were alarmed by the quantities of black smoke billowing out from his private laboratory. This research was quite unofficial; he had bought skyrockets with his own money, and had begun to try to improve their performance by re-designing their combustion chambers (that is to say, the chambers in which the fuel-burning took place). He was also concerned with what is now known as the mass ratio.

The scientific load carried by a rocket is known as its payload. Unfortunately, it takes a large rocket to launch a small payload, as Goddard realized. The original weight of the fully-fuelled rocket, divided by the weight which is left when all the fuel has been used up, is the mass ratio – and the smaller the mass ratio, the more effective is the rocket. If, for instance, the rocket could have an original weight of 10 tons and an 'empty' weight of 5 tons, the mass ratio would be 10/5, or 2. This is quite out of the question even today, and it was even more so when Goddard began his labours.

There were two main things to be done. Propellants had to be made more powerful, and the design of the rocket had to be improved, so that burning a set amount of fuel would give a higher velocity. There was not a great deal that Goddard could do about the fuels, at least so long as he kept to solid powder, and so he concentrated chiefly upon design. Also, he planned to use step-rockets. Tsiolkovskii had thought of the same thing, but Goddard had never heard of Tsiolkovskii's work (neither, for that matter, had anyone else outside Russia). Moreover, Tsiolkovskii was purely a theorist, while Goddard was a practical experimenter. He was not content to design rockets; he wanted to build and fire them as well.

Rocket research costs money. Goddard had no need of the vast

MOON IS ON SALE, ONLY $1 AN ACRE

Long Islander Doing Land-Office Business in Deeds to Crater Bottomland

---

By ROBERT K. PLUMB

Several lawyers in the city were scratching their heads last night in amazement over a new deal that has come to light in Long Island real estate.

There are plenty of deals in Long Island real estate, of course. But in the latest, a Long Islander is selling deeds to one-acre plots for $1. The deeds are to an acre in Copernicus Crater on the northeast quadrant of the moon. So far, there are reported to be 4,500 buyers.

For $1, here is what the lunar buyer gets:

¶A general quitclaim to an acre of good crater bottomland. The fine print disposes of the mineral rights (including uranium). It gives the buyer fishing and winter sports rights near the site he purchased.

¶A brochure describing the wonders of the moon as they are at present envisioned by the developer of the area. The brochure waxes enthusiastic in the time-honored manner of real estate promoters.

¶A map that shows the purchaser how he can see his land through a powerful telescope

Office at Glen Cove

The scheme is the invention of

NEWSPAPER REPORTS OF 'MOON SALES' IN 1919. At that time the idea of lunar travel was not taken seriously, but various hoaxers and tricksters were even able to make some profit by selling plots of land on the Moon to credulous buyers! This cutting, from the *New York Times*, reports one such attempt, which seems to have been moderately successful.

◄ GODDARD'S LAUNCHING OF THE FIRST LIQUID-FUEL ROCKET. The launching took place at Auburn, Massachusetts, on 16 March 1926. Small though it may have been, the vehicle was powered by liquid fuels, and may therefore be regarded as the first of the modern-type rockets.

NEWSPAPER COMMENTS ABOUT SPACE RESEARCH IN 1919. New York papers were quick to seize upon Goddard's comment that a rocket could be sent to the Moon, and later articles tended to ridicule the idea, which is one reason why Goddard subsequently avoided publicity.

sums now being spent monthly by the American and Russian Governments, but he did need more than his small salary allowed, and for some time his work was held up. Then, during the First World War, the United States authorities offered him a grant if he would turn his attention to rocket weapons. Goddard agreed, and produced some promising designs; but his first successful tests were delayed until November 1918, and the Germans surrendered a few days later, so that no further tests were made.

Goddard went back to his original line of research, and it was only a year later that he published the booklet which caused such a stir when the *New York Times* created a sensation out of it. At about the same period, Goddard turned to liquid propellants instead of solids, and he tested his first liquid-fuel motor in 1922, though it was not efficient enough to satisfy him, and he made up his mind to re-design it.

By 1926 he was ready for a full-scale test. He had assembled a strange-looking, spidery vehicle in which the propellants were petrol and liquid oxygen, and he hoped that it would at least show some promise. By modern standards it was very crude; for instance, the launching was carried out simply by opening the liquid oxygen and petrol valves, and then using a blowlamp to ignite the mixture. However, its propellants were of the 'new' variety, and nothing of the sort had been tried before.

Goddard took his vehicle to a remote farm at Auburn, in Massachusetts. Only a few people were there to see the great experiment, just as few people had actually seen Orville Wright's first aeroplane flight more than twenty years earlier. After his experience with the *Times* journalist, Goddard was not at all anxious for publicity.

At last all was ready. The blowlamp was lit, and the rocket fired; with a roar it took off, and we may suppose that the inventor watched it with considerable satisfaction. Its motors operated for $2\frac{1}{2}$ seconds before the propellants were exhausted, and the vehicle reached a speed of 60 miles per hour, travelling 184 feet before crashing to the ground.

This time there were no journalistic sensations. Some time later Goddard made an official report to the Smithsonian Institution, America's leading scientific body, but he certainly did not contact the Press, and it was a matter of years before his success became widely known.

Naturally, the 1926 firing was only a start; its importance historically lies in the fact that it was the first of the new-type, liquid-propellant rockets, so that it marked the dawn of the Space Age.

Goddard had no thought of giving up his research, and he kept working away, though his limited funds held him back. In July 1929 he fired a larger rocket from Auburn, launching a small scientific payload consisting of a barometer, a thermometer and a camera; the roar was sufficiently loud to attract attention, and the *New York Times* produced another headline—METEORLIKE ROCKET STARTLES WORCESTER—followed by a totally inaccurate description of what the rocket and its launcher were like. Dr. Abbot, Secretary of the Smithsonian Institution, felt bound to comment, and he told the Press that 'no such wild project as going to the Moon is contemplated'. No doubt Dr. Abbot was perfectly sincere; he must have believed that the very idea of lunar flight was completely absurd. On the other hand, he could hardly have expressed the contrary view even if he had wanted to do so; he would have been promptly accused of bringing the Smithsonian Institution into disrepute. Forty years ago there were few serious scientists who would have been prepared to believe even in the possibility of an artificial satellite, to say nothing of a vehicle which could send a payload as far as the Moon.

By this time, however, the idea of space-flight was much more in the public eye than it had been at the time of Goddard's earlier paper. The book written by Hermann Oberth had shown that there was a sound scientific basis for what we now call astronautics, and in Germany some practical experiments had been started. For a time Goddard was given a financial grant, and he used it to continue working on rocket design, but he took no steps to make his results available, so that the Germans knew nothing about them.

More rockets were sent up. One, launched in March 1935, rose to more than 1,000 feet, and travelled at a maximum speed of over 700 miles per hour. Goddard was obviously on the right track, but he had no official support from the United States authorities; indeed, nobody except the Germans showed much interest in rocketry—and little notice was taken when the German Government, headed by Adolf Hitler, took over the rocket field which had been set up near Berlin and transferred its workers to a Baltic island, Usedom, where the experimenters were ordered to forget about the Moon and concentrate upon developing weapons of war.

Had Goddard been given funds and equipment, he could have accomplished much more than he actually did, but it was only after the Second World War was well advanced that the menace of the rocket became evident. In 1944 the first V.2 weapons fell upon South England. These were rockets pure and simple, and they incorporated many of Goddard's ideas.

Meanwhile, Goddard had been working not upon rockets, but upon improved fuel pumps and other pieces of equipment for naval aircraft. No doubt he would have returned to his main interests after the Germans had been beaten for the second time, but he was given no chance to do so. On 10 August 1945, shortly before the end of the war in the Pacific, he died in hospital following a throat operation.

Much criticism has been levelled at Goddard, and in particular he has been accused of selfishness for keeping his results to himself. Yet this is quite unfair. He disliked publicity, and kept away from newspaper reporters as much as he could, but he did not hold back any information which might have been useful to his colleagues, and during his lifetime he published a large number of technical papers. Certainly his work was of the utmost value. The huge, complex space-rockets now being sent up from Cape Kennedy and from launching sites in the Soviet Union are the direct descendants of the strange, spidery device that Goddard set off from the Auburn farm more than forty years ago.

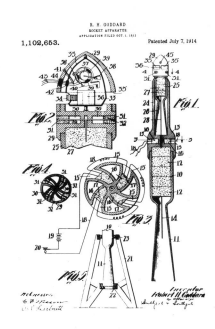

GODDARD'S ROCKET APPARATUS. This plan was the patent design approved on 7 July 1914.

ROBERT HUTCHINGS GODDARD, at work on a rocket in his laboratory at Roswell, New Mexico. This photograph was taken in October 1935, when rockets were still feeble and unreliable; before the war, the space-research idea was not taken at all seriously except by Goddard and a relatively few more pioneers.

The Rocket Flying Field

During the years following the end of the First World War, Tsiolkovskii in Russia and Goddard in the United States were both working hard upon problems of rocketry. Tsiolkovskii confined himself to theory; Goddard planned his first test vehicles with liquid propellants. Neither had heard of the other; and neither became well-known, Goddard because he wanted to keep out of the public eye, and Tsiolkovskii because his writings had simply not caught the popular imagination. It was only in 1924 that the space-travel idea became headline news once more. This time, the man responsible was Hermann Oberth.

On a personal note, it seems to me that this brings the present book into 'modern' times, because Oberth is still very much alive, and I have met him on several occasions. It is probably true to say that his first contribution to astronautics was also his greatest, but he certainly has an honoured place in the history of space research, and his 1924 book, *Rakete zu den Planetenraumen* (The Rocket into Interplanetary Space) remains a classic of its kind.

Oberth was born in 1894, in Transylvania. His father was a doctor, and intended his son to follow the medical profession, but young Oberth had other ideas; his interests were in mathematics and physics, and medicine was not for him, though he did serve in a hospital near the front line during the First World War. At that time Transylvania was part of the Austro-Hungarian Empire, but after the Armistice it was taken over by Roumania; Oberth did not become a German citizen until more than twenty years later.

Nobody could doubt Oberth's methematical ability, and after the war he became a teacher in a country school in the little town of Mediash. All his spare time was spent in working out rocket problems, and he corresponded with Goddard, who—whatever his views about sensation-seeking Pressmen—was always ready to exchange ideas with serious students.

All that Oberth learned made him certain that space-travel would become a real possibility before long. The trouble was that nobody had so far attempted to treat the whole subject in a suitably technical fashion. Actually, Tsiolkovskii had done so, but Oberth could not read Russian, and in any case he had never heard of Tsiolkovskii's work. Goddard, of course, was concerned mainly with upper-atmosphere studies, and his remark about sending a charge of flash-powder to the Moon had been more or less of an aside. Certainly Goddard had no thoughts about designing a space-ship.

Oberth went much further, and eventually he had prepared a short book in which his ideas were put down. Most of the test was mathematical, but the third section included some preliminary suggestions for a rocket vehicle capable of travelling away from the Earth. For some time no publisher would accept his manuscript – after all, Oberth was completely unknown, and his ideas sounded far-fetched. Eventually, in 1924, the book did appear in print, and,

PROFESSOR HERMANN OBERTH, whose book 'The Rocket into Interplanetary Space' was probably the first serious technical discussion of rocket principles. Oberth was closely concerned with all the early research. This photograph of him was taken in 1967, and sent to the author for the present book. At present Professor Oberth is living in Germany, where he continues with his theoretical research.

FRAU IM MOND—*The Girl in the Moon,* the science-fiction film in which Herman Oberth was called in as scientific adviser. These pictures show two scenes from the film. The explorers land on the lunar surface, and set off to explore the landscape.

probably to the publisher's surprise, it sold well. It was hastily reprinted, and before long the second edition too was almost out of stock.

No doubt there would have been some event to spark off a wide interest in space research sooner or later. In a world becoming more and more scientific, the idea was bound to take root. Actually it was Oberth's book that provided the spark, even though it was mainly technical and had not been written for the benefit of the layman. Soon afterwards, two 'popular' writers, Max Valier and Willy Ley, produced non-technical books in which the general principles were explained; Valier's came out first, though in point of fact Ley's was much the better of the two.

The immediate result was that 'Interplanetary Societies' started to spring up. A group was formed in Russia at an early stage; it did not last for long, but of the pioneer societies much the most important was the German *Verein für Raumschiffahrt* (VfR), or Society for Space-Travel. It was established in 1927, under the presidency of one Johannes Winkler. Oberth and almost all other interested researchers in Europe joined it, and within a year it had grown to a membership of over 500.

The VfR had no wish to remain inactive. It wanted to design rockets, and fire them. Unfortunately there was little money available, but then came a most unexpected development. Fritz Lang, the most famous producer in Germany, decided to make a film to be called *The Girl in the Moon*, and he invited Oberth to Berlin to act as technical adviser.

Oberth accepted, though in view of the series of mishaps which followed he may well have regretted his decision later. In the autumn of 1928 he arrived in Berlin, and set to work designing the space-craft to be used in the film. Then, somewhat to his dismay, he found that Fritz Lang had another idea in mind. What could be better publicity than to have an actual rocket launching on the day that the film was due to be released? Oberth was the great pioneer; given the equipment, he could presumably make a rocket that would fly.

What Lang had not realized, unfortunately, was that Oberth had had no experience of organization or practical engineering. It is one thing to make drawings, but quite another to produce a workable machine. Oberth, perhaps unwisely, decided to try. He engaged two assistants, one of whom (Rudolf Nebel) was an ex-pilot of the German Air Force, and the other (Alexander Shershevsky) an aviation student who had left Russia rather hastily and had been making some sort of a living by writing popular articles about flying. Neither knew any more about mechanics or engineering, in the practical sense, than Oberth himself, and neither had any knowledge about rockets. It was not a promising start.

To make matters worse, Oberth had been alarmed by one of his critics, who had claimed that no liquid-fuel rocket could ever work. It was said that as soon as the two liquids were combined, they would simply explode instead of producing a steady jet of gas from the exhaust. It is rather surprising that Oberth took this argument seriously—and had he known about Goddard's more recent work, his fears would have been set at rest immediately; after all, Goddard had successfully fired a rocket powered by liquids three years before Oberth began his task in Berlin. However, Oberth did

Second Repulsor rocket built by members of the German V f R. It is shown being examined by Klaus Riedel, its designer.

Verein für Raumschiffahrt E. V.
Geschäftsstelle Berlin SW 11

Abschußfertige Oberth-Rakete mit dem Abschußrohr

MODEL OF THE OBERTH ROCKET IN ITS STAND. This was the pattern designed by Hermann Oberth in connection with the film *Frau im Mond*, though in fact the practical difficulties of building proved insuperable, and the Oberth Rocket never actually flew.

not know, and he came to the conclusion that he had better find out for himself.

He proved his point, but not without the first of the really serious accidents. During the experiments there was a most unsatisfying explosion, which partially wrecked a laboratory. Oberth narrowly escaped serious injury, and the explosion shook him up much more badly than he or anyone else realized at the time.

Then there was the ever-pressing matter of money; the fund that had been promised by the film company never materialized, and Oberth began to use his own savings. Time, too, was short. *The Girl in the Moon* was going ahead quickly, but the Oberth Rocket was not; there were innumerable design problems, and at last it became painfully clear that the rocket never could be made ready in time. Incidentally, even had the rocket been fully prepared, it would not have been easy to obtain Government permission to fire it.

By now Oberth was almost at his wits' end. Nebel and Shershevsky were of little help, and the only course was to postpone the main plan and prepare a smaller test rocket to fire at the time of the film première. Even this could not be done; the materials were not available, and in any case the project needed a much more experienced mechanic-cum-engineer than Oberth and his assistants. Finally Oberth gave up. He left Berlin abruptly, without telling anyone about his departure, and went back to his country home in Mediash. When *The Girl in the Moon* was released, on 15 October 1929, there was no dramatic rocket launching; the producers announced that the Oberth Rocket had been postponed indefinitely. Actually, it never flew at all—and by this time Oberth had come to the conclusion that it simply would not work.

The whole episode had been something of a fiasco, but it did not damage Oberth's reputation to any great extent. To expect him to build a full-scale rocket in so short a time, and with such limited equipment, was unreasonable. A new, enlarged version of his book appeared, and he was awarded a special prize for it, which did at least something to soothe his ruffled feelings.

Meanwhile, the VfR had not been idle. They had pinned their faith in the Oberth Rocket, but they were not despondent. There was a great deal of general interest in their ideas, and in 1930 Winkler gave a very successful public lecture. (One of those who listened was Hermann Ganswindt, still as argumentative and self-opinionated as ever.) Headed by Nebel, the VfR decided to carry on the experimental work, and to attempt a small liquid-fuel rocket which was to be called the Mirak.

It must be said that Nebel's attitude was not entirely to be praised. He even wanted to carry out a 'fake' launching, putting an ordinary solid-fuel arrangement inside a rocket and passing it off as a liquid-fuel device in order to gain public support. Ley and the other members of the VfR refused to have anything to do with such a trick, and Nebel withdrew his suggestion.

Max Valier, meantime, had interested the German manufacturer Fritz von Opel in the possibilities of a rocket car. This was clearly a useless sort of device, and the VfR leaders were annoyed; they regarded the whole venture as cheap publicity, and they were certainly right. Various experiments were made, none of which showed any promise. Then came tragedy; an explosion wrecked

Valier's laboratory, and Valier himself was killed.

Since the VfR experimenters still knew nothing about Goddard's work, they thought that nobody had ever fired a liquid-fuel rocket, and they were determined to be the first. They obtained the use of a waste area in the northern suburbs of Berlin, now remembered as the *Raketenflugplatz* or Rocket Flying Field, and they worked away ceaselessly. By now Winkler had resigned the Presidency, and was carrying out research on his own—and on 14 March 1931, he sent up a small liquid-propelled rocket from Dessau. Naturally, this was thought to be the first of its kind, but

EARLY ROCKETS, showing run of Nebel and Werner von Braun at the old Raketen-flugplatz of Rocket Flying Field near Berlin in the early 1930s.

it was not long before the VfR followed Winkler's example. Their first two Miraks had exploded, but on 23 May they sent up a much more promising vehicle which they called the Repulsor.

Yet even in 1931 there were signs of trouble ahead. Quite apart from the shortage of money, there were political complications in Germany. Hitler's Nazis were coming to power, and independent, non-military research was not encouraged. One visitor to the Rocket Flying Field was a German officer, Colonel Dornberger, who held the view that these vehicles might eventually be used as weapons of war instead of messengers to the Moon. Though he was unimpressed by much of what he saw, he noted everything carefully and sent in a report. Nebel became a member of the Nazi Party, but most of the other VfR leaders, including Willy Ley, were strongly anti-Hitler, and wanted to have no connection with preparations for the war which would obviously come.

ROCKET CAR; the Opel-Rak, driven by Max Valier.

ROCKET LAUNCHING from the Raketenflugplatz, with members of the VfR organization.

There was one more episode which is certainly worth re-telling, because it had its humorous side. This was the Magdeburg Experiment of 1933, which sounds almost unbelievable today even though it happened less than forty years ago.

It began with a member of the City Council of Magdeburg, who believed in an extraordinary theory according to which the surface of the world lies at the centre of a hollow sphere, so that Australia is above our heads, the Sun lies in the middle of the opening, and the Earth extends beneath our feet infinitely in all directions. (Incidentally, I found recently that there are still people who believe in this remarkable idea; the headquarters of the modern society is also in Germany.) It would seem, then, that a rocket launched vertically upwards would come to rest in the Antipodes, provided that it could be sent up to a sufficient 'height'. The VfR was approached by the Magdeburg City Council, and asked to prepare a rocket which would test the theory. Neither Nebel, Ley nor any of the other experimenters had the slightest faith in hollow Earths, but at least the test would mean a financial grant, and two rockets were actually built and fired. The first failed to rise beyond its launching rack, while the second took off horizontally and ended its career in a ploughed field . . .

The Magdeburg Experiment was pure comedy, but there was little else in Germany to laugh at. Colonel Dornberger persuaded the Nazi authorities to set up a rocket ground of their own, and Wernher von Braun, one of the mainstays of the VfR, joined it. Nebel announced his intention of putting the Society at the disposal of the Nazi Party; Ley and others left Germany for good, and by 1933 the VfR had ceased to exist. Even before then, Dornberger's new research establishment had fired its first rocket, and ideas of space-travel were firmly put aside in favour of the development of horror weapons.

The situation was different in other countries. An American Interplanetary Society had been formed in 1930, but soon changed its name to the American Rocket Society, presumably to avoid ridicule. In England, P. E. Cleator founded the British Interplanetary Society, but met with no official support; I have seen a letter to Cleator written in 1934 by the then British Under-Secretary of State in which it was said that even jet propulsion could never be a serious rival to the airscrew-engine combination for aircraft, and that the Government would not be justified in spending any time or money on it.

War finally came in 1939. Five years later, the crash of the first V.2 weapon upon South England showed, once and for all, that the rocket was something very much more powerful than a toy.

Chapter 12

Peenemünde

PEENEMUNDE, indicated by the black arrow. This was the site of the German rocket base where the V.2 weapon was developed.

WERNHER VON BRAUN, the German rocket pioneer who worked on developing the V.2 at Peenemünde. He is now engaged in rocket research in the United States.

When Colonel Dornberger went to the Rocket Flying Field, he naturally talked with all the VfR team. Among them was a young enthusiast, still in his 'teens: Wernher von Braun. Dornberger realized that Von Braun was particularly skilful and far-sighted, and would be a most valuable member of the official Government project. In 1932, when the new test station was set up at Kummersdorf, south of Berlin, Von Braun joined it, together with Rudolf Nebel and a few other members of the VfR who were ready to throw in their lot with the Nazi Party. By then the VfR itself was more or less dead; the first phase in the German rocket story was already over.

Dornberger was handicapped by official apathy. He had a certain amount of money available, but not nearly enough to satisfy him, and he realized that he would have to produce startling results if he were to be given extra funds. Actually, Kummersdorf did not make a promising start. In December 1932, a test motor was ready, but when Von Braun ignited the fuel there was a violent explosion, and the whole motor was wrecked, together with much of the laboratory.

Better things followed, and two years later the Kummersdorf team managed to send a rocket up to a height of $1\frac{1}{2}$ miles. Moreover, it was a much larger, more complex vehicle than anything that had been attempted at the *Raketenflugplatz*. Dornberger was encouraged, and so were at least some influential members of the Nazi Party. More funds were handed over, and it was decided to transfer the whole base away from Berlin to a site where roaring, possibly exploding rockets would attract less public attention.

Von Braun suggested that an excellent spot would be Peenemünde, on the small Baltic island of Usedom. Dornberger agreed; so did the authorities, and the transfer was duly carried out, with the minimum possible publicity. After that, no official statements were made about what was going on, and members of the Press were definitely not welcome. In fact, the whole rocket project was classed as 'top secret', and for a long time nothing was heard about it. As late as 1943, Professor Lindemann (later Lord Cherwell), the scientific adviser to the British War Cabinet, still thought that the whole rumour about German long-range rockets was a deliberate hoax, which shows that Dornberger had been successful in keeping his activities well out of the public eye.

By the autumn of 1939 the Peenemünde team, expertly directed by Dornberger and with Von Braun as the leading research scientist, had built a rocket which was known as the A.3. It was 21 feet long, and weighed one ton; it was capable of rising to a height of five miles, and, more important, it could be guided to some extent. Certainly the whole project was very different from those of the early days in Berlin, when any rocket which managed to lift itself off the ground was regarded as a major success. For a time Dornberger was provided with enough money to carry out a full-scale programme, and the results were promising. By now, of course, the war had started, and the emphasis was all upon military weapons.

Fortunately for mankind, the whole German war effort was in the hands of one man: the Führer, Adolf Hitler. He was the supreme master, and he could make or break a project simply by a stroke of the pen. Just as the Peenemünde researchers were in full stride, their high priority rating was taken away; funds were reduced, and Dornberger had to struggle on as well as he could. Under the circumstances, it is remarkable that he managed to achieve as much as he actually did.

The critical test was made on 3 October 1942. The new rocket was the A.4, later to become famous as the V.2; it had a total height of almost 50 feet, and it was a complex structure, very different from the relatively simple rockets of earlier years. It was made in four sections—the conical warhead in the nose, weighing one ton and filled with high explosive; the instrument compartment; the fuel tank section, and the tail. All the brains of Peenemünde had gone into its design, and there was no doubt that Von Braun and his team knew far more about rockets than anybody else at the time.

One major development was that pumps had been installed to force the liquids into the combustion chamber at the correct rate. The fuel was alcohol, and the oxidant was liquid oxygen, a troublesome material which boils at a very low temperature and has to be put into the rocket only just before the rocket launching.

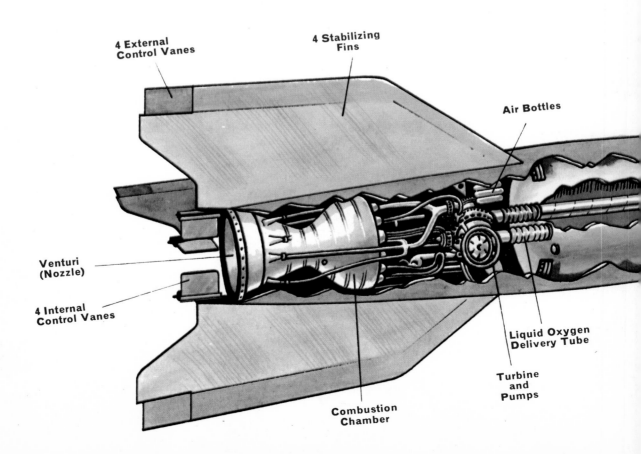

The pumps alone had taken years to design, and they were only one of the many complications. In the A.4, there were any number of things that could go wrong—and the failure of even one of these details would mean the failure of the whole rocket.

During the final preparations, the atmosphere at Peenemünde was tense. Lack of success now would probably mean the end of the whole project. Dornberger and Von Braun were determined that this should not happen, but there was nothing much they could do except watch and hope.

At last the A.4 was fired. The motors roared; smoke billowed out, and the great vehicle lifted clear of the ground, slowly at first and then gaining speed. All went well, and within a few minutes the watchers knew that they had triumphed. In Dornberger's own words: 'For the first time in the history of the rocket we had flown an automatically-guided, jet-driven projectile as far as the limit of the atmosphere . . . and sent it on into practically airless space. We had been working ten years for this day.'

One thing must be made clear. Though the A.4 was designed and used as a war weapon, it was based upon exactly the same principles as those of the later space-vehicles. Indeed, after the war, captured German rockets were taken to America and used for tests. In some ways it is unfortunate that a rocket capable of carrying scientific equipment can also carry high explosive or even a nuclear bomb, because rocket research can be used for evil as well as good. The problem is still with us today. Meanwhile, Peenemünde seemed to have justified its existence, and Dorn-

CROSS-SECTION OF THE V.2 ROCKET,
with a human figure shown for scale.

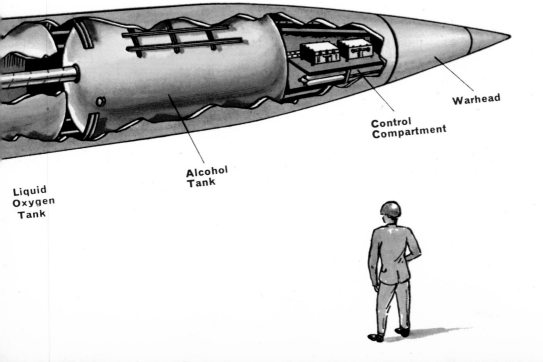

ted Alcohol
ery Pipe to Pump

Liquid
Oxygen
Tank

Alcohol
Tank

Control
Compartment

Warhead

berger hoped that Hitler would give it full support.

Nothing of the sort happened. Apparently, in March 1943 the Führer dreamed that no German rocket would ever fall upon England, and this was enough for him to hold back supplies of money and equipment. Dornberger felt bitterly discouraged, but still he was not prepared to give up. He obtained an interview with Hitler—never an easy matter, particularly at the time when the war was starting to run against Germany—and at last he managed to convince the strange, unbalanced leader that rockets could win the war for him. In July 1943 Peenemünde was given top priority once more, even though Dornberger had to contend with various Nazi officials who did not trust him in the least.

But time was short now, and the years of indecision had wrecked all Dornberger's plans. Moreover, the Allies had at last realized that the stories about long-range rockets were serious. On 17 August 1943, British bombers flew over Peenemünde and dropped some 12,000 tons of bombs upon the rocket station, killing 800 members of the staff. The raid did not put an end to the work, as has been claimed, but it certainly crippled the programme, particularly as Dr. Thiel, one of the main scientists, was killed together with his whole family. A few months later, Nazi officials swooped on Peenemünde and arrested Von Braun and two other key men, on charges of being too deeply interested in space research and too little interested in winning the war. Dornberger soon managed to have them released, but in spite of Hitler's 'top priority' it was only too clear that Peenemünde had to battle against political intrigue as well as research difficulties and hostile bombers.

Of course, it is perfectly true that Von Braun and the other rocket scientists were much more concerned with science than with war. To them, the ultimate objective was space-flight; it so happened that only the military aspect could provide them with sufficient funds and facilities for their experiments.

It was not until the autumn of 1944 that the A.4, now known as the V.2, was ready for use. In September, the first rocket was launched against England. I actually heard it come down; I was in Bomber Command of the R.A.F. at the time, but I happened to be on leave, and I was only a few miles away from the impact point. Obviously I had no idea what had caused the explosion, but later it became known that the rocket attacks were not completely unexpected. In June 1944 a test V.2 sent up from Peenemünde had gone off course and crashed in Sweden, where it had been recovered and handed over to the British authorities—so that its essential design was known even though the details were not.

New vehicles had appeared over England before the arrival of the first V.2. The 'buzz-bombs' or V.1 weapons had become unpleasantly familiar, but they were jets, not rockets, so that they need not concern us here.[1] The V.2s were much more deadly, and it was said that anyone who heard one come down could feel reasonably safe; the worst danger came before the noise of the rocket could be heard. The attack was something out of the ordinary, and it was unnerving even to people as used to raids as Englishmen of the early nineteen-forties.

[1] V stands for *Vergeltung*: in English ,'revenge'. The V.2 was therefore Hitler's second 'revenge weapon'.

(Left) THE V.2. This photograph shows the successful launching of a V.2 rocket. Though designed purely as a military weapon, the V.2 may be regarded as the ancestor of all subsequent space-craft. After the German collapse, numbers of unused V.2s were taken to America and launched for purely scientific purposes.

Luckily, the V.2s were not accurate. All that the Germans could do was to aim them at a really large target, such as London, knowing that they might fall somewhere within the area. Altogether more than 1,000 were launched, most of them at London and the rest at Norwich; over 500 actually exploded in the London area, and killed a total of more than 2,500 men, women and children as well as doing a vast amount of damage to property. The last V.2 fell at Orpington, in Kent, on 27 March 1945. By then Germany was facing defeat; her power had crumbled, and the V.2 launching sites were overrun by the advancing Allied armies, so that the rocket launchings were effectively stopped. On 5 May Peenemünde itself was taken by the Russians, but little was left there. Dornberger, Von Braun and the other research workers had already left, and were in American hands a few weeks later.

They had kept up their efforts until the very last moment, and as late as 8 January 1945, they had fired a rocket to almost 50 miles, at a top speed of 2,700 m.p.h. This was the A.9, which was promising in every way. But there was no time left, and it was impossible to make up for the wasted years when Hitler had starved his scientific team of funds and supplies. With the storming of Peenemünde, all rocket work in Germany stopped.

The story of Peenemünde is curious indeed. Had Hitler taken a different view, and had he not been so slow to realize the importance of the rocket as a weapon, the war might have had a different ending; the Nazis might have overrun the whole of the civilized world, and the outlook would have been black. Yet in spite of its evil background, an amazing amount of brilliant work was carried out. The space-vehicles that now fly to the Moon, Mars and Venus owe much to those experiments carried out more than a quarter of a century ago on a lonely island in the Baltic Sea.

V.2 IN ITS LAUNCHING RACK, 1944. The rocket attack upon South England represented one of the Germans' last bids for victory in the war. In the event, the V.2 weapons killed large numbers of people and caused considerable damage, but the on-slaught came too late, and was too limited, to affect the issue.

Chapter 13

From Europe to White Sands

Peenemünde was the real birth-place of the modern rocket. Of this there can be no doubt; the V.2s which bombarded England during the final stages of the war were precision instruments, compared with which the primitive rockets fired from the *Raketenflugplatz* and by Goddard were no more than toys. They had shown, above all, that the rocket was capable of controlled flight into space.

It is true, of course, that the V.2s were limited to less than 150 miles, so that they could not reach beyond the top of the atmosphere; but they were space-craft none the less. And the Americans, in particular, were quick to realize that the unused V.2s were of the greatest value.

It did not take long for the United States to become rocket-minded. Before the war, lone experimenters such as Goddard had been hopelessly handicapped by lack of money, and had had to depend upon what small grants they could obtain. After 1945, Government money was poured into rocket research to such an extent that there have been rumblings of discontent in certain

ENTRANCE TO WHITE SANDS ROCKET RANGE. This photograph, of the entrance to the White Sands proving ground used for much of the early post-war rocket research, was taken by Arthur C. Clarke, who is shown standing next to the warning notice-board. Subsequently White Sands was found to be inconveniently small, and the main rocket work was shifted to Cape Canaveral (now re-named Cape Kennedy).

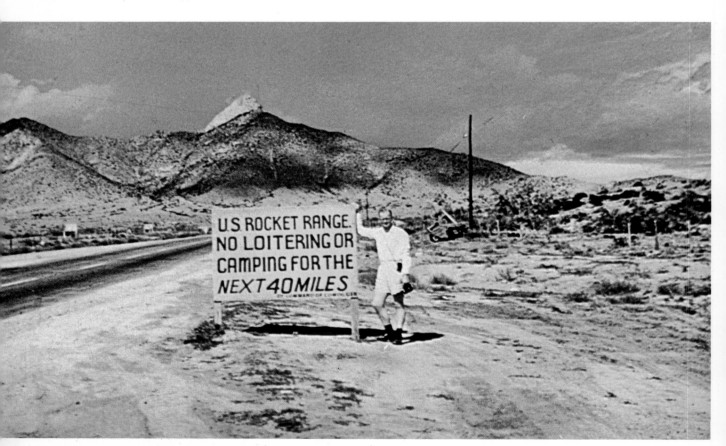

quarters ever since.

One familiar, hackneyed argument is: 'Why spend money upon trying to reach the Moon, when there are so many people on Earth living at starvation level?' The question is by no means unreasonable, but it can be answered at least in part (quite apart from the fact that if all available money were used wisely instead of being squandered upon armaments, there would be plenty of funds available to feed the starving millions and reach the Moon as well). First, space research involves much more than sending a man to the Moon It will affect all branches of science, including medicine, and it will add tremendously to human knowledge. Secondly, it must be admitted, with regret, that the main costs of rocket research would have been incurred in any case, for purely military purposes. Let us repeat that a vehicle capable of sending a probe toward the Moon is also capable of dispatching a nuclear bomb. No Government is ready to spend vast sums upon peaceful, scientific projects; but when weapons of destruction are to be considered, the money is always forthcoming, whether the taxpayers like it or not.

Peenemünde had been stormed by the Red Army, but the leading German scientists, including Von Braun, had fallen into American hands. They were speedily transferred to the United States and put into positions of responsibility, so that a full-scale programme was soon under way. The Russians certainly began work at the same time, but for some years the Soviet authorities said very little about what was going on. Britain, seriously crippled by the war, could do no more than play a comparatively minor role; a rocket range was set up at Woomera in Australia, north-west of Adelaide, and launchings of high-altitude rockets began there in 1947, but there was insufficient resources to attempt anything more ambitious.

So far as America was concerned, the first essential was a proper testing range. The site selected was White Sands, in New Mexico, a wild area of white gypsum dunes and scrubby vegetation, well away from any townships. It measured 125 miles by 40 miles, so that it was large enough to be useful. Captured V.2 components were taken there as early as the summer of 1945, before Japan followed Germany into defeat, and test launchings began soon afterwards.

Quite apart from any military aspect, there was the question of using rockets to explore the upper part of the Earth's atmosphere. Goddard's forecasts made in his 1919 paper were very close to the mark, and the early White Sands work was concerned largely with this aspect; the rockets carried scientific instruments, not high explosive. A purely American rocket, known as the WAC Corporal, was developed soon after White Sands started work, and it proved to be very effective, reaching heights of more than 40 miles without a great deal of difficulty.

Unfortunately this was not high enough; a more powerful rocket was needed. Then came a real windfall in the shape of various undamaged V.2s, which were shipped across from Germany and handed over to the White Sands scientists. The first of them, sent aloft in March 1946, went out of control and lost an all-important fin within twenty seconds of take-off, but others were much more encouraging, and on 17 December 1946, a V.2 rose to the dizzy

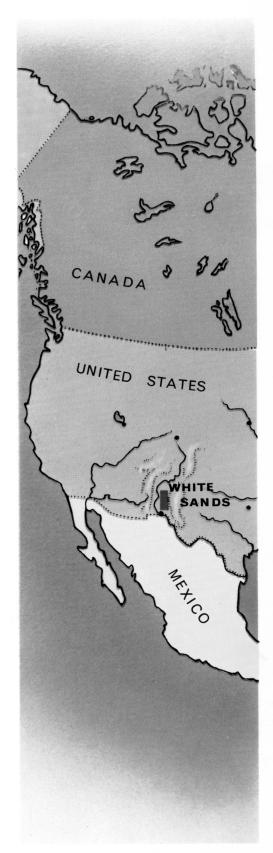

POSITION OF THE WHITE SANDS PROVING GROUND in New Mexico.

ROCKET RESEARCH AT WOOMERA. The Woomera proving ground in South Australia has been the scene of many launchings, largely for upper-atmosphere research. This photograph shows the dry duct and the mast of the Europa 1 rocket; the rocket itself is still sheathed by the bulky square service tower.

THE EARTH FROM A TIROS WEATHER SATELLITE. The Tiros series of meteorological satellites was extremely successful, and led to considerable advances in our knowledge of the behaviour of pressure systems. In this photograph, the cloud masses are well shown.

altitude of 114 miles. This was easily a record, and it remained so for five years.

One trouble was that the supply of V.2s was limited, and each rocket could be used once only. This, in fact, is probably the worst drawback of the simple scientific rocket. It blasts off; it rises to its peak altitude; and then it falls—crashing to the ground and destroying itself utterly. Instrument packages may often be separated and brought down gently by parachute, but the rocket itself, much the most costly part of the experiment, is certain to be a total loss. The whole procedure is wasteful, and for this reason alone is most unsatisfactory.

There was obviously no chance of saving any of the V.2s once they had been launched. An empty V.2 still weighed 4 tons, and no parachute could slow down its headlong drop through the atmosphere once its motors had stopped firing and it had passed its peak height; when it hit the White Sands desert, it would make a 60-foot hole. This happened every time, as was only to be expected. There were a couple of awkward moments; the fourteenth V.2 went off course and was deliberately crashed, by remote control, when it was found to be heading for Mexico. And on 29 May 1947, a V.2 actually did land in Mexico, though fortunately it came down on a hill and there were no international protests.

The whole series extended over more than six years. The first V.2 was launched successfully on 28 June 1946, reaching 67 miles above White Sands, and carrying instruments for studying various features of the upper atmosphere. The last was that of 19 September 1952. Altogether there were sixty-three launchings, of which over forty were successful. The greatest altitude was that of the launching on 22 August 1951, when a V.2 reached no less than 132 miles. This seems very little today, but at the time it was regarded as excellent—as indeed it was.

Yet nothing could alter the fact that the V.2 had been designed as a war weapon, and had to be adapted for scientific use. It could carry a ton, but it was not ideal, and in any case it was merely a start to the programme. Relatively speaking, the American WAC Corporal rocket was more efficient, but it was not so large or so powerful. Another early vehicle, the Aerobee, also showed real promise, but perhaps the most important experiment carried out from White Sands was that of 24 February 1949, when the first step-arrangement was brought into action.

We have already noted that pioneers such as Tsiolkovskii and Goddard had suggested the step-principle, which involves mounting one rocket on top of another. A modern step-vehicle is immensely complicated, and the various stages are designed together. The situation at White Sands was different. What was done was to take an American WAC Corporal, mount it upon a V.2, and launch it in the hope that nothing would go wrong. Of course, everything was worked out as carefully and accurately as possible, and there was nothing 'hit or miss' about it, but nobody really knew whether the experiment would work.

Actually, the launching was a triumphant success. One minute after blast-off the V.2 had reached a height of 20 miles, and was moving at nearly 1 mile per second. At that point the WAC broke away and continued under its own power, using its motors for 40 seconds and accelerating to nearly $1\frac{1}{2}$ miles per second. The now-empty V.2 rose to 100 miles, after which it fell back to the ground and crashed 20 miles away from its launching site; it had been aloft for only five minutes, but it had done its work well. The WAC climbed on for another 90 seconds, and at its peak soared to almost 250 miles above White Sands. Since the atmosphere at this height is to all intents and purposes negligible, it is justifiable to claim that for the first time a man-made vehicle had reached true space. Then the WAC too dropped back, and landed 80 miles away from its launching-point after a flight lasting for a total of 12 minutes.

There was one note of anti-climax. It is not easy to keep track of a comparatively small vehicle falling at a tremendous rate, and when radio signals ceased nobody knew just where the WAC had hit. Neither could it be found. Its shattered remains were finally located almost a year later.

Even while the V.2 tests were still going on, new-type rockets were being developed at White Sands. In particular there was the Viking, of greatly improved design; the first of the series went up in 1949, and No. 7, on 7 August 1951, reached 135 miles, moving at a maximum speed of 4,100 miles per hour. Cameras were carried in most of the Vikings, as well as in some of the other types of rockets, and for the first time it became possible to look at photographs of the Earth taken from high altitude. The curvature of the globe was clearly shown, and the pictures caused a great deal of interest when they were published. Even the earnest members of the International Flat Earth Society found some difficulty in accounting for the curved horizon!

As rockets of better design and greater power were developed, the experimenters began to complain that White Sands was too small. Possibly the accidental flights toward Mexico gave cause for alarm, and it seemed that something would have to be done. The ideal solution was to have a launching ground near the coast, so that used-up rockets could fall harmlessly in the sea. A proper warning system could eliminate any danger to shipping, but a launching site place inland was no longer practicable.

Almost a century earlier, Jules Verne had selected Florida for his launching ground. The American Government did the same, though admittedly for rather different reasons. The selected site was Cape Canaveral, which appeared to have every possible advantage, particularly as the British authorities raised no objection to having tracking stations erected on the Bahama Islands. While the work at White Sands was still in full swing, Cape Canaveral was made ready, and the first launching there was attempted on 19 July 1950. It failed, but it was the forerunner of many brilliant successes. Just as the focus of attention had shifted from Peenemünde to White Sands, so it now began to shift from White Sands to Canaveral.

NIGHT LAUNCHING OF VIKING 13, one of the most successful of the rockets of the important Viking series.

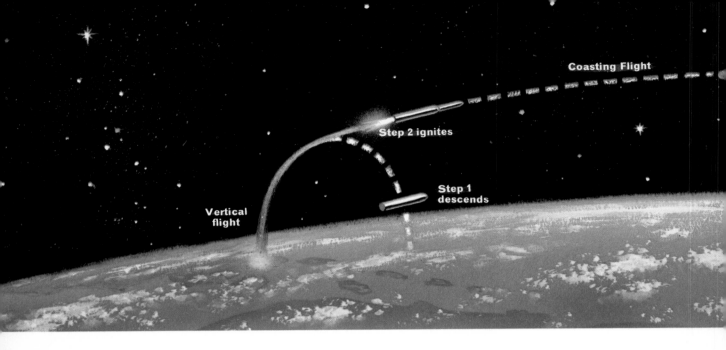

Coasting Flight

Step 2 ignites

Step 1
descends

Vertical
flight

Chapter 14

Operation Vanguard

On 29 July 1955, it was officially announced from the White House that the construction and launching of small unmanned satellites had been approved by the United States Government, and that the first practical experiments were scheduled to take place some time between July 1956 and December 1958.

The announcement caused immense interest all over the world. It was headline news in almost all newspapers; television programmes were interrupted, and there were comments from scientists and non-scientists alike. The world was becoming rocket-conscious, and there could no longer be any doubt that Governments were really serious about sending vehicles beyond the Earth.

Three days later, the sixth congress of the International Astronautical Federation (the I.A.F.) opened in Copenhagen. The I.A.F., a loosely-knit organization consisting of representatives of various Interplanetary Societies, had been created in 1949, but the Copenhagen meeting was the first to which the Soviet Union had sent delegates. Sedov and Ogorodnikov, the Russians present at the congress, made the prompt statement that a Soviet artificial satellite also might be expected. Not many people paid much attention . . .

The idea of an artificial satellite was anything but novel, since it had been described by Tsiolkovskii and others. Even before 1955, workers such as Wernher von Braun had published elaborate plans for a vehicle which was to move round the Earth at a height of perhaps 1,000 miles, serving as a combined observatory, laboratory, meteorological station and refuelling base. But a

THE EARTH as photographed from a high-flying artificial satellite.

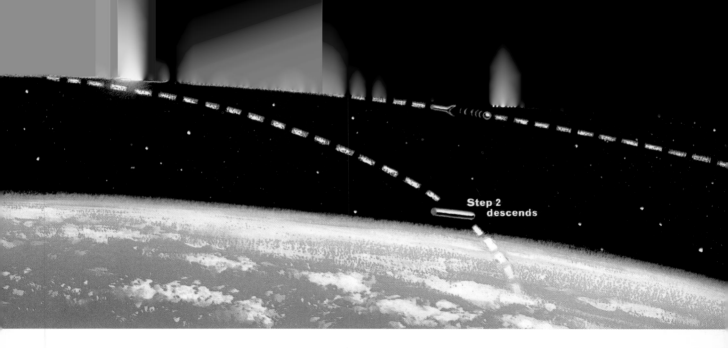

Step 2
descends

manned satellite then seemed far in the future, and even a tiny vehicle no larger than a football would prove difficult to launch.

Delving into the literature, we find that the resourceful Jules Verne had put forward some sort of a scheme for a man-made moon. This was in his novel *The Begum's Fortune*, which may not rank among his best books, but which is worth considering here because it raises some important principles.

In the story, two cities are built—Frankville, ruled by the benevolent Dr. Sarrasin, and Stahlstadt, held in the iron grip of Professor Schultz, of whom Verne wrote that his general appearance 'was decidedly unpleasant to others, though he himself was perfectly satisfied with it'. Schultz makes up his mind to destroy Frankville by firing a lethal shell at it, using a powerful cannon of his own invention. He duly fires the shell at an initial speed of 10,000 yards per second, but his plan fails; instead of falling on Frankville or anywhere else, the shell simply continues to circle the Earth, because it is travelling so fast that it becomes an artificial satellite.

Before finding out where Verne's errors lie, let us examine the situation a little more carefully. First, it will be helpful to suppose that the Earth has no atmosphere, so that we can ignore air resistance. Secondly, let us suppose that we can emulate Verne's Professor Schultz, and fire shells out of our cannon at ever-increasing speed. And thirdly, let us assume that we have mounted our cannon on top of a peak, high enough to tower above all obstructions. The diagram, which makes no pretence of being drawn to scale, will give the general idea of what is meant.

We now start our firing. Shell No. 1, ejected at low velocity, will describe a curve and will fall to the ground. Shell No. 2, ejected at a higher velocity, will travel further before it touches down. Shell No. 3, with still higher velocity, will go an appreciable part of the way round the world. But what of Shell No. 4? Fired at just over 17,000 m.p.h., it will never land at all. It will 'fall', but it will never come any closer to the ground. When it has been right round the Earth, it will return to its original point of departure; that is

PROFESSOR SCHULTZ' CANNON. In his novel *The Begum's Fortune*, **Jules Verne described how Professor Schultz built a cannon with which he hoped to fire a projectile to destroy the city of Frankville—but instead merely managed to launch an unintentional earth satellite! This woodcut, from the original edition of Verne's book, shows the cannon as built in Schultz' city of Stählstadt.**

PROFESSOR SCHULTZ' PROJECTILE, aimed at the city of Frankville, passing harmlessly overhead in a closed orbit around the Earth. This is another illustration from the original of Verne's novel *The Begum's Fortune.*

to say, it will strike the cannon once more.

This is what Professor Schultz's shell would presumably have done, though Verne gives us no further details. Basically, the theory is sound enough. A projectile sent into a perfectly circular orbit, at this particular velocity, round an airless world would behave in such a way.

The main flaw is, of course, that the Earth is not airless. Eject a shell at anything like 17,000 m.p.h.—even assuming such a thing to be possible—and it will promptly be heated to melting point by friction against the air; actually, it will be crushed and destroyed even before it can leave the cannon, in the same way as Verne's manned Columbiad would have been. Moreover, to launch a projectile into a perfectly circular orbit would be almost impossibly difficult, and the slightest departure from a circle would mean that a projectile fired at low height would strike the ground somewhere or other, because it would be travelling in an ellipse. With all artificial satellites (and with the Moon), the point in orbit closest to the Earth is termed the perigee, while the furthest point is known as the apogee. It is the perigee distance which matters most.

To make sure that this vitally important principle is made clear, it will perhaps be helpful to give a few figures. If we launched our shell at the required velocity to keep it in orbit round the airless Earth, i.e. at about 5 miles per second or over 17,000 m.p.h., it would 'fall' about 15 feet in one second, as shown in the next diagram. If the Earth were flat, then after a second's flight the shell would be 15 feet nearer the ground. But the Earth is not flat; it is to all intent and purposes spherical, and at a horizontal distance of 5 miles, the ground also falls away by 15 feet. Therefore, the shell is no nearer the ground than when originally launched. If the shell is launched at 6 miles a second, its height above the ground will increase; but it will not escape into space—remember that the Earth's escape velocity is 7 miles per second. Our 6-mile-per-second shell will enter an elliptical orbit, with its perigee at the original launching site and its apogee on the other side of the world.

Obviously, we can forget all about cannons and shells except for the purposes of explanation. If a real earth satellite is to be sent up, it must be dispatched by rocket power, and it cannot move at a low altitude. To achieve a stable, long-lasting orbit, it must go up to a height so great that it will be more or less unaffected by air-drag; that is to say, at least 100 miles. There is another refinement, too. If the orbit is elliptical (as will certainly be the case), then it is the perigee distance which is all-important. At apogee, we may assume that our satellite will be well beyond the limits of the effectively resisting atmosphere; otherwise, it will not become a satellite at all. But when it moves toward perigee, it may enter the denser layers, and be subject to drag. Curiously, the result will be that the perigee height will remain much the same, but the apogee height will lessen; in other words, the orbit will shrink. And when the orbital size has become sufficiently small, the satellite will spiral down and be destroyed in the lower atmosphere.

The simplest way to launch a satellite, one might think, would be to place it in the nose of a rocket, send it above the atmosphere, and then give it a 'sideways jerk' to put it into orbit. But things are seldom so simple as they appear, and the only really practicable method is to send up the launcher in a pre-determined curve, so that when it arrives at the required position it can eject its load suitably; the third diagram shows what is meant, though a great many complications have been deliberately left out. It is hardly necessary to add that the launching-vehicle has to be a step-arrangement, and that it takes a massive launcher to put even a small satellite into orbit.

One more point should be stressed. As soon as an artificial satellite has been put into orbit, it behaves in precisely the same way as a natural astronomical body would do. The orbit will be exactly the same whether the body is made up of rock, stone or man-made steel; or, for that matter, thin plastic. It is only when the body enters the resisting part of the atmosphere that its mass becomes important in working out its movements (apart from certain minor effects due to radiations from the Sun, appreciable only with balloon satellites whose masses are negligible). So, as always, we are back with Kepler's Laws.

Returning to a satellite moving in a circular orbit, it is not hard to show that at an altitude of roughly 100 miles, the orbital period is about 88 minutes, and the orbital velocity 17,450 m.p.h. As soon as the satellite comes much lower, it is doomed; air-drag pulls it to destruction. But if it is in a higher orbit, its period will be more than 88 minutes, and its velocity will be less; gravity decreases with distance, so that at greater altitudes the Earth's pull is not so strong. At 500 miles, for instance, the orbital velocity will

BRAKING EFFECT OF THE EARTH'S ATMOSPHERE ON AN ARTIFICIAL SATELLITE. If, near perigee, the satellite encounters appreciable atmospheric drag, its perigee distance will remain much the same during successive orbits, but the apogee distance will be steadily reduced. Eventually, the satellite will drop into the denser layers of atmosphere, and will be destroyed.

SOLAR PROMINENCE, photographed by W. M. Baxter on 12 June 1966. The telescope used was Baxter's 4in. refractor at his private solar observatory at Acton, just outside London. The photograph was taken with the aid of a monochromatic filter.

be a mere 16,660 m.p.h., and the period 101 minutes. Since the atmosphere at this height is so thin, there will be virtually no drag, and the satellite will become a permanent member of the Solar System – unless it is deliberately brought down.

It seems worth while here to give a table showing how velocity and period for a stable, circular orbit change with distance:

There are points of special interest in the last two examples in the table. If a satellite is launched into an equatorial orbit at 22,300 miles, it will complete one journey in 23 hours 56 minutes, which is precisely the time which the Earth takes to spin once on its axis. Therefore, the satellite will remain above the same point all the time, as it will keep pace with the rotating Earth. Satellites of this sort have actually been sent up for communications purposes. The idea was a purely British one, due originally to Arthur C. Clarke, and I shall have more to say about it in Chapter 18.

The final entry is, of course, for our one natural satellite: the Moon, which does move at 239,000 miles at an average velocity of

2,268 m.p.h., and completes one journey in 27.3 days. Here the orbit is somewhat elliptical, not circular, but the basic principle remains unaltered. Again it is worth noting that celestial mechanics makes no distinction between natural bodies and those which are man-made. We can even take the argument a step further, and consider the Earth, which is moving round the Sun at a distance of approximately 93,000,000 miles at a mean orbital velocity of 66,000 m.p.h., or $18\frac{1}{2}$ miles per second. Its orbit is completely stable; there is certainly no need for us to attach rockets to the world and fire them periodically to prevent ourselves from falling into the Sun. Neither need we give extra power to an artificial satellite, once we have put it into the right path and given it the right initial velocity.

All these considerations are familiar to many people nowadays. They were decidedly novel in 1955, even though the whole project had been widely discussed in scientific circles. The main trouble was that the rockets of the nineteen-fifties were much less powerful than those of the present time.

Plans were not lacking, and one is reminded of the MOUSE

Height above the Earth's surface, in miles	Orbital velocity m.p.h.	Orbital period	
		hours	minutes
100	17,450	1	28
200	17,250	1	30
300	17,060	1	34
400	16,850	1	37
500	16,660	1	41
1,000	15,780	1	59
2,000	14,415	2	36
5,000	11,750	4	45
10,000	9,410	9	20
22,300	6,872	23	56
239,000 (from Earth's centre)	2,268	27.3 days	

EFFECT OF LAUNCHING VELOCITY UPON A SPACE VEHICLE. If the initial velocity is less than 5 miles per second, the vehicle will not enter orbit, but will fall back to the ground. At 5 miles per second the orbit will be circular; between 5 and 6.9 miles per second, the orbit will be elliptical; over 7 miles per second the vehicle will escape from the Earth altogether. This is why 7 miles per second is known as the Earth's escape velocity.

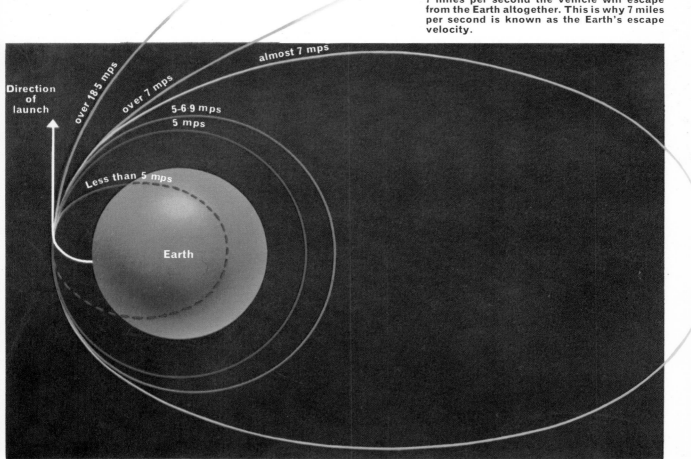

DIFFERENT ORBITS FOR ARTIFICIAL SATELLITES: the polar (passing over both the North and South Poles) and the equatorial. Each orbit has its own particular advantages, but also its own particular drawbacks. By now, satellites have been sent into orbits at many different inclinations from 0 degrees to 90 degrees.

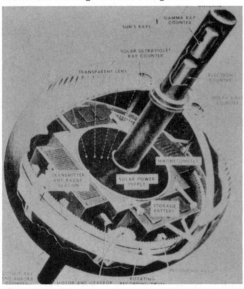

THE 'MOUSE'—an abbreviation for 'Minimum Orbit Unmanned Satellite, Earth'. This was designed by Professor S. F. Singer, of the United States, before the official announcement of the earth satellite programme in 1955. The MOUSE was never actually built, but represented a notable theoretical study.

(Minimum Orbit Unmanned Satellite, Earth) described by Professor S. F. Singer of Maryland. The MOUSE was to be used for upper atmosphere research, and was to be about a foot in diameter, moving at about 200 miles up and making one revolution in 90 minutes. However, it was to be put into a path carrying it over the poles instead of above the line of the equator. This would have various advantages, but it would also be rather more difficult, since with an equatorial orbit one can take advantage of the Earth's own rotation; a mountain on the equator is being carried round at a velocity of almost a third of a mile per second, so providing a useful bonus for a satellite launched eastward. (To launch westward, of course, would mean extra velocity, as the Earth's spin would be a handicap instead of a help. This is one reason why, even today, few satellites are launched westward.)

There was a special reason for the timing of the American announcement of 1955. The period between mid-1957 and the end of 1958 was to be called the International Geophysical Year (I.G.Y.), during which scientists of all countries had undertaken to co-operate in collecting observations to tell us more about all aspects of the Earth. It may be added that the I.G.Y. was a triumphant success, and was the greatest international scientific programme ever undertaken, though doubtless it will be surpassed in the future.

Originally, this particular period had been selected because it was known that the Sun would be at its most active, with many spot-groups and solar storms which would have pronounced effects upon the Earth. It was a happy coincidence that rocketry had progressed just far enough for there to be at least a good chance of satellites being launched during the eighteen months that the I.G.Y. was to last. The first suggestions had come earlier, with a report presented to Congress by James V. Forrestal, then Defense Secretary, in December 1948, but it had then been too soon to give even an approximate time-scale. All the Forrestal Report really said was that the idea of a satellite programme had been given official sanction.

During the next year or two after 1955 there were regular reports from Cape Canaveral, where Project Vanguard, as it had been christened, was in progress. Many of the details were kept secret, for military reasons; the 'cold war' that followed the German overthrow was uppermost in most people's minds, and nobody really knew what the Russians were or were not doing in the field of rocketry. Certainly the Soviet statements were rare, vague, and almost totally uninformative.

I will claim, with all due modesty, that in a book written within a few weeks after the 1955 announcement, I gave my view that 'there is no reason to disregard Soviet claims to have reached a stage technically equal to that of the West, and it is quite possible that bigger and better satellites will be sent up from the far side of the Iron Curtain'. But when I made this comment, I was doing little more than guess; I had no 'inside knowledge'. And I was not, of course, the only writer to think in such a way.

All the same, the events of 4 October 1957, came as a decided shock. It was on that day that the Space Age began, considerably earlier than had been generally expected. And it started not with a whimper, but with a very pronounced bang.

Chapter 15

4 October, 1957

Nowadays we are used to the Russians springing surprises on us in their space programme. We were not used to it in 1957, and it came as a shock when on 4 October, without the slightest warning, Sputnik 1 soared into orbit and proceeded round the world in a path which took it from about 580 miles at apogee down to a mere 135 miles at perigee.[1] Its original period was slightly over 96 minutes. It carried a radio transmitter, and the characteristic 'bleep! bleep!' signals were picked up by receivers in many countries, East and West.

Later information from Moscow stated that the launcher had been a three-step arrangement. Step No. 1 carried the vehicle to a height of 35 miles, and reached a speed of 4,500 m.p.h. in 2 minutes. The second step exhausted its propellant at a height of 140 miles, by which time the velocity had risen to 12,500 m.p.h. The third stage, containing the Sputnik itself, then 'coasted' in a curved path for 5 minutes, reaching a height of 300 miles. Its motors were then started, driving the vehicle more or less horizontally and increasing the speed to around 18,000 m.p.h. At this point the Sputnik was ejected, and both it and the now-fuelless third step of the launcher remained in orbit.

I have never known so much general interest over a scientific experiment, either before or since. I remember trying to persuade one agitated telephone inquirer that the Russian satellite would neither disrupt the Moon, interfere with the weather, or land devastatingly in her back garden. Usually, however, people wanted to know whether the satellite would be visible—and if so, what would it look like?

Actually, the Sputnik itself was always too faint to be seen with

HEADLINE IN THE *DAILY EXPRESS* (London) on 5 October 1957, announcing the successful launching of Sputnik 1, the first artificial satellite, on the previous day. This Russian achievement came as something of a surprise in Great Britain and America, though it was known that the Soviet workers had been making great progress with their rocket research.

[1] The modern practice, thoroughly justifiable scientifically, is to use kilometres instead of miles. I propose to retain the mile as the unit of measurement in the present book, however, for the excellent reason that everyone understands what it means.

DAILY EXPRESS

17,814   SATURDAY OCTOBER 5 1957   1 a.m. forecast. Some drizzle; bright spells later

The first 'Flying Saucer' travels at 17,000 m.p.h.

SPACE AGE IS HERE

Soviet satellite circling world in 95 minutes

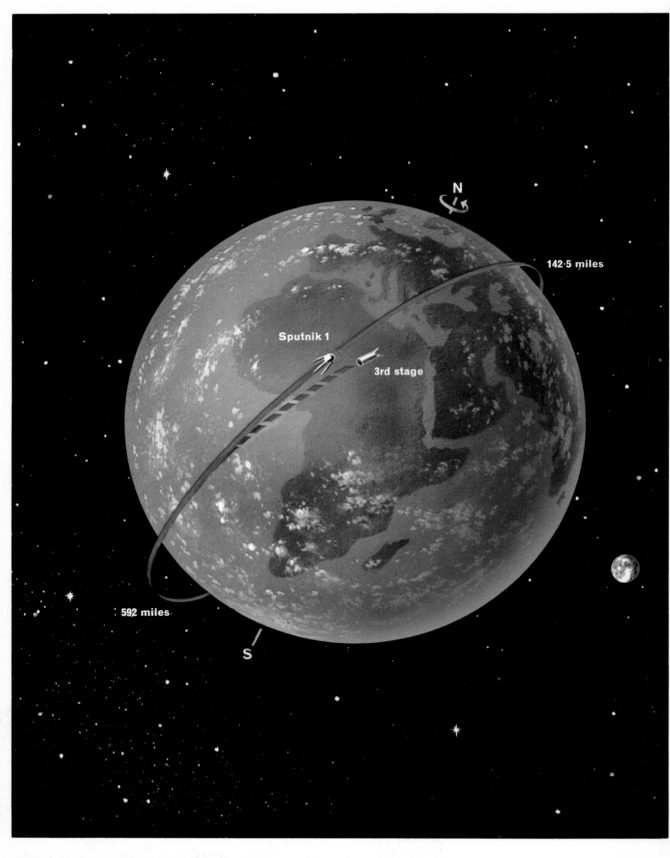

ORBIT OF SPUTNIK 1 ROUND THE EARTH, at the time of its initial launching on 4 October 1957. Sputnik 1 remained in orbit until January 1958, after which it decayed in the lower atmosphere.

the naked eye. The rocket was brighter, and was not difficult to locate; it surpassed most of the stars when at its best, and could be seen crawling slowly among the constellation-patterns.

It would be idle to pretend that reactions in the West were uniformly enthusiastic. In America, there were feelings that the Russians had not 'played fair', presumably because they had not announced beforehand that their satellite was ready. One irritated U.S. Rear-Admiral described the Sputnik as 'a hunk of iron that almost anyone could launch'. Unfortunately, it was only too clear that at that period Project Vanguard was not ready to send up a piece of iron or anything else.

The Sputnik (Russian term for 'satellite' which has now become part of our own language) was small by modern standards. It was spherical, with a diameter of only about 20 inches, and apparently it carried little apart from its transmitter. Its importance lay not in itself, but in the fact that it had been launched successfully. Its signals were duly picked up, and it was also tracked by the new 250-foot radio telescope at Jodrell Bank, then still in the last stages of construction. The Jodrell Bank team had a somewhat hectic time, because the radio telescope had not been designed with any thoughts of being used for satellite tracking, and in any case it was not ready to be put into operation. In particular, it was teeming with painters, and more than once there were sliced cables to be mended when the whole giant structure began to twist and turn so as to follow the rapidly-moving Sputnik. However, much valuable information was collected, notably the discovery that the satellite was spinning.

Three weeks after the launch, Sputnik 1's batteries apparently went dead. The only hope of tracking it further was by radar; and following an urgent message from Moscow, the Jodrell Bank team was able to send the necessary information—the first, but by no means the last, piece of East-West co-operation in space.

Another discovery made from Jodrell Bank was that although the Sputnik and the final stage of its launcher had begun moving in similar orbits, the rocket soon started to gain on the satellite; in other words, its orbit was shrinking more quickly (see Ills. on page 94). This was not surprising. Sputnik, as we have noted, was only about 20 inches in diameter. The third stage of the launcher seems to have been a cylinder more than 60 feet long, which explains why it appeared so much more conspicuous. Air drag near perigee affected it differently, and it came down more quickly; so far as we know, it re-entered the dense atmosphere, and was destroyed, on 1 December. Sputnik itself lasted longer, and remained aloft until 4 January 1958. Then it, too, came to the end of its career, and shared a similar fiery fate, but it had done all that its makers could have hoped of it.

The chief cause for alarm in the United States was that instead of being well ahead in what now came to be called the 'space race', America was considerably behind. There were various causes. It has been said that rivalry between different American research teams had prevented full co-operation, and it was also suggested that the plans had not been sufficiently clear-cut, so that several systems were being studied at once instead of the main attention being concentrated upon the most promising line. It is pointless to revive these questions, which are of no interest today, but at any

MODEL OF SPUTNIK 1, the first Russian earth satellite, on display at the Exhibition of National Economic Achievements in Moscow in the autumn of 1957.

THE 250-FOOT RADIO TELESCOPE AT JODRELL BANK. This is still the world's largest fully-steerable radio telescope. It was not designed for tracking earth satellites, but it was pressed into service in the early days of practical space research. It has been announced that an even larger instrument is to be built within the next few years.

rate it was obvious that the Russians had developed propellants of surprising power.

One result of the Sputnik was that all cynics of space-research were silenced permanently. Even after the Vanguard announcement of 1955, it was still claimed by some reputable scientists that the whole idea of launching space-probes would remain impracticable for a great many years, if not for ever; but nothing of the sort could be said after 4 October 1957. The Space Age had begun.

Almost before the initial shock had subsided, the Russians sent up another vehicle, Sputnik 2. Unlike the original tiny satellite, this was a properly instrumented body, said to be cylindro-conical, and more than five times as massive as its predecessor; it weighed something like half a ton. Its equipment was capable of studying cosmic rays, short-wave radiations, and the temperatures and pressures in the upper part of the atmosphere. The apogee height was greater than that of Sputnik 1, and its original revolution period was almost 104 minutes, so that it could enjoy a longer life-span; in fact, it remained up until 14 April 1958. During its final orbit of the Earth, when it was already self-luminous because of the friction against the air-particles, it was well seen over wide areas.

The really controversial feature of Sputnik 2 was that it contained a live dog, whose name, Laika, will always be remembered. Laika was the first of all living space-passengers, but there was no hope of her safe return to Earth. She was sent up, with automatically-recording instruments attached to her body, so that her reactions could be studied as a prelude to the launching of human crews; but at that stage in research, the re-entry problem—that is to say, the method of bringing a satellite down without burn-out in the atmosphere—had yet to be solved. Laika lived on for some

SPUTNIK 2, the second Russian earth satellite which was launched on 3 November 1957; this is a model on display at the Exhibition of National Economic Achievements in Moscow, in early 1958. Sputnik 2 carried a live dog, LAIKA (below)—the first mammal to be sent into space.

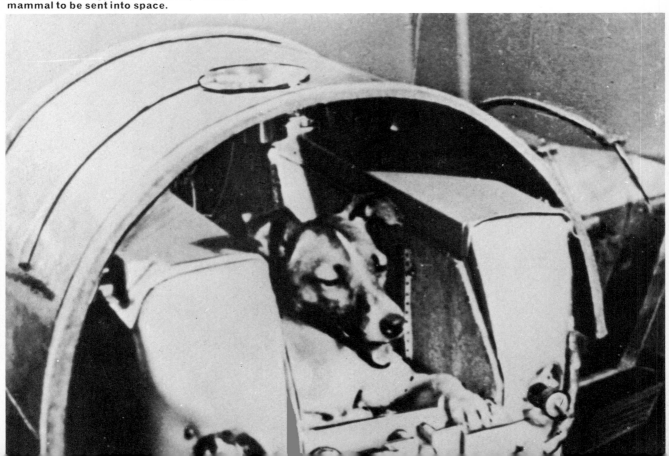

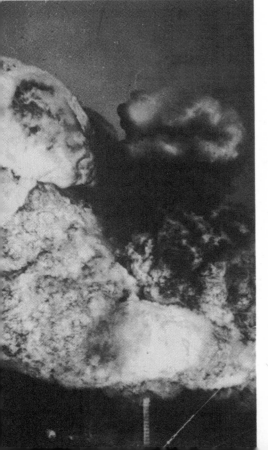

time, but was dead long before Sputnik 2 spiralled to destruction 162 days after having been launched.

There were voluble protests against the use of a dog in such a way. Of course, there are two sides to the matter, and in speaking publicly against the experiment I was, I think, in the minority; at any rate, I was strongly criticized, though I remained unrepentent. (I agree, of course, that no deliberate cruelty was involved, which is more than can be said for 'sports' such as fox-hunting, still, for some obscure reason, legal in Britain.) Other animals have been launched since, both by the Russian and American teams, but Laika remains the only passenger to have been officially doomed from the moment of take-off. Efforts were made to bring down the later animals, and in most cases these efforts were successful.

It must be admitted that the Sputniks effectively diverted world attention from Project Vanguard, still continuing at Cape Canaveral. It is probably true to say that the main American desire now was to get some kind of satellite into orbit, no matter how small it might be—and it is also probable that the first serious attempt at launching, on 6 December 1957, was made earlier than would have been the case but for the Sputniks. Not surprisingly, it failed. After days of delay due to minor troubles, the launching was scheduled for just before noon. The rocket carrying the 6-inch satellite blew up almost immediately, and exploded with considerable violence, though luckily there were no casualties. The satellite was thrown clear, and its transmitters continued to 'bleep', though I cannot vouch for the story that one American scientist implored a colleague to 'go and put that thing out of its misery'!

Yet these were the pioneer days, and mishaps were only to be expected. Within two months after the initial fiasco, the U.S. team headed by Wernher von Braun, late of Peenemünde, managed to launch a satellite, Explorer 1, which may have been small (6 inches across) but which carried instruments destined to make vitally important discoveries. And then, on 17 March 1958, Vanguard at last proved itself. This time there were no explosions, and Vanguard 1 soared into the sky.

I have dwelt at some length on these first launchings, because they are part of history. To give similar details for all the satellites and probes which have followed would be quite out of place here; in the Appendix, I have listed the most important launchings of the first few years of space research, but full information belongs to technical books, not to a general survey. It is time to turn to tracking methods, and to the uses to which satellites have been put. Yet nobody who was actively interested in astronautics during the late nineteen-fifties will ever forget the excitement of the days when man-made vehicles at last broke free from the forceful grip of our parent Earth.

UNSUCCESSFUL VANGUARD LAUNCHING, 1957. The experiment was a failure, since the rocket blew up on the ground.

EXPLOSION OF VANGUARD; the site was enveloped in clouds of smoke, and the launching vehicle was destroyed. It was not until 1958 that the Americans were first able to emulate the Russians in sending up an earth satellite.

Chapter 16

Tracking the Satellites

When the first Sputniks were launched, many people in many countries went outdoors at night to look for them, but without knowing just what to expect. In those early days it was often supposed that a satellite might look as large as a walnut or even a football. By now, of course, most non-scientists as well as scientists have seen the various bright satellites which have been sent up; it has been said that, in particular, the two American Echo vehicles which are extremely brilliant, have been observed by more people than any other artificial objects in all history, not excepting Big Ben and the Statue of Liberty.

Modern satellite-hunting is a popular hobby, as well as being a rewarding one. It is rather surprising to find that visual observations of some satellites, carried out with binoculars and a stop-watch, are of definite use to space-research teams; but such is the case.

At the beginning of 1968 there were something like 1,000 separate objects in orbit round the Earth, moving at various heights and at various speeds. Some of them may be regarded as permanent. For instance, the original Vanguard of 1958 will stay up for something like 300 years, because its orbit is sufficiently high above the denser parts of the atmosphere; Telstar, the first successful communications satellite, which was launched in 1962 from Cape Canaveral, will remain circling the world for at least 10,000 years, because even at perigee it is still 600 miles above sea-level—and at this height, air-drag is negligible. Others are more temporary, and will have come down before this book appears in print, either by natural decay due to air-resistance or by being summoned home by remote control.

Not all of these objects are intentional satellites. Many last stages of launchers are still in orbit, and there are also many 'fragments', due to accidents or mere debris. For example, there was a mishap in June 1961, when an American Ablestar rocket exploded, putting over 200 separate objects into paths round the Earth—where most of them remain, useless and in some ways irritating.

For tracking purposes, satellites, last stages of launchers, and

RUSSIAN SATELLITE TRACKING STATION AT ZVENIGOROD, some way from Moscow. This photograph, taken by Gregory Moliakov, shows the author standing by one of the 'camera pavilions' from which earth satellites were tracked during the early days of space research. The picture was taken in 1960.

fragments may be discussed together. And let me stress that I do not propose in this book to give detailed instructions of how to make predictions and work out the observations; all I hope to do is to indicate the general lines of attack, after which those who have become seriously interested will perhaps feel inclined to turn to a more technical treatise such as *Observing Earth Satellites*, a recent book by Desmond King-Hele, one of Britain's leading satellite-hunters. It is also worth noting that the needs and methods have altered considerably since the Space Age began in the autumn of 1957.

To begin with, it is obvious that satellites are of many kinds. They have different uses, to be described in Chapters 17 and 18; they are of different sizes and different shapes. Some of the most interesting satellites, such as the Telstar and Early Bird communications vehicles, are much too faint to be seen without good optical equipment. On the other hand, the U.S. Echo satellites, which are nothing more nor less than plastic balloons totally without instrumentation, are much too brilliant to be overlooked even by the most myopic sky-watcher. Every time they come into regular view during evenings, they attract widespread attention. They have also, needless to say, been responsible for a great many flying saucer reports.

Although an artificial satellite behaves in the same way as a natural astronomical body as soon as it has been put into a stable path, there are various points to be borne in mind. Once a satellite is completely out of the atmosphere (or, more accurately, so far out that there is no perceptible air-drag), its position can be predicted for weeks or months in advance, and it can always be found, provided that it is large enough to be detectable at all. But when a satellite is being affected by air-drag, its movement becomes less predictable, partly because our knowledge of the density of the upper atmosphere is not perfect. True, our estimates now are much better than they were in 1957; the pioneer satellites showed that the higher regions of the air are much denser than had been thought, and, of course, the denser the air, the greater the drag it will produce.

This is also one of the main reasons for making accurate observations of satellites. When we know what is happening to them, we can work out the density of the atmosphere in the regions in which they are moving—and this density is not entirely constant.

To locate a naked-eye satellite, all that need be done is to look at the appropriate column in one of the daily newspapers, note the time and direction at which the satellite will be visible, and then go outdoors and observe. With clear skies, success is virtually certain. The prediction may be in error by a minute or two, but this should cause no difficulty. For fainter satellites, of course, one needs the official tables, which are issued to observers who are serious about the matter and who have already submitted enough reliable measures of the easier objects.

If a satellite is bright, anyone with a fair knowledge of the constellation patterns will be able to pick it out at once. In any case, a few moments' watching will show that it is in motion—and I need hardly add that no natural body, except for a meteor, has an apparent movement quick enough for it to be 'caught in the act', so to speak. Lofty satellites take some time to crawl across the sky

DISTANCES FROM EARTH OF SOME OF THE EARLIER SATELLITES; the weather satellite Tiros 1, the balloon vehicles Echo 1, Echo 2 and Pageos, and the Intelsat vehicle, which had a very eccentric orbit.

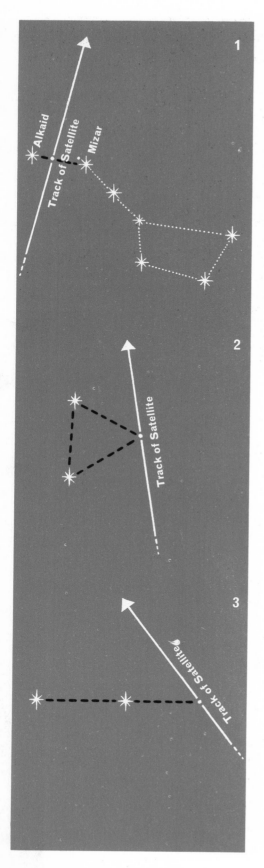

from one horizon to the other, but satellites at relatively low altitudes hurry along. Then there are the 'winkers' and the 'flashers', to say nothing of the satellites which show slower, more ponderous changes in brilliancy.

There are four methods of satellite observing to be considered: visual, photographic, radio and radar. Of these, only the first two are within the scope of the average amateur tracking enthusiast.

For visual observing, the simplest equipment consists solely of a stop-watch, though it is very desirable to have at least a working knowledge of the constellation patterns. The method is to time the moment when the satellite reaches a point which can be 'fixed', usually by passing between two stars which can be identified later.

Let us consider Mizar and Alkaid in the famous Great Bear, as shown in the diagram, and assume that we are to observe a naked-eye satellite such as Echo 2. Having looked up the prediction, we go outside a few minutes before Echo is due, settle ourselves down, and wait. As the satellite passes between Mizar and Alkaid, perhaps two-thirds of the way toward Alkaid, the stop-watch is started; let us say that a telephone is available, so that as soon as the observation has been made it is possible to listen to the Speaking Clock. The stop-watch is stopped at a known time; let us say 21 hours 10 minutes 30 seconds. We find that the watch has run for 1 minute 10.0 seconds. A simple subtraction sum must now be worked:

| | 21 hours 10 minutes 30.0 seconds |
| minus | 1 minute 10.0 seconds |

$=$ 21 hours 9 minutes 20.0 seconds

which was the time that Echo 2 reached our fixed point. The observation is complete.

Generally, matters will not be so easy as this, and satellites seem to have a perfect genius for avoiding positions between two suitable stars, but there are various modifications; we may obtain a fix when the satellite forms an equilateral triangle with two stars (Diagram 2) or is lined up with two stars (Diagram 3). The observer can work this out for himself. Incidentally, it is not often that a satellite passes directly in front of a star, hiding or occulting it. I have seen such an event only three times, and although I am not a regular satellite observer I have made a good many measurements during the past few years.

Naturally, one has to be sure of the stars used as 'anchors'; if the stars are wrongly identified, the results will be very peculiar indeed. Moreover, the stop-watch must be accurate. An observation must be correct to within one second of time and half a degree of arc if it is to be of any use at all; to give some idea of what this means, it is worth noting that the angular separation between Dubhe and Merak, the 'Pointers' in the Great Bear, is 5°. Reliable naked-eye satellite observations are of value, and should be sent in to an official data centre.

When an observer has 'qualified', he will be able to obtain regular predictions for the fainter satellites not dealt with in any daily newspapers. He will also need optical aid. A powerful astronomical telescope is of limited use, because it is bound to have a small field of view, and to try to locate a dim, quick-moving satellite in such a way is rather more troublesome than looking for the

TIMING THE POSITION OF THE ECHO BALLOON SATELLITE. The measurement is made at the instant when the satellite passes between two known stars (upper diagram), forms an equilateral triangle with two known stars (centre) or is aligned with the two known stars (lower). Since the positions of the stars are known, the position of the satellite at this particular moment can also be found, and the results used to correct the orbital predictions for the future. Visual satellite tracking of this sort has been of great value for satellites of many kinds, and is still carried out.

PHOTOGRAPH OF THE CARRIER ROCKET OF SPUTNIK 1, taken on 10 October 1957 by K. Kiseleva at Pulkovo Observatory, near Leningrad. The stars are shown as short trails, since the photograph was taken with a time-exposure; the rocket appears as a straight line. The interruption in the middle of the rocket trail is deliberate, and is made so as to provide a means of reference.

THE HEWITT CAMERA, designed at the Royal Radar Establishment, at Great Malvern, specifically for photographing earth satellites. It is really an adaption of the Schmidt principle, enabling large areas of the sky to be covered with a single exposure.

proverbial needle in the equally proverbial haystack. Binoculars are much better, particularly if the field of view is large and the light-grasp good. Average binoculars will bring at least 200 satellites within range, which is quite satisfactory. A good star-atlas is also an essential, so that the fainter stars used as reference points can be identified.

In the early days, the famous 'Moonwatch' system was organized by the Smithsonian Astrophysical Observatory in Cambridge, Massachusetts. Here, a team of about ten volunteers, each equipped with a small telescope, covered an arc of the sky, each observer being responsible for one particular area so that the expected satellite would be unable to avoid detection by one or more members of the team. The Moonwatch programme still continues, and has yielded useful results.

In most branches of modern astronomy, photography has replaced the human eye. To some extent this is also true in satellite work, and special cameras have been developed, notably the Baker-Nunn (U.S.A.) and the Hewitt (Britain). Both are extremely accurate, extremely complex and very expensive; the Baker-Nunn, with its mounting, weighs nearly three tons. Fortunately, the amateur satellite-watcher need not go to such lengths. Even with an ordinary camera, bright satellites may be recorded easily. All that need be done is to leave the camera shutter open, pointing at the right area of the night sky, and wait until the satellite has come and gone. The resulting picture will show the characteristic star-trails, together with the different sort of trail left by the satellite.

I am well aware that the directions given above are not adequate for the would-be serious observer. I can only repeat that in a general survey, it would be out of place to go into too much detail about tracking methods; but the information is readily available in technical works, and I can only hope that at least some of my

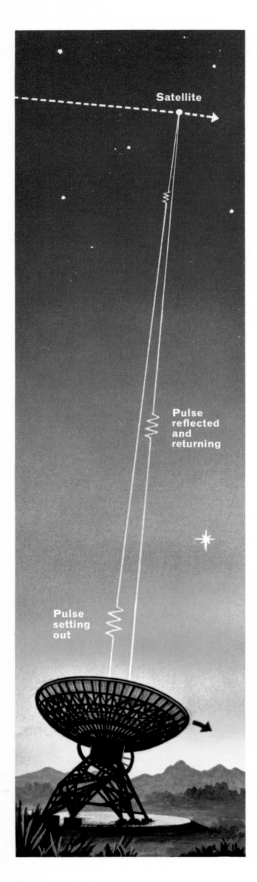

readers will feel interested enough to take the matter further.

Before turning to other methods, let us note that there are occasions when a satellite vanishes abruptly from view when it is in full flight across the sky. This will certainly mean that it has passed into the Earth's shadow, and has been eclipsed; its source of sunlight has been cut off, so that it can no longer be seen. The natural Moon, of course, can undergo eclipse in precisely the same way, but the process is more gradual, and the Moon does not (usually) vanish completely, because some of the Sun's rays are bent on to its surface by the effect of the atmospheric layers surrounding the Earth.

Another method of tracking is by radio. Here, special equipment is needed, and in any case the method is confined to 'active' satellites—that is to say, satellites which carry transmitters and are sending out signals at known frequency. As only about 5 per cent. of satellites now in orbit are so equipped, pure radio methods are very restricted, though they are of course highly accurate.

In passing, it is quite wrong to assume—as many people do—that the great 250-foot 'dish' at Jodrell Bank is used regularly as a satellite tracker. Admittedly, it was called in during the eventful early days, but it was not designed for such a task, and it is fully employed on much more fundamental research. It was built to detect and study the long-wavelength radiations coming from the depths of space, and could not be spared for following puny satellites, even if it were really suitable (which it is not).

Radar tracking is a different matter, and is less limited, since it does not depend upon any transmitter carried in the satellite. Basically, the principle is to use a movable saucer-shaped dish which can send out radio waves in an almost parallel beam, and then detect the 'echo' as the waves are bounced back from its target. There are several difficulties to be faced, of which the most pressing is the cost; a proper installation needs an expenditure of money which is astronomical in every sense of the word. Moreover, the directional accuracy is poor when compared with that of the camera, and the performance of radar equipment falls off quickly with the increased distance of the target. Even more annoying is the fact that some common materials, notably fibreglass, are more or less transparent to wavelengths commonly used in radar (say 3 to 10 centimetres). To such a radar installation, a fibreglass satellite would be undetectable,

Most or all of these hazards can be overcome, and the various methods of keeping track of the satellites complement each other, so that it is not often nowadays that an important or interesting satellite is permanently lost. As the 'space population' increases, matters will become more difficult, but for the moment the situation seems to be well under control.

Few people, except those actively engaged in space research, will spend their time in tracking down faint satellites and identifying them. Yet satellite-spotting has now become an entertaining and useful hobby among many amateurs, and it is fascinating to watch the tiny specks of light which cross the sky, making their way among the stars and giving visible proof that the natural bodies of the Solar System, created thousands of millions of years ago, have at last been joined by newcomers fashioned by the ingenuity of mankind.

TRACKING EARTH SATELLITES BY MEANS OF RADAR. A pulse is 'bounced off' the satellite. The advantage of the method is that it can be applied to satellites which have no transmitters on board, and it has been of great value, though it also has marked disadvantages.

Chapter 17

The Van Allen Zones

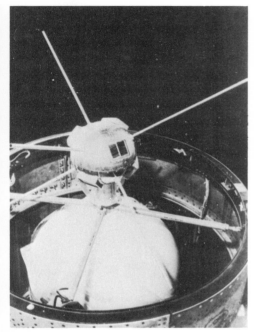

EXPLORER 1, the first successful satellite sent up from the United States. It was launched in 1958 by the team led by the German rocket expert Wernher von Braun.

ORBIT OF EXPLORER 1, showing the parts of the orbit during which the satellite was illuminated by the Sun.

When the United States team headed by Wernher von Braun launched Explorer 1, on 1 February 1958, it did so in a decided atmosphere of anti-climax. America had been beaten in the first lap of the 'space race'; two Russian Sputniks had already been sent up, and the second at least was surprisingly massive, whereas Explorer was a tiny thing. World attention had been switched away from Cape Canaveral, and the American space programme was in danger of being regarded (quite unjustifiably) as something of a wry joke.

Yet in the long run, the dwarf Explorer proved to be much the most effective of all the early satellites. It weighed a mere 31 pounds, but it was crammed with miniature equipment, and it carried, among other things, a Geiger counter, which is an instrument used to detect charged particles and high-energy radiation. One of its tasks was to investigate the frequency of cosmic rays at various heights above the Earth.

Cosmic rays are not true rays at all; they are the nuclei of atoms, and they come from 'the depths of space'. The Sun is admittedly one source of them, but most originate far away across the Galaxy, and we are still ignorant of their origins. Since they represent a possible hazard to astronauts venturing beyond the screen provided by our atmosphere, it was clear from the outset that they would have to be investigated. Explorer I was only the first of many cosmic-ray satellites.

Explorer's orbit was decidedly elliptical, with a perigee at 224 miles, an apogee at 1,585 miles, and an initial period of just under 115 minutes. Its estimated lifetime was ten years, so that as I write these words (1968) it is still moving round the Earth; of course it was always far too faint to be seen with the naked eye, and it sent

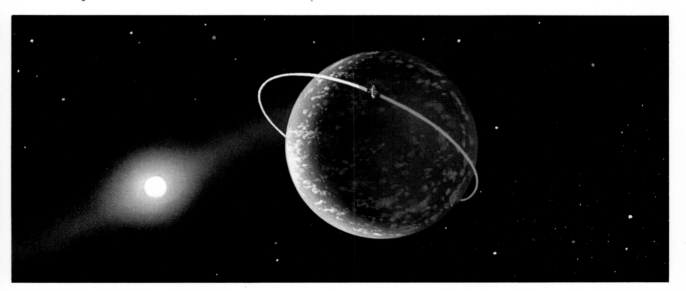

REPLICA OF LUNIK 3, launched by the Russians on 4 October 1959. This was described at the time as 'an automatic interplanetary research station'. Lunik 3 went round the Moon, and sent back the first photographs of the averted hemisphere which is always turned away from the Earth.

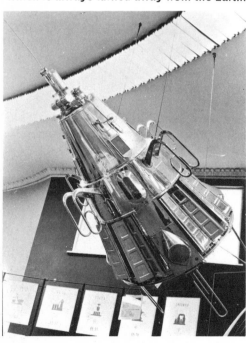

SPUTNIK 3, a purely scientific earth satellite launched by the Russians on 15 May 1958. This was one of the most successful of the early Soviet satellites, and transmitted information of great value.

back its information by means of its own transmitter.

At first everything seemed normal. The cosmic ray counts were expected to increase with height, because the Earth's air prevents the relatively massive cosmic-ray primaries from reaching ground level. Quite predictably, the counts went up. Then, at a height of about 600 miles, they stopped completely—and this happened each time Explorer went through the 'critical height', though unfortunately its transmissions were somewhat restricted and the information was not complete.

The situation was most peculiar, and at first the American research team, headed by James van Allen, simply did not know what to make of it. It was absurd to suppose that the region above a set height of 600 miles was completely free from cosmic ray particles; on the other hand, it did not seem that anything had seriously upset the Geiger counters carried in the satellite. Something was wrong somewhere, and it was tacitly assumed that the instruments on Explorer 1 must be at fault.

Van Allen had his doubts. Suppose that above the critical region, there were so many particles that the counters on board the satellite could not cope with them, and had become jammed? This would provide a good reason for the sudden apparent falling-away to zero, though at that time there was no explanation for such an abundance of particles.

The main drawback about Explorer 1 was that it could not store its information. It had to transmit immediately—and if it were not conveniently placed with respect to a recording station, then the information would be lost. The obvious answer was to send up another satellite, carrying equipment of the same kind but with a tape-recorder added. Explorer 2 was a failure, and never achieved orbit, but on 26 March 1958 Explorer 3 was successfully launched into a path which carried it between 119 and 1,741 miles above the Earth; this time the revolution period was slightly over 115 minutes. Ninety-three days later it fell back into the denser atmosphere, and was destroyed, but by then it had fulfilled its task.

Note, incidentally, that Explorer 3 was much less long-lived than Explorer 1, because its original perigee distance was smaller. Each time it came to its closest point—that is to say, every 115 minutes—it was meeting with definite resistance from the air, so that its orbit contracted relatively quickly and it could not survive for long.

Explorer 3 completely confirmed the results obtained by its predecessor, and it also confirmed Van Allen's theory. Up to a height of 300 miles, there was a gradual increase in the number of charged particles. Then, up to 600 miles, there was a more rapid increase. Above 600 miles, the counters became jammed. Van Allen estimated that the actual particle numbers might be anything up to 35,000 per second, which was far too high to be dealt with by any self-respecting Geiger counter. Meanwhile, the Russians had joined in the research with their massive vehicle Sputnik 3, which was sent up on 15 May 1958 and did not decay until 6 April 1960. Two Soviet space-scientists, Vernov and Chudakov, came to conclusions very similar to those of the Americans.

It seemed that there must be a zone of intense radiation, and studies with later probes led to the picture of two distinct zones, appropriately named in honour of Van Allen. The outer parts were beyond the range of the early satellites, and were investigated with vehicles which were not designed to return to Earth; I shall have more to say about them later. Our ideas have changed somewhat of late, and it is now thought that the Van Allen Zones should more properly be regarded as a single belt with a gradual change in nature with increasing distance from the Earth, but the basic idea has not been altered. It is perhaps fitting that the first really great discovery to be made by means of an artificial satellite should have come from a team headed by Wernher von Braun, who had spent so much of his early life in experimenting with feeble, unreliable rockets at the old Flying Field near Berlin.

It was one thing to discover the Van Allen Zones, but quite another to explain them. Before attempting to try, we must look more carefully at the Earth's magnetic field.

Everyone knows that the Earth is magnetic; were it not so, then our ordinary pocket compasses would not work. To delve into the causes of this magnetic field would be beyond my present scope, but of its importance there can be no doubt at all, and of course it is bound to affect the charged particles coming from space. Some particles, at least, will be trapped by the magnetic field, and will be unable to break free, so that they will simply spiral to and fro. Speculations about trapped particles of this kind had been made before the Space Age by Størmer of Norway, Alfvén of Sweden and Poincaré of France, but until the flights of the Explorers there could be no proof.

The inner part of the Van Allen Zone appeared to be made up of high-energy protons; the outer part, of high-energy electrons. Both sets of particles were presumably trapped by magnetic forces, but it was not easy to explain how the particles arrived there in the first place, and even now this problem has not been fully solved.

Let us consider the inner zone first. It seems to be reasonably constant, and may be due to cosmic-ray particles. Because these particles are so energetic, they can pass through the Earth's magnetic barrier and collide with the atomic particles in the upper air, producing various other particles—including neutrons. Neutrons have no electric charge at all, and so they are blissfully unaffected by magnetic forces; they can therefore travel in any direction even when in a strong magnetic field. On the other hand, they do not last for long, and after a few minutes they decay once more into protons and electrons. It may well be that the neutrons

THE VAN ALLEN ZONES, detected from the U.S. satellite Explorer 1. These are zones of intense radiation surrounding the Earth, and have been found to be of immense importance. They are due to particles trapped by the terrestrial magnetic field.

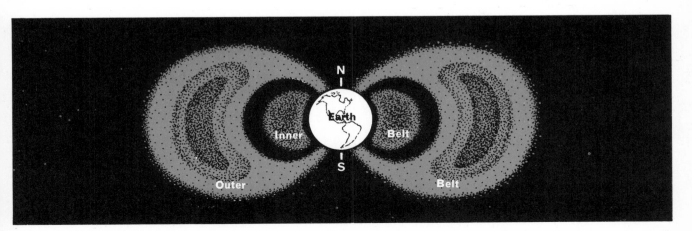

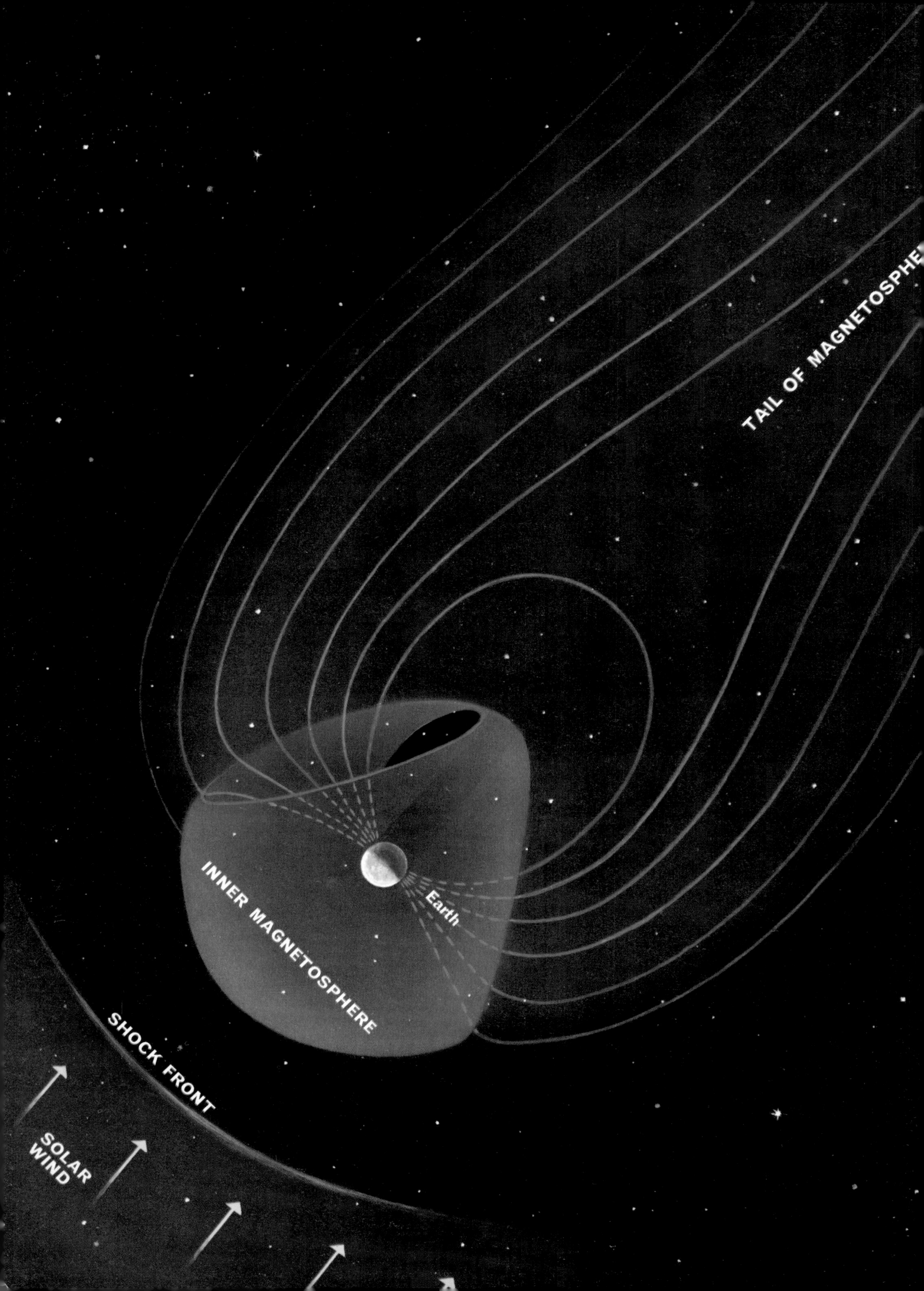

TAIL OF MAGNETOSPHERE

INNER MAGNETOSPHERE

Earth

SHOCK FRONT

SOLAR WIND

which travel away from the Earth after their creation in the upper atmosphere are responsible for the protons in the lower part of the Van Allen Zone.

There are various weaknesses in this theory, but it seems to be the best put forward so far, and we must await the results of further research. In any case, the origin of the outer part of the radiation zone, made up principally of electrons, is clearly different. Unlike the inner region, the outer Van Allen Zone is variable, and is strongly influenced by events taking place in the Sun, so that we must do our best to see just where the connection lies.

The Sun, as we have noted, is a star; it is quite mild on the stellar scale, but immensely energetic judged by our everyday standards. Also, it is known to be sending out constant streams of particles, making up what is known as the solar wind. (Here, too, we owe the discovery to space-probes, though the existence of the solar wind had been suspected on theoretical grounds as long ago as 1896, by the Norwegian scientist Olaf Birkeland.) It seems quite likely that these solar-wind particles supply the outer part of the Van Allen Zone with its particles, though here too there are various puzzling facts which remain to be cleared up.

Of course, there is no chance of observing the solar wind directly. Its particles move at something like 900,000 m.p.h. as they reach the orbit of the Earth, and on an average there are only about ten of them per cubic centimetre, so that they are quite undetectable visually, though instruments carried in satellites and space-probes have no trouble in studying them.

Various satellites have been put into highly elliptical orbits specially to examine the Earth's magnetic field at great distances, and the results have been in good agreement. We have also learned a great deal about the extent of the magnetic field itself, and we have found that it is confined to a definite region. On the side of the Earth facing the Sun it is 'squashed-in', so to speak, and ex-

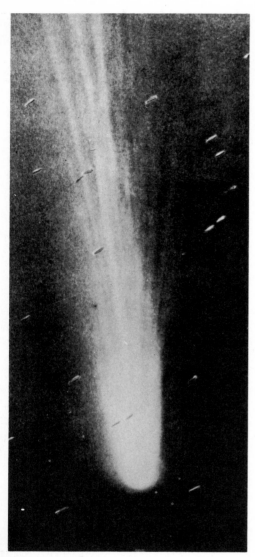

MRKOS' COMET OF 1957, photographed from Byurakan Observatory in the U.S.S.R. This was the second naked-eye comet of 1957, and was seen in the autumn; it was comparable with the comet of April of the same year (Arend-Roland), but lacked the characteristic 'spike' or reverse tail. Like Arend-Roland, Mrkos' Comet has a period so long that it will not be seen again for many centuries.

tends out to only about 40,000 miles, but on the side of the Earth turned away from the Sun it extends out to a much greater distance. In fact, the 'magnetosphere' is shaped rather like a teardrop, with a tremendously long tail.

It has been said that the Earth represents a blunt obstacle in the flow of the solar wind. As the wind comes in toward us, it meets the magnetic field of the Earth, and a shock-wave forms. Inside the shock-wave is a turbulent region, inside which again is a definite boundary called the magnetopause. The magnetosphere proper lies on the Earthward side of the magnetopause, while on the far side of the world, away from the Sun, the shock-wave weakens much as the disturbed wake of a ship will do across the water.

All this may sound rather confusing, and we have to admit that the Earth's surroundings are much less straightforward than we used to think, but at least the general picture is starting to become clear. Without the help from satellites and space-probes, we should still know very little about the magnetosphere.

As an aside, there are two astronomical matters of interest in connection with the solar wind and the Van Allen Zone. First, there are the tails of comets, which always point more or less away from the Sun. As noted in Chapter 1, a comet is a flimsy object made up of relatively small particles (perhaps icy in nature) together with thin gas; a large comet may have an impressive tail. Unfortunately, great comets have been rare of late, and the only recent example was Ikeya-Seki of October 1965, which made a brief, spectacular showing in some parts of the world but which was a grave disappointment in Europe.

It is a great pity that we cannot guarantee the appearance of another bright comet before 1986. In this year our old friend Halley's Comet is due back once more, and there is no fear that it will disappoint us, but evidently it is not so brilliant as it used to be long ago—and this is another indication that comets, as a class, are short-lived. Every time they return to the neighbourhood of the Sun, material is evaporated from the nuclear regions, and the result is a steady deterioration.

Encke's Comet is a case in point. It has a very short period (only $3\frac{1}{3}$ years) and it has now been seen at almost fifty different returns; not many centuries ago it may have been a naked-eye object, but it does not now aspire to such eminence, and it has even been suggested that it will 'die' before the year 2000. There are, of course, some cases of periodical comets which have ceased to exist; the most famous of these is Biela's Comet, which split into two fragments in 1846, was seen for the last time in 1852, and subsequently bade us farewell in the guise of a shower of meteors. But interesting though they may be from the purely astronomical point of view, comets have also told us more about matters such as the solar wind, and as such they are of equal importance to the space-research enthusiast. It has even been suggested that a probe might be dispatched to rendezvous with a comet and collect 'samples' for subsequent analysis. This may be done one day, though not yet. (Jules Verne, needless to say, wrote a novel about a journey to a comet—the theme was very much to his liking—but it must be admitted that this particular story is by no means one of his best.)

When travelling inward towards the Sun, a comet moves head-first; actually, it does not usually develop much of a tail until it is reasonably near perihelion, even if it does so at all. When it has passed its closest point, and has begun its outward journey, it travels tail-first, as shown in the diagram. It used to be thought that this behaviour must be due to 'light repulsion', since light does exert a slight pressure, and the Sun is intensely brilliant. Nowadays we know better; the repelling effect of sunlight would be too weak to make a comet's tail act in this way, and the solar wind must be held mainly responsible.

Then there are the auroræ or Polar Lights, beautiful glows which are seen in the night sky, mainly from high latitudes. They are certainly connected with the Sun, and are usually associated with disturbances such as the brilliant, short-lived outbursts known as solar flares. It used to be thought that the process was quite a simple one, with electrified particles from the Sun striking the Earth's upper air making it glow. The discovery of the Van Allen Zone has caused some re-thinking, and it now seems that auroræ are produced by particles which enter the outer part of the Zone, are accelerated by some process as yet unknown, and cascade downward, making the lovely glows at heights ranging from around 200 down to as little as 60 miles.

Auroræ occur at both polar zones, but the Northern Lights are the better known; they are well seen from countries such as Norway, Iceland and North Canada, while the southern auroral region is limited chiefly to uninhabited areas. From North Scotland, auroræ are common enough, but a Londoner may go for years without seeing a good display, and anyone who stays in, say, San Francisco will be lucky to see one aurora over the course of a lifetime. The best chances occur when the Sun is active, as happens at the time of solar maximum every eleven years or so. The next maximum is due in 1969.

Auroræ are commonest when large, active spot-groups are crossing the Sun's disk, but by no means every large sunspot will produce an aurora; exact predictions cannot be made, and brilliant displays usually take us quite by surprise. However, it is fairly safe to assume that during the period between late 1968 and late 1970 there will be various auroræ bright enough to be spectacular, and at least some of these will be seen from latitudes as low as 50° north or south.

There is no need to emphasize the scientific importance of the solar wind and the Van Allen Zone, but there is another point also to be borne closely in mind. The Zone is a wide belt in which radiation is intense. For an astronaut to stay there for long would be inviting trouble; the human body does not take kindly to overdoses of radiation, and to attempt to set up anything in the nature of a permanent manned space-station in the Van Allen region would be courting disaster. Fortunately, it now seems that nothing of the sort will be strictly necessary, and the elaborate orbital bases planned by Von Braun and others not many years ago have been falling steadily into disfavour. It may well be that the Van Allen Zone has killed them completely.

I have strayed somewhat from my historical sequence, but there seemed to be no alternative, and there is, after all, every excuse for dwelling to some extent upon the first of the great discoveries made by an artificial satellite. The Van Allen Zone is of fundamental importance to astronauts, astronomers and physicists alike.

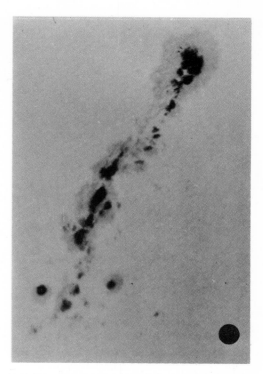

GIANT SUNSPOT GROUP, photographed on 28 February 1967 by W. M. Baxter. The telescope used was a 4in. refractor. To this scale the full diameter of the Sun would be 36 inches. The black disk represents the Earth shown to the same scale.

Chapter 18

Satellites of Many Kinds

The first of all artificial satellites, Sputnik 1, carried little more than its 'bleep, bleep' radio transmitter. It was important not in itself, but simply because the Russians had shown that it could be launched. But there is a great difference between sending up a simple object and dispatching a fully-instrumented satellite, and it was not long before really sophisticated vehicles were in orbit round the Earth.

The Russians took the lead, because they were able to develop more powerful propellants than those used by the American teams. This meant that the Russians did not have to worry about every ounce of weight, and they could install comparatively heavy pieces of equipment without a qualm. The early United States launchings were much less ambitious from this point of view, but there was compensation to be found in the remarkably skilful use of miniature-sized instruments. As we have noted, the first major discovery, that of the Van Allen Zone, was made from the midget Explorer 1.

At the end of the first ten years of the Space Age, the gap between Russian and American 'brute force' had narrowed to a great extent, and the United States, too, could send up massive vehicles. The present position in the unhealthy and distinctly childish 'space race' is uncertain, and I do not propose to discuss it, largely because I have no patience with it. Suffice to say that both

METEOR CRATER, ARIZONA; an aerial photograph taken by the author in 1963. The crater, in the Arizona desert, was formed by the impact of a meteorite in prehistoric times; it is almost 1 mile in diameter, and is the best known example of a crater of this type.

nations are able to launch complex equipment without bothering too much about its dead-weight.

The scientific information gained from the many satellites has been quite amazing. Much of it has been made generally available, but there are still some subjects which are kept strictly secret upon military grounds; this attitude applies particularly to the reconnaissance or 'spy' satellites which are sent up on missions over forbidden territory.

I have no wish to speculate, and I propose to confine myself to a general survey of some of the information which has been released. Much of this is, of course, American; the Russians are not inclined to say much about some aspects of their programme. For instance, over 100 vehicles of the Cosmos series were launched before the end of 1967, but very little has been said about just what these satellites have been doing. Rather than guess, it is better to wait until the Soviet authorities decide to tell us.

There were various investigations which could be carried out only from satellites or space-probes, and which were tackled almost immediately. In particular, there were cosmic rays and meteoroids, both of which had been regarded as potential hazards to manned flight beyond the atmosphere.

I have already said something about cosmic rays, which are high-speed particles—mainly atomic nuclei—coming from space. Some of them come from the Sun, but most originate beyond the Solar System, and possibly beyond the Galaxy. The heavier particles, or 'primaries', smash into the upper air, and break themselves against the air-particles; the fragments or 'secondaries' are broken in turn, and after a whole series of collisions it is only the remnants which reach ground level. This is fortunate for us, since the primaries may well be dangerous. But for the atmospheric screen, life on Earth might never have developed.

Even Explorer 1, first of the American satellites, carried a Geiger counter to deal with cosmic-ray studies, and it was this which led to·the quite unexpected discovery of the Van Allen Zone. Since then, many other satellites have continued the research, and we know a great deal more about cosmic rays than we did before October 1957, even though the mystery of their origin has still to be solved.

Larger particles, genuinely 'solid', belong to a different category. There can be few people who have not seen shooting-stars, and anyone who has visited a major museum will have seen specimens of meteorites. As we have noted, a shooting-star or meteor is smaller than a grain of sand, and burns itself out in the upper air; a meteorite is more nearly related to an asteroid or minor planet, and is massive enough to complete its drop through the atmosphere without being destroyed. Also, it was known in pre-Space Age days that there are numerous micro-meteorites, too small and non-massive to create luminous effects when they enter the air. All these various bodies may be referred to jointly as 'meteoroids'.

It had been claimed that any astronaut venturing above the atmosphere would at once be battered to pieces by a sort of cosmic bombardment. The large meteorites were no real danger, because they are so rare; but shooting-star meteors were known to be much more common, and the micro-meteorites were more common still. Any space-craft staying aloft for more than a few minutes would

THE NORTON-FURNAS AEROLITE, the largest known example of an aerolite or 'stony meteorite'. It is on display at the Institute of Meteoritics at Albuquerque, New Mexico. The author is here examining the aerolite together with Dr. Lincoln La Paz, Director Emeritus of the Institute.

FRAGMENT OF THE BARWELL METEORITE. This meteorite fell at Barwell, in Leicestershire, on Christmas Eve 1965. Many fragments have been recovered; this one, weighing 1¾ pounds, was found by the author some weeks later. The total weight of the meteorite, before break-up during the final descent through the atmosphere, may have been well over 100 pounds, which is a record for known British meteorites.

be certain to receive several hits. And though both meteors and micro-meteorites are small and flimsy, they are moving at great speeds, which would presumably make them unpleasantly penetrating.

The Russians soon began to study meteoroids with their Sputniks. On 15 May 1958 they launched Sputnik 3, of which the instrumented cone weighed almost 3,000 pounds and was 10 feet long. It carried a whole array of scientific instruments, including (of course) cosmic ray counters, and also equipment to record micro-meteorite hits. It remained up until 6 April 1960, and it was widely observed; it was easily visible with the naked eye, and its cone shape made it vary and 'flash' in an intriguing manner. The rocket which sent it into its final orbit stayed aloft until 3 December 1958, and was much brighter than Sputnik 3 itself, since when at its best it outshone even Sirius, the most brilliant star in the sky.

Since then, meteoroids have been under constant survey from space-vehicles, and the results obtained between 1958 and 1968 showed clearly that the early fears had been wildly exaggerated. Micro-meteorites cause frequent impacts, and these can be recorded; one method has been to use a microphone, so that each hit produces an audible 'ping' capable of being transmitted to the ground. Yet the penetrative power is slight enough to be dealt with by a tough hull, and the danger of collision with a larger body, massive enough to cause a bad hole, is very slight indeed.

Sputnik 3 was also a pioneer vehicle in the study of upper-atmosphere density. When first launched, on 15 May 1958, it had a

CONTRACTION OF THE ORBIT OF SPUTNIK 3, due to atmospheric drag near perigee. Eventually the satellite descended into the lower atmosphere, and was destroyed.

perigee height of 135 miles and an apogee of 1,167 miles, which meant that it was not expected to be permanent; the air-drag at 135 miles is quite marked, and it was predicted that the Sputnik would come to the end of its career after it had been round the Earth about 8,000 times. As the months went by, the orbit slowly contracted; by 30 November 1958, the perigee was reduced to 105 miles, and the apogee to only 245 miles. The diagram shows how markedly the orbit altered between May and November. As always, the perigee was affected much less than the apogee height.

And yet Sputnik 3 survived throughout 1959, and well into 1960. It was not until 6 April of that year that it finally came down, after having been round the world 10,037 times and covering a total distance of 278,000,000 miles. During 1959, there were periods when its orbit did not seem to be altering at all.

There could be only one explanation. Since no extra power was given to the satellite once it had been put into orbit, it could be affected only by air-drag; and since it lasted for longer than expected, then the air-drag was clearly less than expected. In other words, the atmosphere at and around the Sputnik's perigee height was thinner than the earlier measures had indicated. During 1958 the Sun was at its most active, and there were numerous spot-groups and flares, but by 1959-60 the solar maximum was past. This lessening activity proved to be the key to the problem of Sputnik 3.

Solar events seem to have an influence upon the density of the upper air. Below 60 miles or so above ground-level, the density remains more or less constant, but at greater altitudes there are pronounced variations. When the Sun is active, the upper air becomes denser than its average value; when the Sun quietens down, the density of the top part of our atmosphere decreases again. The changes are small enough (and, in any case, the density at such heights is equivalent to what we could normally call a laboratory vacuum), but they are sufficient to affect the movements of a satellite. The expected lifetime of 8,000 revolutions for Sputnik 3 had been worked out according to measures made early in its career, in 1958, when the Sun was particularly energetic. Later on, the solar disturbances slackened, and the drop in upper-air density was the reason why Sputnik 3 lasted for more than 2,000 extra revolutions.

The same sort of thing has been found with later satellites, and the effect can now be allowed for in predicting just when a vehicle will delay—though, of course, it is still difficult to be really accurate.

In addition to analyzing and measuring the upper atmosphere, satellites can also be used to help that much-maligned man, the meteorologist. Weather forecasting is far from being an exact science (as I know to my cost; I worked on it for some months during early 1945, after I had stopped flying with the R.A.F., and to say that my department produced consistently reliable results would be straining the truth dangerously). But if we are to understand the way in which the atmosphere behaves, we must study all of it, not only the lower parts in which we live. To obtain a general view of the air-masses, we must use satellites.

The first weather satellite was Vanguard 2, launched from Cape Canaveral on 17 February 1959. It was only 20 inches in diameter,

LAUNCHING OF THE WEATHER SATELLITE TIROS 2, on 23 November 1960. The launching took place from Cape Canaveral (now Cape Kennedy); the vehicle was a three-stage Delta rocket. The 280 pound satellite was put into a nearly circular orbit, with a perigee of 387 miles, an apogee of 453 miles, and an initial revolution period of 98 minutes. During its active lifetime it sent back many valuable pictures of weather systems.

but it was sent into a high orbit—perigee 350 miles, apogee 2,065 miles—so that it will remain circling the world until near the end of the present century. It carried special equipment to look down on the Earth and measure the cloud cover, and it proved to be quite successful.

The next step was to obtain actual pictures of weather systems, and this was started on 1 April 1960, with Tiros 1. Here the diameter was 42 inches, and two television cameras were carried, capable of covering systems extending over 650,000 square miles. The quality of the pictures turned out to be remarkably good, and by the time that its batteries failed, after 78 days, more than 23,000 photographs had been obtained. In particular, a major storm developing off the Australian coast was recorded earlier than it would otherwise have been. Other vehicles of the same series followed—the last, Tiros 10, went up on 2 July 1965—and all in all, it may be said that these weather-spotters were among the most successful of the first American satellite programmes.

Incidentally, Tiros 3, sent up on 12 July 1961, transmitted operational data about a hurricane, 'Anna', and it subsequently photographed another hurricane two days before detection by conventional methods, so giving extra warning time. It is likely that by the end of the nineteen-seventies there will be regular patrols by weather satellites, so that potentially dangerous storms will be located soon after being formed, and people living in the affected areas will be able to take due precautions. By now the Tiros series has been succeeded by more complex vehicles, of which Nimbus 1, launched on 28 August 1964, was the first.

There was a by-product of the Tiros photographs inasmuch as it proved possible to study the break-up of ice-packs in frozen waters. It was even claimed that for work of this sort, a satellite might well be more effective than an aircraft.

Satellites of the Tiros or Nimbus type depend for their value upon the equipment they carry, but use can also be made of satellites which are totally 'dead'. The way in which a satellite moves depends partly on the amount of air-drag (if it is low enough to be affected at all) and partly on the mass and shape of the Earth. Early studies showed that the Earth is very slightly pear-shaped, and that it is flattened at the poles by about 250 feet less than was previously supposed. Measured through the equator, the Earth's diameter has been found to be 7,926.36 miles; measured through the poles, only 7,899.78. This gives a flattening of 1/298.2, instead of the older value of 1/297. The difference from the earlier estimates is slight, but Earth-study scientists find it important, and it was established only by very careful observations of the movements of suitable satellites.

There is also the possibility of navigation by satellite observing, and here too the Americans took the lead, with Transit 1B, launched on 13 April 1960. It seems rather doubtful whether sea or air navigators will ever rely upon satellite fixing, because much more convenient methods are available, but the scope is there should it ever become necessary.

More important are the 'geodetic' satellites, such as those used for measuring the Earth's degree of polar flattening. The first active geodetic satellite was Anna 1B, sent up on 31 October 1962; it is 3 feet long, and will remain aloft for some 3,000 years. Anna,

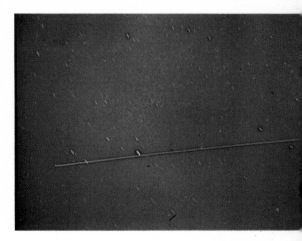

TRAIL OF THE U.S. BALLOON SATELLITE ECHO 1, photographed by Henry Brinton. Echo 1 was a 'passive reflector', and was a very conspicuous naked-eye object. It decayed in the atmosphere in May 1968, after having made 36,031 circuits of the Earth. It had lasted for 3,544 days.

ANOTHER PHOTOGRAPH OF THE TRAIL OF ECHO 1. The trail is seen against the background of stars in Aquila (the Eagle), of which the leader is Altair.

◀ THE EARTH; a wide area photographed from a Tiros weather satellite, with whole meteorological systems clearly shown.

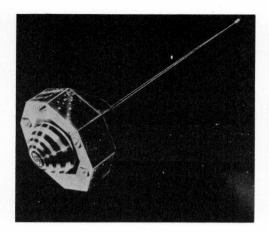

GEOS-A, the 'geodetic satellite' used to make measures for investigating the shape and form of the Earth. This was an American vehicle, and was the first of its kind. Various successors have since been launched, and have provided very useful information. We now know much more about the form of the Earth than we used to do before the age of practical space research.

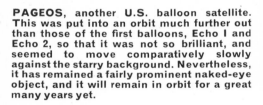

PAGEOS, another U.S. balloon satellite. This was put into an orbit much further out than those of the first balloons, Echo I and Echo 2, so that it was not so brilliant, and seemed to move comparatively slowly against the starry background. Nevertheless, it has remained a fairly prominent naked-eye object, and it will remain in orbit for a great many years yet.

TELEVISION PICTURES BY SATELLITE (far right). This photograph was taken from the BBC Television programme of 23 July 1962, and shows the New York skyline; the picture was relayed by Telstar, the first television satellite.

named in honour of its four sponsors (the American Air Force, Navy, National Aeronautics and Space Administration, and Army) was a 'flasher'; that is to say it carried an optical beacon which winked, so that the effect could be quite startling. Observations of it proved extremely helpful to those scientists engaged in studying the form and characteristics of the Earth, and the same was true of another flasher, Explorer 29 of 6 November 1965. Explorer 29 was more commonly known as Geos A (short for Geodetic Explorer), and was put into an orbit which never brings it much below 700 miles. It will last for some 50,000 years, so that there is no urgent rush to study it before it decays in the upper atmosphere.

Pageos (Passive Geodetic Explorer), of 23 June 1966, is not an active satellite. It is simply a balloon, with negligible mass. It was put into a nearly circular orbit at over 2,500 miles above the ground, so that its lifetime will be immensely long, and it may be regarded as a permanent addition to the Solar System. Since it is almost 100 feet in diameter, it is quite bright, and its great distance means that it seems to be a slow mover. It is only too easy to confuse Pageos with a star, since it has to be watched for some minutes

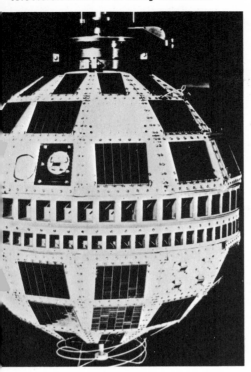

before its motion becomes really obvious.

But of all the satellites, those which have attracted most public attention are the communications vehicles. Here the first launchings were American, but, as we have noted, the idea was British. The man responsible was Arthur C. Clarke, known equally as an astronaut (armchair variety, to use his own term); science-fiction novelist, and underwater photographer.

Arthur Clarke was an early member of the British Interplanetary Society, and has served as its Chairman. So far as Britain is concerned, he and P. E. Cleator stand out as being the two writers who did most to publicize the space-research idea at a time when any talk of sending vehicles to the Moon was officially classed as wild speculation. Most of his predictions have come true, and I cannot think of any instance in which he has been shown to be badly wrong, even though the rate of progress has been quicker than expected.

In 1945 Clarke wrote an article for the periodical *Wireless World* which is now regarded with some reverence, even though it caused absolutely no excitement at the time. His scheme was to set up three satellites in a '24-hour' orbit, moving round the Earth in the plane of the equator at a height of 22,300 miles. As shown on pp 118-9, this would mean that each satellite would seem to stay still in the sky, since it would keep pace with the rotating Earth,

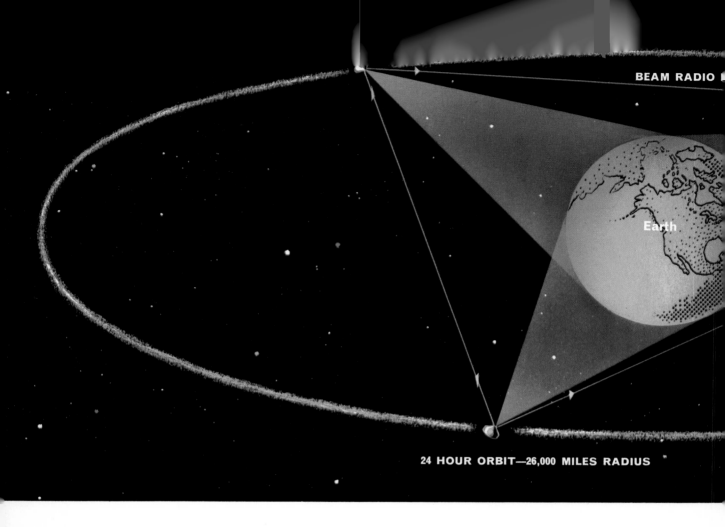

Earth

24 HOUR ORBIT—26,000 MILES RADIUS

and would remain over the same ground position. If the vehicles were equally spaced, at least one of them would be visible from any point on the Earth's surface further than 8° from the poles. They could thus act as world-wide radio and television relays.

In 1945 television had not yet taken a grip, and there was no serious thought of an artificial satellite. Yet it was only 18 years later that the first Transatlantic television link by satellite actually took place, and was seen by 200,000,000 people. I watched that programme, and to my mind the worst omission was that the name of Arthur Clarke was not mentioned at all. I suggest that a 24-hour orbit of this sort should justifiably be referred to as a Clarke orbit.

As with geodetic vehicles, communications satellites are of two varieties, active and passive. A passive satellite merely serves as a reflector, while an active one is itself a source of transmissions. Rather surprisingly, the pioneer attempt, by the Americans, was of the second type. On 18 December 1958 Project Score was launched; it was an 85 feet by 10 feet cylinder weighing about 4 tons, and it was designed to receive messages from the ground, record them on tape, and then re-transmit them when ordered to do so. Score was a definite success, and introduced itself to the world at large by relaying a perfectly audible Christmas message from General (then President) Eisenhower. The satellite remained in orbit for a month or so, and fell back to destruction on 21 January 1959.

Various other vehicles were launched as communications satel-

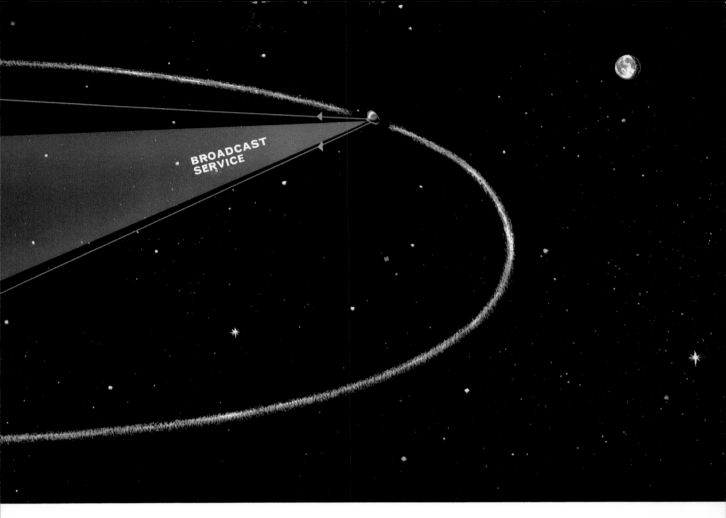

BROADCAST SERVICE

CLARKE ORBITS. The idea of using orbital satellites as television relays originated in 1945, and was due to the British scientist Arthur C. Clarke, who pictured satellites in 'stationary' orbits—moving round the Earth at 26,000 miles, and so completing one revolution in the same time that the Earth takes to spin once on its axis. Clarke's predictions have since been completely vindicated.

lites, and special mention must be made of the Echo balloons, to be described below. However, it was in July 1962 that the full impact of the new technique was felt. On the 10th of that month, the first Telstar satellite went into orbit, going round the Earth every 158 minutes at a distance ranging between 600 and 3,500 miles above the ground. Since it was a mere $34\frac{1}{2}$ inches in diameter, with a weight of 170 pounds, it was well below naked-eye visibility. During its fifth circuit, some rather vague pictures were sent across from the United States to France and England by way of the satellite. Tests went on according to plan, and on the evening of 23 July the first full-scale Transatlantic exchange took place, lasting for twenty minutes. The British receiving station at Goonhilly Down, in the West Country, worked perfectly, and from my Sussex home I was able to look at my screen and see a baseball game actually being played in America. The second programme, sent from Europe across the Atlantic, involved over fifty cameras, in nine countries ranging from the Mediterranean to the Arctic Circle.

I suppose Telstar was the vehicle which really drove home the idea that communications satellites had come to stay. Inevitably, others followed. Syncom 1 (14 February 1963) was the first attempt at a launching into a Clarke orbit. With Early Bird, sent up on 6 April 1965, a Clarke orbit was practically achieved. The path is almost circular, and the revolution period 23 hours 57 minutes, with an expected lifetime of well over a million years.

By now, communications satellites are no longer novel, and television links in this way are accepted as part of normal life. There is no longer anything strange in sitting in a house in London or New York and watching events taking place in, say, Tokyo. Moreover, the Russians have launched efficient communications vehicles of their own. Things were very different in 1945, when Arthur Clarke wrote his original paper; but when I asked him, not long ago, whether he were surprised at what had happened, he replied dryly that he would have been astounded if events had taken any other turn.

Quite apart from everyday considerations such as television links, there are long-term possibilities such as the setting-up of orbiting astronomical observatories. On the surface of the Earth, astronomers are hopelessly handicapped by the blanket of atmosphere. Not only is it dirty and unsteady, but layers in it are opaque to many of the interesting radiations coming from the Sun and stars. If we are to examine the full range of wavelengths, we must send instruments above the atmosphere. Balloons, of course, can be useful, but the only proper answer—short of a research base on the Moon—is an astronomical satellite. The first attempt, OSO (Orbiting Solar Observatory) was made on 7 March 1962, and for 77 days scientists received a continuous stream of data about solar radiations and associated phenomena. Other astronomical vehicles have been launched since, though we have yet to see a large telescope in operation from above the atmosphere.

Satellites, as we have noted, are of various sizes and various

ECHO II, a 135-foot aluminium-coated balloon used as a passive radio reflector. Ever since its launching, Echo II has remained a conspicuous naked-eye object. In this prelaunch photograph it is shown undergoing visual inspection by a technician riding a smaller balloon at Lakehurst, New Jersey.

shapes. Explorer 6 of 1959, one of the most successful of the early vehicles sent up to study the Van Allen Zone, was nicknamed the Paddle-Wheel, for reasons which will be obvious from one glance at a picture of it. Yet most of the really important satellites are below naked-eye visibility, and it is somewhat ironical that the only two man-made moons which are familiar to many millions of people are the passive communications satellites Echo 1 and Echo 2, both of which are strikingly conspicuous but neither of which carries any instrumentation at all.

Echo 1 was launched on 12 August 1960. It was nothing more nor less than a balloon made of transparent plastic material 0.02 inches thick, coated with an 0.0005-inch layer of aluminium to make it a good reflector. During the launching procedure it was folded, and was inflated in space by 30 pounds of powder which turned into a gas when exposed to the rays of the Sun. The final diameter of the balloon was 100 feet, and the orbit ranged between 945 miles at perigee out to 1,049 miles at apogee.

Echo 1 was designed as a reflector of very strong radio beams, to provide a high-quality telephone circuit. It proved to be a success in Transatlantic experiments; in itself it cost almost nothing, but of course it had to be launched by the usual step-rocket arrangement, and the ground equipment needed was decidedly costly. It was followed, on 25 January 1964, by Echo 2, which was rather larger (diameter over 120 feet) and ranged between 640 miles at perigee to 820 miles at apogee.

Because the Echo vehicles had practically no mass, and were so far out that they were to all intents and purposes unaffected by

UK-3, THE FIRST ALL-BRITISH ARTIFICIAL SATELLITE, undergoing solar illumination spin tests at the Goddard Space Flight Center. The satellite was successfully sent into orbit by an American launching vehicle.

A BRITISH UPPER-ATMOSPHERE ROCKET: the Black Knight, shown on its launching pad at Woomera in Australia. So far no British launcher has put a satellite into space, but many upper-atmosphere vehicles have been sent up, mainly from the Woomera range.

COSMOS 144, one of the long series of similar vehicles sent up by the Russians. Many Cosmos vehicles were safely recovered a few days after having been launched.

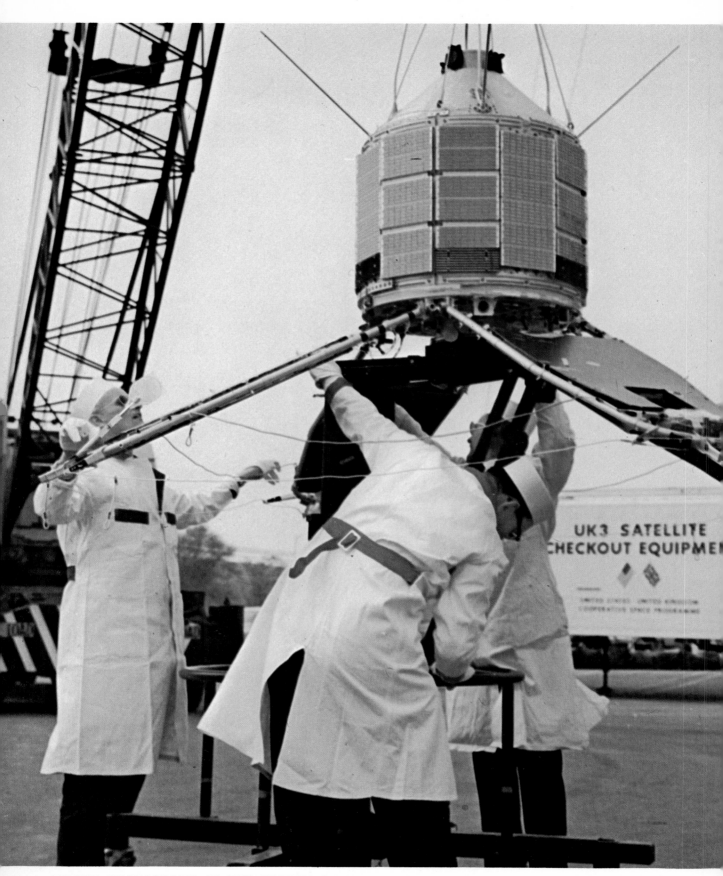

COLOUR PHOTOGRAPH OF THE BRITISH SATELLITE ARIEL 3, taken before launching at Lompoc, California. Like its predecessors, Ariel 1 (April 1962) and Ariel 2 (March 1964), Ariel 3 was purely British in construction, but was sent into orbit by an American launching vehicle.

airdrag, their movements were particularly interesting. They were affected by light-pressure from the Sun, and also by solar wind, so that their orbits altered in an unusual manner, and their overall descent was extremely slow.

Both Echos were very easy to find, and indeed nobody could overlook them. No. 2 was always the brighter, because it was larger and lower; it seems almost like a small lamp crawling across the starlit sky. Both vehicles were punctured by meteoroid impacts, and the gas inside them escaped, but of course there was nothing to make them collapse as a child's Christmas balloon will do when holed. Echo 1 finally came down in 1968; Echo 2 is still in orbit.

Since 1963, some satellites have been dispatched into very eccentric orbits. Explorer 18, better known as Imp 1, was the first of these. On 27 November 1963 it was put into a path which carried it out as far as 120,000 miles, or roughly half the distance of the Moon, so that it cut right through the Van Allen Zone and appreciable portions of the magnetosphere; a full revolution round the Earth occupied nearly four days, so that when near apogee it was very faint and very slow in movement. A much more recent example is Intelsat 2 of 26 October 1966, whose orbit at the end of the following month carried it between 2,100 miles and over 23,000 miles in a period of more than 12 hours. Like Early Bird, it is to all intents and purposes permanent, with a life expectation of about a million years. Whether it will be tracked for all that time is rather dubious, since it is a small cylinder measuring only 3 feet in length!

It was another obvious step from the straightforward satellite to a vehicle which could be manœuvred about from one orbit to another, and here the Russians took the lead, initially with their first Polyot vehicle in late 1963. This, however, leads us on to the problem of re-entry, or sending up satellites and bringing them down intact—that is to say, making them descend through the atmosphere slowly enough to avoid their being overheated and destroyed by friction against the air-particles.

The re-entry problem had always been regarded as one of the most difficult in astronautics, and many elaborate plans for coping with it had been put forward by Von Braun and others. In the event, it was solved by the Russians with unexpected ease. As early as 1960, Sputnik 5 was successfully recovered. The series of Cosmos satellites, which began in 1962 and was still in progress in 1968, included many vehicles which were launched, kept up for a few days, and then brought back undamaged.

So far, most of the satellite launchings have been made by America and Russia. The first British vehicle, Ariel 1, was dispatched on 26 April 1962, and Ariel 2 followed on 27 March 1964, but in both cases the launching vehicles were American, and it was only the satellite itself which was British-built. General de Gaulle has joined the space club with some small satellites which are purely French affairs, launched from sites in the Sahara, but it will be a long time before any nation seriously rivals the U.S.A. and the U.S.S.R.; nobody else has the money and the resources. Japan is likely to be next in the field. The first attempted Japanese satellite launching, in late 1966, was unsuccessful, but before long we may expect the Rising Sun to take its place in space-research projects.

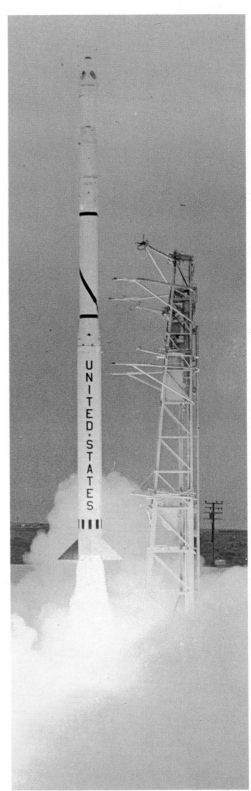

LAUNCHING OF ARIEL 3 from the Western Test Range at Lompoc, California, on 5 May 1967. The orbit was a polar one, and the launching vehicle was an American four-stage Scout.

Chapter 19

Man in Space

By the end of the nineteen-fifties, the 'space race' between the United States and Soviet Russia was in full swing. It is no secret that the Americans had been angry and disappointed to have been beaten in their attempt to be the first to launch an artificial satellite, and there was immense determination to win the next round.[1] The aim was, of course, to put a man into orbit.

It would be quite wrong to suppose that the only object behind space research is to send a man to the Moon; indeed, in some respects the manned flight project is far from being the most important branch of astronautics. When it comes to making scientific measurements, instruments are usually more reliable than men. They are less fragile, and—a vital point—they are expendable, so that risks can be taken with them. On the other hand, no instrument can 'think' in the generally-accepted meaning of the word, and instruments also need to be maintained, which means that they must be handled. Moreover, Man is an inquisitive animal, and he would still want to go to the Moon even if the long-term benefits to the human race were certain to be as slight as those of—say—climbing Mount Everest.

There was also the question of prestige, ever-dominant in the

[1] Regrettably, we must also admit that the whole space project was, and to some extent still is, bound up with military preparation. The discovery that Russian rocketry was well ahead of that of the U.S.A. came as an unpleasant shock, and it was this that caused the feeling of alarm at the time of Sputnik 1. I do not propose to discuss military space projects, and I will do no more than mention the notorious 'West Ford' experiment of 1963, in which the American authorities sent up vast numbers of tiny copper needles so as to form a belt round the Earth suitable for use as a sort of 'artificial ionosphere' for the purposes of radio communication in time of war. Since a permanent belt of needles would completely ruin many branches of radio astronomy, there were understandable protests from scientists all over the world. Fortunately the needle belt proved to be temporary, and no lasting damage was done, but it is to be hoped that nothing of the sort will be attempted again.

COMMANDER ALAN SHEPARD, the first American in space. In 1961 he made a successful sub-orbital flight from Cape Canaveral (now Cape Kennedy). The flight was a complete success.

MAJOR (later Colonel) **YURI GAGARIN,** in his space-suit; on 12 April 1961, Gagarin became the first astronaut in human history when he made a successful flight round the world in Vostok 1. He made no further flights, but took a leading part in training other astronauts. In March 1968 he was tragically killed in an air crash over the Soviet Union.

ENOS (left), a male chimpanzee who experienced a space-flight in preparation for the U.S. Mercury series of manned flights. Enos remained in space for 201 minutes, and returned to Earth quite unharmed.

MONKEY ABLE (below), an American-born Rhesus, one of two monkeys carried in the nose cone of a Jupiter missile during a rocket test carried out from Cape Canaveral (now Cape Kennedy) prior to the Mercury series of manned launchings.

MISS SAM (above), a Rhesus monkey, placed in the environmental container of the Project Mercury space capsule for launching at Wallops Island, Virginia, in a test of the capsule's escape equipment.

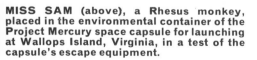

RUSSIAN SPACE TRAVELLERS OF 1959 (right); a dog, Otvazhnaya, and a rabbit. The animals were sent into space on 2 July, and returned safely. Photographed by N. Rakhmanov.

(right) **GEMINI ASTRONAUTS** White and McDivett shown in a training spacecraft on 14 May 1965, at Galveston, Texas. Both astronauts subsequently made space voyages. Major White became the first American to 'walk' in space; he was one of the three astronauts killed in a disaster during training at Cape Kennedy in January 1967.

A GIANT SWING! (below) Astronaut Elliott See whirls upside-down while his ankles and wrists are strapped to a training device at Cape Kennedy. The exercise was designed to keep the astronauts in good physical condition, and to subject them to various motions and stresses to be expected in a space-flight. See never went into space; he died tragically in an air crash.

CREW TRANSFER IN SPACE. (below) American space engineers at the Langley Research Center in Virginia are shown testing equipment and techniques for transfer of crews between orbiting spacecraft.

TESTING FOR THE MERCURY SERIES OF MANNED LAUNCHINGS; a device to simulate the roll, pitch and yaw of a capsule in orbital flight. Devices of this sort were essential in the training of American astronauts, and presumably for Russian spacemen as well.

SIMULATED LUNAR ENVIRONMENT at Houston Manned Spacecraft Center in Texas, where the Apollo astronauts have been trained.

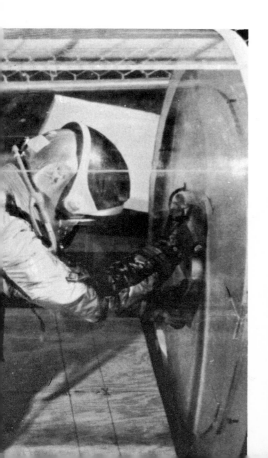

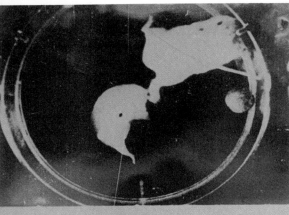

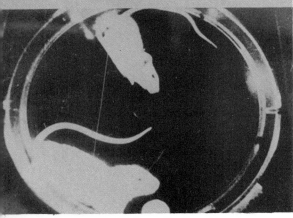

SPACE DOG. Belka, a Russian dog, who made a successful space flight in August 1960. Photographed by Y. Abramochkin.

MICE IN FREE FALL. These mice were among the earliest animals sent up in an American rocket. They did not orbit, but during their descent they were photographed in a state of free fall; automatic cameras were used. Experiments of this kind were essential in preparation for the manned launchings of later years.

minds of politicians. But an unsuccessful attempt, ending in disaster, would receive quite the wrong sort of publicity, so that neither the Americans nor the Russians were inclined to hurry matters.

By 1958 the National Aeronautics and Space Administration (NASA) had been set up, with its headquarters at Washington, D.C. And on 27 January 1959, it was announced that seven young Americans were to be selected for special training, and that one of these would be the first United States astronaut. Project Mercury, the man-in-space project, was under way, and everything possible was done to speed up the time when it would be reasonable to make the great experiment. Of the seven original volunteers, most have achieved fame. Alan Shepard and John Glenn, in particular, will always be remembered in history as being the original United States space-pioneers; Virgil Grissom, as well as being the second American to travel beyond the atmosphere, was one of the three victims of the terrible disaster at Cape Kennedy at the start of the Apollo programme, eight years later—on 27 January 1967.

At the start of Project Mercury, there were two separate problems. First, the astronauts themselves had to be trained, and this was no light task. Each started off with exceptional qualifications, both physical and mental; each was an experienced flyer in conventional aircraft, and each was dedicated to the idea of space-flight. But the training itself was rigorous by any standards, and not many young men could have come through it successfully. The would-be astronauts had to show that they possessed the ability to cope with any situations which might arise, and they had to put up with extreme discomfort—as, for instance, being whirled around in a device known as a centrifuge, which is the nearest possible ground approach to the sensation of a space-launch.

One immediate trouble was that there are some features of orbital flight which cannot be 'faked' on Earth. In particular, it is impossible to produce weightlessness, or zero gravity, except over a very short period by suitable manœuvring in an aircraft. At that time nobody had much idea of whether the effects of 'zero g' would be harmful or not, and there was still a lack of information about the risks due to radiations encountered above the atmosphere. The only course was to go and find out, and it was plain that the first astronauts would need immense courage. Also, they had to be scientifically competent, and they had to know every detail of the craft in which they were to ride.

The other problem was that of the space-ship itself. It could not take off too rapidly, because this would mean that the tremendous acceleration would crush its passenger; it had to be much more complicated than an unmanned vehicle, and there was no room for error. If a pilotless vehicle crashes to destruction, the only loss is in time and money. If a manned vehicle is wrecked, then a life is lost too.

There was also the question of re-entry into the atmosphere, which, as we have noted, had always been regarded as particularly difficult. Various schemes had been put forward in the pre-satellite days; for instance, it had been proposed to fit the vehicle with wings, so that the re-entry into the atmosphere would be made in an upside-down position with the wings being used to keep the craft down rather than buoy it up. Another idea was to send the

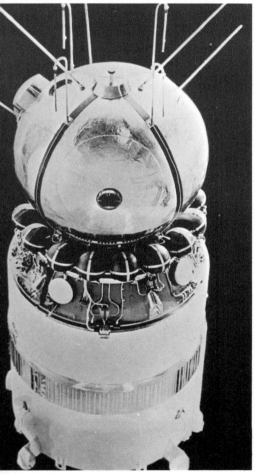

VOSTOK 1: SPACEMAN'S COUCH. It was in Vostok 1 that Yuri Gagarin made his pioneer journey on 12 April 1961. This picture was taken at the Exhibition of National Economic Achievements in Moscow.

VOSTOK SPACECRAFT; a photograph taken at the Exhibition of National Economic Achievements, Moscow, in late 1961.

vehicle in and out of the atmosphere in an elliptical path, so that after its first passage through the resisting air it would return to the safety of space to cool down before returning, at a lesser speed, for another encounter. But by 1958 it was obvious that the only practicable method was to use rocket braking. Here, rocket engines are fired against the direction of motion, so that they will slow the vehicle down. Careful control of these retro-rockets will ensure that by the time the ship has dropped into the dense air, it will be moving relatively slowly, and will not be burned or melted, though inevitably the outer hull will become very hot.

All these problems were tackled by the Project Mercury team. Meanwhile, experiments on the same lines were going on in the Soviet Union. On 15 May 1960, the Russians launched a 4½ ton vehicle, Sputnik 4 (sometimes termed Spacecraft 1) which carried a dummy pilot. The original orbit had a perigee of 183 miles and an apogee of 422 miles; the plan was to allow the craft to stay in orbit for some days and then bring it down, so that it was plainly a dress rehearsal with everything except the human factor. However, it was not successful. When the retro-rockets were fired, by remote control, something went wrong, and instead of coming down the Sputnik was merely forced into a different path; the perigee distance remained the same, but the apogee height increased. Radio contact was lost on 8 July, and it seems that the vehicle came down nine days later.

Sputnik 5, launched on 19 August, more than made up for this disappointment. This time there was no dummy pilot, but there were two live dogs, Strelka and Belka, whose experiences on board the space-ship were watched by Russian scientists on television screens. On the following day the Sputnik was brought down; the capsule containing the dogs was ejected, and landed with no trouble at all, while the main vehicle touched down not far away. The re–entry problem had, apparently, been solved. Also, both dogs were quite unharmed, and were none the worse for their adventure.

Still it was too early to risk a human passenger, and there were further mishaps ahead; for example, another Sputnik came back into the air too quickly, and was destroyed. But by the beginning of April 1961 it looked as though the Russians were set to orbit a man, and there was a general feeling of expectancy. Of course, there were still some sceptics, and I have kept some of the sarcastic letters (mainly anonymous) which were sent to me after I had been questioned on the B.B.C. Television News, on 10 April, and said that in my view the attempt would be made before the end of the month. Actually, the vital date was 12 April, when the space-ship Vostok 1 blasted off, carrying as passenger Major Yuri Gagarin of the Soviet Air Force.

Yuri Alexeyevich Gagarin was born on 9 March 1934, at the village of Gzhatsk, near Smolensk. There was nothing particularly notable about his family. His father was a carpenter, and was far from rich; indeed, there was little money to spare for food, and none at all for luxuries. Altogether there were four young Gagarins, two older than Yuri and one younger.

Just as Yuri had started to attend the local school, the Germans attacked Russia and spread the war into Eastern Europe. The Smolensk area became a battlefield, and there followed a period of

GEMINI 7, launched in December 1965. Here, one of the astronauts, Frank Borman, is shown together with Alan Shepard, who had earlier been the first American to go into space, and who has since played a major part in astronaut training.

Nazi occupation. The older Gagarin children were deported to the west, but somehow or other they survived. Yuri stayed on at Gzhatsk, together with his parents and his younger brother Boris. Food was desperately short, and even grass had to be eaten when nothing else could be found.

When the Germans were finally driven out, Gzhatsk had to be completely rebuilt. A new school rose from the ruins, and Yuri went there. His first task was to learn how to read, after which he could begin his true education—rather later than most boys, but this was hardly his fault! He developed a keenness for science, and when still in his teens he had progressed far enough to attend a training course at an apprentices' school near Moscow. He intended to become a metalworker, and did actually qualify in his chosen trade.

Yet his main interest was in flying; he had been hypnotized by aircraft ever since he had seen his first machine—an old Russian fighter which had crashed near his home during the early stages of the war. He joined a flying club, and had his first taste of piloting. It did not take him long to 'get the feel' of it, and he felt able to apply for entrance to the Orenburg Air Force School. By the time he had graduated as a test pilot, he had also married. When he volunteered for training as an astronaut, in 1959, he seemed to have every qualification needed to be the world's first space-man.

There were plenty of other candidates, and there was a long, tough training period which was presumably much the same as that of the Mercury astronauts; Gagarin, Glenn, Shepard, Grissom and the others must have been carrying out their tests during the

VIRGIL I. GRISSOM, who became the second American in space when he made a sub-orbital journey soon after Alan Shepard. Grissom later completed a successful orbital mission, but lost his life in January 1967 during a tragic accident during a pre-launch rehearsal at Cape Kennedy.

same period. At last all was ready, and by 12 April 1961, Gagarin was strapped down inside the cramped cabin of Vostok 1, waiting to be hurled beyond the atmosphere. I remember asking him whether he felt badly frightened. He replied that he had no time to think about anything but the matter in hand; there was so much to be done that he had to concentrate grimly.

Gagarin was launched at seven minutes past six G.M.T. (9.07 Moscow time). Excluding the last stage of the carrier rocket, the Vostok weighed $4\frac{3}{4}$ tons, so that it was roughly of the same mass as the dummy craft which had been sent up earlier. When blast-off came, the pilot felt crushing pressure as the acceleration grew; during the worst period—mercifully brief—he was unable to move, and an untrained man would certainly have lost consciousness. Yet as soon as the Vostok reached its peak velocity of 17,500 m.p.h. the engines were cut, and all sensation of weight vanished. Gagarin was in orbit, and was experiencing the strange sensation of zero gravity.

He was scheduled to make only one circuit of the Earth, with his height ranging between 112 and 203 miles. There were many observations to be made, and he had to keep in touch with ground stations as well as he could; then, of course, would come the descent, perhaps the most risky part of the whole operation. The Vostok would be slowed down by its retro-rockets, and would drop back into the atmosphere, losing speed until the danger of overheating was over and parachute braking could be applied to his capsule. Luckily all went well, and, to quote the official Russian account, 'the Vostok landed safely in the prearranged area of the Soviet Union at 10.55 Moscow time, 07.55 G.M.T.' The total flight time had been 1 hour 48 minutes.

The first space-trip had been carried through without a hitch,

and it was at once clear that several of the most dreaded 'bogeys', such as what had been called space-sickness, did not apply. Gagarin had shown that astronautics could become a practical science instead of a mere dream. It was doubly tragic that he should lose his life in an ordinary air-crash eight years later.

I have been saying that the Space Age began on 4 October 1957, with Sputnik 1. However, there are grounds for claiming that a better date would be 12 April 1961, with the flight of the Vostok. In any case, the seeds had been well and truly sown.

Inevitably, Gagarin's success swung world attention away from Project Mercury, but the American programme was well under way even though preparations had taken longer than had been hoped. And less than a month after Gagarin, the first American astronaut was sent up in the craft Mercury 3, more commonly known as Freedom 7.

Of the seven trainee pilots, the honour fell to Commander Alan Shepard of the United States Navy. Shepard was older than Gagarin; he had been born at East Derry, in New Hampshire, in 1923, and during the war he had served as a deck officer on board a destroyer. He began Navy flight training in 1946, and won his wings in the following year, after which he graduated as a test pilot for jets. By the time he started training as an astronaut he had over 3,500 flying hours in his log book.

On 5 May 1961 he blasted off from Cape Canaveral, and reached an altitude of 116 miles. He did not go round the Earth; his flight was 'sub-orbital', or in other words an up-and-down hop. The whole trip was over in about a quarter of an hour, and his capsule landed in the sea some 300 miles away from the launching-site. Over 500 reporters and technicians on board the aircraft-carrier *Lake Champlain* saw him step from a helicopter after he had been successfully picked up from his capsule, and, incidentally, the whole flight was broadcast, with a suitable running commentary. I listened to it from my Sussex study, and it was heard all over the world. This was in sharp contrast to the Russian procedure; even Soviet citizens had been told nothing about Gagarin's flight until the trip had been completed.

A second sub-orbital flight, with Virgil Grissom as pilot, was undertaken on 21 July 1961; the Cape Kennedy disaster was still over six years ahead, though on this occasion Grissom had a narrow escape from drowning when his capsule started to sink after splash-down at the end of the journey. Still Project Mercury was not ready to send an astronaut right round the world, but the Russians were quick to follow up their first success, and on 6 August the second Vostok went up, with Herman Titov as pilot. The general plan was very much like that of Vostok 1, but there was one important difference. Gagarin had stayed aloft for only 1 hour 48 minutes. Titov remained up for over 25 hours, during which he went round the Earth seventeen times.

This proved to be the last Soviet manned flight for over a year. Before Vostok 3 was dispatched, the Mercury team too had achieved a full orbital journey.

The first 'orbital American' was Lieutenant-Colonel John Glenn of the United States Marine Corps. He was the oldest of the original seven volunteers on the short list; he was born in Ohio in 1921, and enlisted in the naval air cadet programme a few weeks after

THE EARTH, as photographed by Major Titov from the Soviet vehicle Vostok 2 in 1961.

AFTER LANDING: THE RECOVERABLE CAPSULE OF THE VOSTOK. Unlike the Americans, the Russian astronauts have always made the practice of coming down on the land rather than in the sea. This photograph was taken in 1961.

BLAST-OFF OF GEMINI 4, on 3 June 1965. The astronauts, White and McDivett, were continuing the overall space programme. It was during this flight that Major White made the first U.S. 'space-walk'; previously this had been accomplished only by Colonel Alexei Leonov of the U.S.S.R.

Japan launched her attack and drew the United States into the world war. In March 1943 he won his wings as a second lieutenant in the Marine Air Corps, and before the end of the war he had flown on many combat missions in the Pacific area. He decided to remain in the armed forces after the Japanese surrender, and subsequently he was engaged in active service in Korea. During his career in the Marine Corps he won many decorations—about which he is noticeably reticent!

Glenn's craft was Mercury 6, otherwise known as Friendship 7. As usual, many preliminary tests had been carried out (on 29 November 1961 a chimpanzee named Enos had made two orbits in a test vehicle, and had come through unscathed, albeit somewhat peevish), and, as with Shepard, Glenn was to have his entire flight covered by television, sound radio and the Press. There was nothing remotely secret about his blast-off, and during the trip he was in touch with ground stations all the time.

Glenn was launched on 20 February 1962. He was aloft for 4 hours 55 minutes, and the period of weightlessness amounted to all but a quarter of an hour of this, so that – like Titov – he had plenty of time to get used to the sensation. Weightlessness did not prove uncomfortable; Glenn even called it 'a pleasant experience', and he soon adapted himself to it. There were minor points to be borne in mind; once, for example, he left a film canister floating in mid-air, while he reloaded a camera, and accidentally knocked against it, so that it floated out of sight behind an instrument panel. But there was no sensation of sickness or giddiness, and it seemed that the human frame would, if suitably trained, stand up to zero gravity conditions much better than the pessimists had forecast. In fact, Glenn's experiences were much the same as those of the earlier astronauts.

Only a few land areas were visible during the trip, because of cloud cover, but Glenn gave a graphic description of the scene. 'The horizon itself is a brilliant, brilliant blue and white,' he wrote later. 'As the Sun moves toward the horizon a black shadow of darkness moves across the Earth until the whole surface, except for the bright band at the horizon is dark. This band is extremely bright just as the Sun sets, but as time passes the bottom layer becomes a bright orange and then fades into reds, then on into the darker colours, and finally off into the blues and blacks.' The colours seen when looking down at the ground were, he said, much the same as those seen from an aircraft flying at 50,000 feet or so.

One minor mystery concerned the 'fireflies', which achieved notoriety at the time. These were small, bright specks which seemed to move along with the space-craft, drifting slowly to and fro. Similar specks were seen later by both American and Russian astronauts, and it seems that they may have been due to paint flaking off the hull. At all events, they originated with the space-craft, and were not lurking in orbit!

Such were Man's first ventures into space. Less than four years separated Sputnik 1 from Vostok, or Explorer 1 from Freedom 7. Most of the alleged 'fatal' objections to manned flight beyond the atmosphere had been shown to be anything but fatal, and there seemed no obvious reason why the Moon should not be reached in the foreseeable future.

MAJOR WHITE IN SPACE. Edward White is here shown outside **Gemini 4,** during his space-flight of June 1965. The photograph was taken by the command pilot, McDivett.

THE END OF THE FLIGHT OF GEMINI 4. After a completely successful flight, Gemini 4 comes down in the sea, and the two astronauts are duly picked up.

Chapter 20

Space Meeting and Space Walks

THE ARABIAN PENINSULA, photographed from Gemini 4 in June 1965 by James McDivitt and Edward White. Seif dunes (sand) are shown to the lower left. The eastern tip of the Arabian peninsula is shown, with the Gulf of Oman to the north.

(Below) SPACE DOCKING. The Agena spacecraft floats above the Earth, as Gemini 8 (launched 16 March 1966) manœuvres. The antenna of the Agena shines on its 8-foot staff above the docking cone at the right.

I have described the first space journeys—by Gagarin, Shepard and Glenn—in some detail, because they are of historic as well as scientific interest. Of course it is undeniable that, for instance, Shepard's 15-minute hop was much less ambitious than some of the subsequent flights, such as that of Astronauts Lovell and Aldrin in late 1966; but Shepard's was the first in the American programme, just as Gagarin's was the first of all.

To describe all the later flights in the same way would mean a good deal of repetition, and would be out of place here, so that it may be better to select a few instructive 'highlights'. However, there may be some use in giving a brief table of all the manned flights achieved between April 1961 and the end of 1966, which marked a definite pause in the programmes. All these flights were successful. It has often been suggested that in previous attempts the Russians had lost several astronauts, and there were strange reports from radio amateurs that 'desperate voices' had been heard, presumably those of Soviet space-men beyond all hope of rescue. I can hardly credit that these reports are meant to be taken seriously; they sound absurd by any standards, and I do not for one moment believe that the Russians have had any unannounced mishaps. It was rather remarkable that up to the end of 1966 there were no casualties at all; the early record of aeronautics was much less unblemished. Indeed, the only 'space victims' of the first phase were some of the luckless animals used as test passengers. (To be strictly fair, I suppose one must also include a Cuban cow, which happened to be in the wrong place at the wrong time when an unsuccessful American navigational satellite, Transit 3A, crashed in 1961. It is gratifying to note that the Cuban Government did at least afford the cow a State funeral, as a victim of Imperialist aggression!)

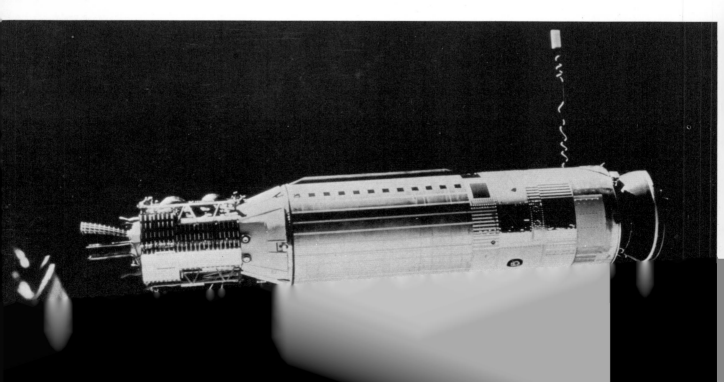

The tragedy of January 1967, which cost the lives of Astronauts Grissom, White and Chaffee, came as an even greater shock because there was no precedent. However, this belongs to the second phase, and meanwhile here is the 1961–6 table:

	Date	Spacecraft	Crew	Flight-time: days	hrs.	mins.	Number of Orbits
1961	April 12	Vostok 1	Gagarin		1	48	1
1961	May 5	Mercury 3	Shepard			$15\frac{1}{2}$	Sub-orbital
1961	July 21	Mercury 4	Grissom			$15\frac{3}{4}$	Sub-orbital
1961	Aug. 6	Vostok 2	Titov	1	1	18	17
1962	Feb. 20	Mercury 6	Glenn		4	$55\frac{1}{2}$	3
1962	May 24	Mercury 7	Carpenter		4	56	3
1962	Aug. 11	Vostok 3	Nikolayev	3	22	22	64
1962	Aug. 12	Vostok 4	Popovich	2	22	57	48
1962	Oct. 3	Mercury 8	Schirra		9	13	6
1963	May 15	Mercury 9	Cooper	1	10	$19\frac{3}{4}$	22
1963	June 14	Vostok 5	Bykovsky	4	23	6	81
1963	June 16	Vostok 6	Tereshkova	2	22	50	48
1964	Oct. 12	Voskhod 1	Komarov, Yegorov, Feoktistov	1	0	17	16
1965	Mar. 18	Voskhod 2	Belyayev, Leonov	1	2	2	17
1965	Mar. 23	Gemini 3	Grissom, Young		4	53	3
1965	June 3	Gemini 4	McDivitt, White	4	1	56	62
1965	Aug. 21	Gemini 5	Cooper, Conrad	7	22	56	120
1965	Dec. 5	Gemini 7	Borman, Lovell	13	18	35	206
1965	Dec. 15	Gemini 6	Schirra, Stafford	1	1	$51\frac{1}{2}$	15
1966	Mar. 16	Gemini 8	Armstrong, Scott		10	42	$6\frac{1}{2}$
1966	June 3	Gemini 9	Stafford, Cernan	3	0	21	44
1966	July 18	Gemini 10	Young, Collins	2	22	$46\frac{3}{4}$	43
1966	Sept. 9	Gemini 11	Conrad, Gordon	2	23	17	44
1966	Nov. 11	Gemini 12	Lovell, Aldrin	3	22	30	60

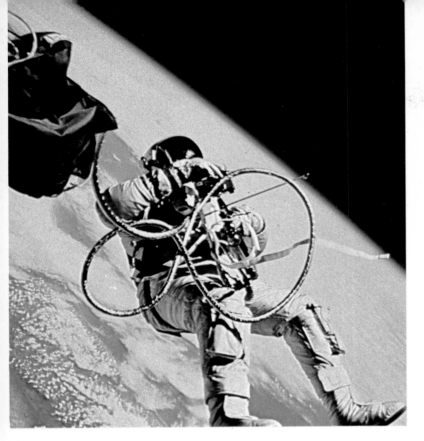

SPACE-WALKING: (left) another spectacular Gemini picture. It was found that activity outside the space-craft resulted in very severe physical strain.

A SPACEMAN'S VIEW OF SUNRISE. (below) This is a painting by Colonel Alexei Leonov, who in 1965 became the first man to go outside an orbiting space-craft. In addition to his scientific achievements, Leonov is also an accomplished amateur artist.

COLOUR PHOTOGRAPH OF VOSTOK 4 (bottom), the Russian space-ship which carried Colonel Popovich into orbit on 12 August 1962. At the time of the launch, Colonel Nikolayev in Vostok 3 was already circling the Earth, so that for the first time there were two astronauts in orbit at the same moment.

Of these, the Vostoks and Voskhods are Russian; the rest, American. Those who suspect a misprint in the table may note that Gemini 7 really was launched before Gemini 6, as will be described below. Also, up to the end of 1966, the number of astronauts who had made more than one trip each was seven Americans (Grissom, Cooper, Schirra, Stafford, Young, Conrad and Lovell) and no Russians.

It is convenient, in an historical framework, to end a preliminary table with 1966, because this was a definite marking-point. The Russians launched no manned vehicles for a long time after their success with Voskhod 2 in March 1965, so that they were clearly preparing for another major step. The Americans, for their part, completed their Gemini series in November 1966, and prepared to embark upon a new series, the Apollo. It was this Apollo venture which began with the tragedy at Cape Kennedy.

During 1961–6, the keynote was sound, steady progress, and the overall results confirmed the preliminary findings of Gagarin, Glenn and others. No fatal hazards were encountered, and the bogeys of space-sickness and meteoritic bombardment faded perceptibly, though there were some uneasy reservations about the former (particularly, from all accounts, on the Russian side). Neither was the radiation danger as serious as had been feared.

Now let us select a few of the highlights.

The first is again a Russian one. It began on 11 August 1962, when Major Andrian Nikolayev was launched in Vostok 3, and began to orbit the Earth between 111 and 145 miles, completing one circuit every $88\frac{1}{2}$ minutes. Just under a day later, Colonel Pavel Popovich took off in Vostok 4, and entered a similar orbit. There were two space-craft going round the Earth at the same time, which was a new departure; at one stage the Vostoks were

GEMINI 7, as photographed from Gemini 6. This is one of the most spectacular space-pictures taken during the Gemini series of launchings, which began in 1965 and ended in 1966.

COLONEL ALEXEI LEONOV, who was sent into orbit on 18 March 1965 and became the first man to go outside an orbiting space-craft.

VALENTINA TERESHKOVA (now Mrs. Nikolayev), as she was shown on Russian television during her space-flight. She was launched in Vostok 6 on 16 June 1963; Colonel Valery Bykovsky in Vostok 5 was already in orbit, and at one time the two space-craft were close to each other.

no more than three miles apart, and millions of people in the U.S.S.R. saw the two men on their television screens. Both were busy making notes, conducting observations and having their meals. Later, Popovich said that Nikolayev's craft looked like a small moon in the distance. On 15 August the two astronauts landed safely, about 150 miles apart and within six minutes of each other. Both had travelled over a million miles in space.

As usual, the hulls of the Vostoks were strongly heated during the final drop through the air. Nikolayev wrote that the effects were 'weird. First smoke, then flame. First red, then orange, yellow and blue. There were nasty crackling sounds. As deceleration slackened it was like being in a cart on a very bumpy road, but it smoothed out before I separated by capsule from the spaceship and landed by parachute.' It must have been decidedly alarming, but other astronauts, before and since, have had similar experiences.

The next flight of special interest was that of Vostok 6, in June 1963. This time the pilot was a woman, Valentina Tereshkova. When she took off, there was already a space-craft in orbit (Vostok 5, carrying the Soviet colonel Valeri Bykovsky), and the general procedure was much the same as with Nikolayev and Popovich. The selection of a woman for a space-journey caused some raised eyebrows in Western countries, but the Russians, very justifiably, saw nothing strange in it—and certainly Valentina Tereshkova proved every bit as skilful as the male pilots. Incidentally, she has since married Andrian Nikolayev, and has a daughter who will doubtless be proud to say that both her parents have been into space!

The year following the ascent of the first space-woman was outwardly uneventful, though plenty of activity was going on. Both the U.S. Mercury programme from Cape Kennedy—the new name of Cape Canaveral—and the Soviet Vostok series had been completed, and it took some time for successor projects to get under way. The new phase was started with the Russian Voskhod 1 of 12 October 1964. The main item of interest here was that of the three crew members, one, Boris Yegorov, was not a trained astronaut in the full sense of the word, though of course his training had been intensive judged by ordinary standards. He was a doctor, 27 years old and with a special interest in space medicine; he was not a jet pilot, and his role was obviously confined chiefly to medical problems. The flight of Voskhod 1 was rather unexpectedly short, but the Russians stressed that all the programmes scheduled for it had been carried through. The Soviet news agency also published a list of some of the food carried; roasted chicken fillet, cottage cheese, fruit and sweets were all on the menu.

Again the next highlight was Russian. On 18 March 1965 Pavel Belyayev and Alexei Leonov went up in Voskhod 2, destined to be the last Soviet manned vehicle for a long time. Belyayev was the senior pilot, but it was Leonov who took the limelight. During the trip, he put on a space-suit and went outside the Voskhod, so becoming the first astronaut to go for what may graphically though rather misleadingly called a 'space-walk'. The feat was shown on television, and was, naturally, watched with considerable excitement by scientists and non-scientists alike. Leonov did not go far beyond his ship, and he stayed out for only a short time, but he certainly made history.

One obvious question is: 'Why did he not drift away?' Actually there was no reason for him to do so, though he carried a safety-cord in case of accidents. If we look back at the analogy of two ants on the rim of a rotating bicycle-wheel, the situation becomes clear. Each ant is moving in an orbit round the central point, the hub of the wheel; but the two insects are travelling in the same path at the same rate, so that they remain in company. One ant may be said to represent Leonov, and the other ant will stand for the Voskhod.

On the other hand, it would be wrong to suppose that the procedure is without its risks. There is no fear of falling, but the walker it totally dependent upon his space-suit, which must be pressurized and made as effective a shield as the hull of a space-craft. Leonov's was described as a miniature cabin consisting of a metal helmet with a transparent visor, a multi-layer hermetic suit, gloves, and specially designed footwear. The air-pressure inside was only about half that which we normally experience, and this was one reason why any exertion was very tiring—a point verified later by the Americans. Also, a meteor puncture would have been disastrous.

Leonov's achievement caught the public imagination more strongly than any space exploit since 1962, but the Russians did not follow it up. They launched no more manned vehicles during the period which concerns us at the moment (pre-1967), but meanwhile the new American programme, known as Gemini, had been made ready. Test vehicles were launched on 8 April 1964 and 19 January 1965, and then, on 23 March 1965, Virgil Grissom and his co-pilot Young made the first ascent in a Gemini craft. Grissom had been in space before, since he had followed Alan Shepard with a sub-orbital hop, but this was his first major flight.

A new departure on this occasion was that Grissom and Young proved able to manoeuvre the Gemini from one orbit to another,

THE FIRST SPACE-WALKER: Colonel Alexei Leonov outside Voskhod 2. This photograph is a still from a Russian film. Leonov and his colleague, Belayev, were launched on 18 March 1965.

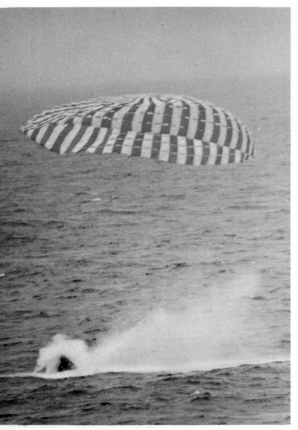

SPLASH-DOWN OF GEMINI 9, on 6 June 1966, with Astronauts Stafford and Cernan. The method of final descent, with parachute braking, is well shown in this photograph.

SPLASH-DOWN OF GEMINI 3, in March 1965. The astronauts were Virgil Grissom and John Young. One of them is being hoisted aboard a recovery helicopter from the U.S.S. *Intrepid* off Grand Turk Island in the Atlantic.

using brief power-bursts from steering rockets. And from Gemini 4, in the following June, astronaut Edward White far exceeded Leonov's space-walk, since he stayed outside for 21 minutes and moved around on the end of his safety-cord by means of a hand-held gas gun. He also took some superb photographs, which were vastly better than anything so far published by the Russians.

The next step was to achieve a space 'rendezvous'; that is to say, send up a space-ship and bring it together with an object already in orbit. This was more or less managed in December 1965, when Gemini 6 was launched and brought within one foot of the already-orbiting Gemini 7, so that the crews could see each other and make signals at each other through their windows. Gemini 8, however, caused some anxious moments. There was a successful 'docking' operation with an unmanned Agena rocket which had been put into orbit to act as a target, but 20 minutes later the Gemini began to roll and yaw because of what was later found to be a short-circuit in the electrical system. It took the astronauts, Neil Armstrong and David Scott, some time to stop the tumbling motion, but they managed to do so by using power-bursts from the rockets designed for use during the final drop to Earth. They then separated the Gemini from the Agena, and landed safely, though some 500 miles east of the planned area. This incidentally is why Gemini 8 made $6\frac{1}{2}$ circuits of the world instead of a whole number; the flight was ended sooner than had been originally scheduled.

Troubles of this sort were only to be expected sooner or later, and it was fortunate that the safety precautions, plus the coolness and strict training of Armstrong and Scott, prevented a disaster. Since then there have been several trouble-free docking man-œuvres, and during one of them, with Gemini 11, Charles Conrad and Richard Gordon reached a record height of 850 miles above the ground. Subsequently, Gordon went outside the Gemini and 'hooked' the Agena with a 100-foot tether; the two vehicles were then slowly separated, until the line was taut. There was certainly no danger of the Agena drifting away.

Yet Gordon found the exertion of his hooking operation almost too much for him, and he was blinded by perspiration inside his helmet, so that he had to cut short his space-walk and come back into the cabin after 44 minutes instead of staying out for the planned two hours. Other space-walkers, too, have found that any physical activity under such conditions is exceptionally tiring. The problem is very real, but no doubt it will be overcome, just as all the others have been. And the Gemini series ended on a most encouraging note, when Edward Aldrin spent 2 hours $9\frac{1}{2}$ minutes outside the twelfth and last vehicle, coping with the conditions remarkably well.

So ended the second phase in the manned exploration of space. The Vostok, Mercury, Voskhod and Gemini projects had been carried through, and each had made major contributions. By the close of 1966, it was reasonable to suppose that men would land on the Moon within the next few years.

When tragedy came, on 27 January 1967, it was not in 'outer space', but a mere 200 feet off the ground. The first of the Apollo flights, planned to end with the first trip to the Moon some time before 1970, had been scheduled for 21 February, with a crew made

THE END OF THE FLIGHT OF GEMINI 5, on 29 August 1965. Gordon Cooper is hoisted
aboard the recovery helicopter from the U.S.S. *Lake Champlain.* He and his fellow-astronaut
Charles Conrad had landed in the Atlantic Ocean an hour earlier, after being in orbit for
eight days—a record up to that time.

COLONEL VLADIMIR KOMAROV, Hero of the Soviet Union. Colonel Komarov was one of the crew of three who made a successful space-flight in 1964, but was killed in 1967 when the braking apparatus of his space-craft Soyuz 1 failed.

up of Lieutenant-Colonel Virgil Grissom, Lieutenant-Colonel Edward White and Lieutenant-Commander Roger Chaffee. Grissom was one of the seven original astronauts of Project Mercury; White had been the first American 'space-walker', and Chaffee, at 31 years of age the youngest of the three, was making ready for his first venture into space. The three were in their take-off positions, during a routine rehearsal, when there was a sudden outbreak of fire—too quick and too complete for any rescue operations to be carried out. The atmosphere inside the cabin was pure oxygen, and when fire broke out the three astronauts had no chance.

The reaction all over the world, from America to Britain, Russia and all other countries, was one of stunned horror. The fact that project Apollo would be seriously delayed took second place in people's minds—and quite rightly so; it was the personal tragedy which was so deeply felt. And the dangers were again brought home a few days later, when two aerospace technicians, Bartley and Harmon, were killed in much the same way in another test capsule.

Grissom, White and Chaffee had been well aware of the risks they were running, had they not possessed immense courage, they would not have volunteered for training as astronauts. There is, unfortunately, little more that can be said. They were the first victims of astronautics; unhappily they were not the last, since within a few weeks tragedy struck again.

When Colonel Komarov was launched in the latest Russian spacecraft, Soyuz 1, there was every reason to expect a new phase in the Soviet manned spaceflight project. Komarov had already made one flight, and was eminently suited to his task; there had been some doubts about his absolute physical fitness, but these had been dispelled, and nobody could foresee the disaster which lay ahead. Evidently things went wrong almost from the start. When Komarov came in to land, his braking equipment failed; the parachutes did not open, and Soyuz 1 crashed down, so that Komarov must have been killed instantly. Certainly he could not be faulted; the trouble lay in the space-craft itself. Again there were very genuine feelings of shock and sadness all over the world.

Astronauts, perhaps above all people, know the risks they are running. Every time they go into space they are gambling with their lives, and they are perfectly aware of the fact; their courage is beyond all praise. Grissom, White, Chaffee and Komarov have been the first victims of Man's progress into space. Let us hope that they will also be the last.

Rockets Toward the Moon

In writing about the story of astronautics since 1957, it is almost impossible to keep to a strict historical sequence, because there have been so many projects going on at the same time. I have not attempted to try, and I have described the pre-1967 period with regard to artificial satellites (manned and otherwise) without taking account of the various probes sent out to the Moon and planets. Now let us deal with the same period in respect of rockets dispatched toward the Moon.

There has never been any serious doubt that the Moon must be our first target, not because it is a friendly world—it is anything but that!—but because it is so much nearer to us than any other natural body. To recapitulate: its mean distance from the Earth is 239,000 miles, roughly a hundred times less than the minimum distance of the closest planet, Venus. Also, the Moon shares in our journey round the Sun, and never wanders away from us.

The diagram given here may help to show how near the Moon really is. The circle on the bottom left-hand page represents the Earth, and the circle on the upper right stands for the Moon, drawn to its correct relative size and distance. This is clearly not very far, and it means that we can examine the Moon in considerable detail even with modest ground-based telescopes.

The first attempt at a lunar probe was made by the United States team in 1958. It failed, as did three subsequent attempts in the same year, but in 1959 the Russians launched three 'Lunik' vehicles, of which one went past the Moon, one landed there, and one went on a round trip, sending back photographs which were then of unique interest. It was not until 1964 that really good close-

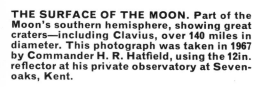

THE SURFACE OF THE MOON. Part of the Moon's southern hemisphere, showing great craters—including Clavius, over 140 miles in diameter. This photograph was taken in 1967 by Commander H. R. Hatfield, using the 12in. reflector at his private observatory at Sevenoaks, Kent.

range pictures were obtained, and only in 1966 was the first 'soft landing' managed by an unpiloted rocket. All the same, the story goes back almost to the start of the Space Age—and the idea of lunar travel is, as we have seen, very ancient indeed.

Before saying much about the various probes, it seems necessary to give a brief description of the Moon itself. I propose, however, to confine myself mainly to the outstanding problems which have been, or will be, cleared up by means of space research methods.

The Moon is a small world, a mere 2,160 miles in diameter, and with 1/81 of the mass of the Earth. It seems certain that it and the Earth were never one body, and that the Moon has always been separate; presumably it was formed in the same manner as the Earth, around 4,700 million years ago, and it should be regarded as a secondary planet rather than as an ordinary satellite. Yet it is very different from our own planet. It has a low escape velocity of only 1½ miles per second, and this means that it has lost virtually all of any atmosphere it may once have had. There may be a trace left, but the ground density must be much less than 1/10,000 of that of the Earth's air at sea-level; even 1/100,000 may be an over-estimate. It is fair, then, to say that the Moon is to all intents and purposes without an atmosphere.

This has many far-reaching consequences, First, there is no blanket to protect the surface; at noon on the equator the temperature must rise to well over +200° Fahrenheit, while at lunar midnight a thermometer would register below −250° Fahrenheit. Also, the Moon is a slow-spinner, and takes 27.3 Earth-days to complete one rotation. This is also the period taken for the Moon to go once round the Earth—or, more accurately, the centre of gravity of the Earth-Moon system—and the result is that the same hemisphere is always turned toward us. From our home-based observatories, we can never see the 'back' of the Moon. I shall go further into this interesting matter in Chapter 22.

The lack of any effective shield means, too, that there is no protection against the various short-wave radiations coming from the Sun and from space. There is a similar lack of protection against meteoroids, and the surface of the Moon must be continually bombarded by small solid particles; there is no atmosphere to burn them up on their way to the ground.

Any small telescope will show the main surface details. To begin with, there are the various darkish areas known as seas (Latin: maria). For centuries now it has been known that there is no water on the Moon, and that the so-called seas are vast dry plains without a trace of moisture in them, but the old names have been retained; thus we have the Mare Imbrium or Sea of Showers, the Mare Nubium or Sea of Clouds, the Oceanus Procellarum or Ocean of Storms, and so on. The outline map given here should allow the main maria to be indentified without difficulty.

Some of the maria are bordered by what may be termed mountain ranges, though it must be made clear that these are basically different from our own ranges such as the Himalayas and Rockies. In general, the lunar mountain chains are given familiar names; thus the large, well-formed Mare Imbrium has part of its border made up of the lunar Apennines and Alps. The heights are considerable, and the loftiest peaks on the Moon reach to more than 25,000 feet above the general level of the surface.

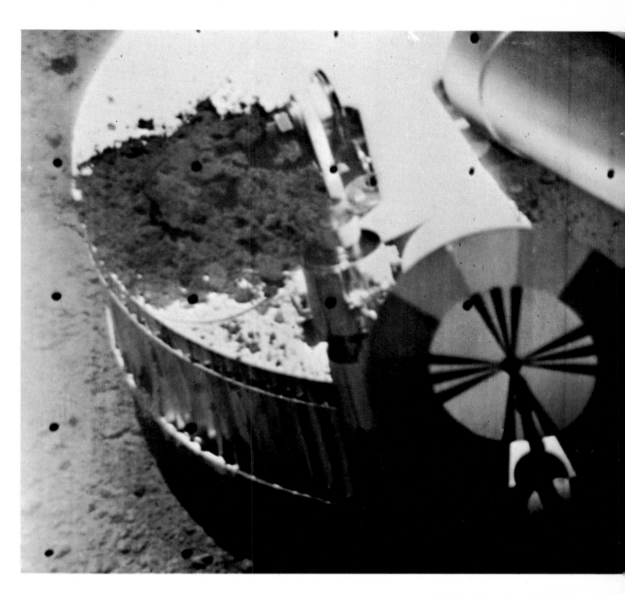

PHOTOGRAPH OF THE MOON'S
SURFACE FROM SURVEYOR 3, 26
April 1967. This is a colour reconstruction, showing the lunar 'soil' and the
footpad of the space-craft.

LUNAR ROCK, PHOTOGRAPHED IN
COLOUR from Surveyor 1 (launched 31
May 1966) from Cape Kennedy. This
picture is a colour reconstruction. Three
black and white pictures were taken
through the three colour filters in the
spacecraft's television camera; from
these, positive transparencies were
made and projected together through
three similar filters, and the triple pro-
jection was photographed.

The most interesting formations are, however, the walled formations known generally as craters. There are tens of thousands of them, ranging from huge ramparted plains over 150 miles across down to tiny pits. Some of them, such as the noble, 64-mile Theophilus, have massive central elevations; others, notably the dark-floored, 60-mile Plato, have interiors which seem perfectly flat when viewed from Earth, apart from minor craterlets and hills here and there. And there are some craters, such as Tycho in the southern part of the Moon and Copernicus in the Oceanus Procellarum, which are the centres of strange systems of bright streaks or rays, surface deposits which have not yet been really satisfactorily explained.

As well as these major structures, there are less obvious features such as the low swellings known as domes; the clefts or rilles; and the less common faults. The clefts look superficially not unlike the cracks visible in dried mud, but there is no doubt that they are in fact collapse trenches; many of them are found to be made up of strings of small craters. Of the faults, the best-known is the Straight Wall, which is not straight and is not a wall. It lies in the Mare Nubium, and is easy to see with a small telescope when suitably illuminated.

The earliest lunar maps were drawn up during the first decade of the seventeenth century (an Englishman, Harriott, seems to have priority), but it was not until 1837 that two German observers, Wilhelm Beer and Johann von Mädler, completed the first accurate chart. It is interesting to find that up to recent years, most of the lunar mapping work was done by amateur astronomers; professionals, as a class, regarded the Moon as rather dull and parochial. The situation has altered now, of course, and excellent photographic atlases have been compiled, mainly in Japan and America.

The craters are named after famous scientists of the past. The original list was drawn up by an Italian named Riccioli as long ago as 1651, but it has been extended since, and works fairly well on the whole. The situation with regard to the orientation of Moon maps is much less satisfactory. In astronomy, most photographs and drawings are shown with south at the top and north at the bottom, since this is the view given by an astronomical telescope; with the Moon, 'west' has always been taken as the left-hand side when south is at the top. The American astronautical authorities, however, publish their maps and photographs with north at the top, and reverse east and west. Since the present book has an historical slant, I am retaining the classical method: south at the top, west to the left.

There has been endless discussion about the origin of the Moon's craters. Some somewhat improbable ideas have been put forward from time to time (coral atolls, for instance, and even the scars left by atomic bombs), but by now only two theories are seriously supported. Some astronomers believe the craters to be due to volcanic action, so that they are in the nature of calderas; others consider that the craters were produced by meteoritic bombardment, so that they are of the same basic type as the spectacular Meteor Crater in the Arizona desert near Winslow. Actually, there must be craters of both kinds, just as there are on the Earth. So far as the main formations are concerned, it has always seemed to me

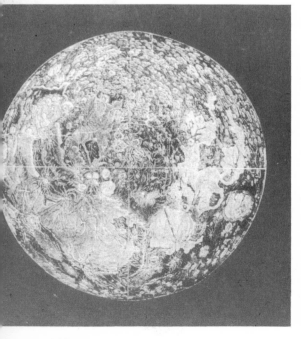

MAP OF THE MOON drawn by Littrow in 1832. Though very rough by modern standards, the main features are clearly recognizable. The first really good map was drawn by W. Beer and J. H. Mädler in 1837–8. By now, of course, visual work in mapping the Moon has been superseded by photographic methods, and the Orbiter space-craft of 1966–1968 have provided really detailed photographs of the whole of the lunar surface.

that the impact theory has fatal weaknesses, and that the craters show every indication of being calderas; nothing that has happened during the past few years has caused me to alter my view, but no doubt we shall know for certain before long.

Major changes on the surface of the Moon belong to the remote past, but it seems that there are minor outbreaks occasionally, presumably volcanic. These show up as transitory red glows, not easy to detect even by experienced observers who know just what they are looking for. To go into details about them would mean too great a digression here, and I mention them merely to show that our knowledge of the Moon is still very far from complete.

One theory of the recent past was of vital importance astronautically. In 1955 T. Gold, then of the Royal Greenwich Observatory, published a long paper in which he claimed that the dark maria were dust-filled, so that a space-craft incautious enough to land there would sink out of sight with devastating permanence. Practical lunar observers were not in the least impressed with the theory, simply because it made no pretence of fitting the observed facts (incidentally, it presupposed the craters to be of impact origin). However, it was taken very seriously indeed by the United States space-planners, as indeed it had to be. Not until 1966 did the first controlled landings on the Moon finally dispose of it.

In short, the Moon is a world virtually without atmosphere, totally without water, and presumably without any sign of life; the temperatures are extreme, the rotation slow, and the surface unprotected from the radiations and tiny particles from which we on Earth are screened. All the same, it has remained Target No. 1, and it would be a magnificent site for an astronomical observatory and a physical laboratory.

It may be useful to start by giving a list of the various Moon-shots attempted in the 1958–66 period. Those which may be regarded as successful are dignified by an asterisk.

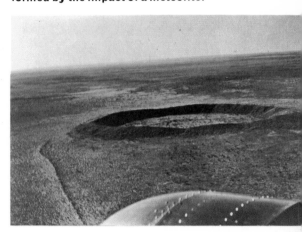

WOLF CREEK CRATER, Australia, photographed by G. J. H. McCall. This crater was formed by the impact of a meteorite.

CRATER LAKE, OREGON, photographed by G. J. H. McCall. This is a volcanic structure, and may well be of the same type as the large craters of the Moon.

Date of Launch		Name	Country	Notes
1958	Aug. 17	Able 1	U.S.A.	Failed after 77 sec. at 12½ miles (explosion of lower stage of launcher).
1958	Oct. 11	Pioneer 1	U.S.A.	Reached 70,840 miles.
1958	Nov. 9	Pioneer 2	U.S.A.	Failed when 3rd stage failed to ignite.
1958	Dec. 6	Pioneer 3	U.S.A.	Reached 66,220 miles.
1959	Jan. 2	*Lunik 1	U.S.S.R.	Passed within 4,660 miles of the Moon on 4 January.
1959	Mar. 3	Pioneer 4	U.S.A.	Passed within 37,000 miles of the Moon on 5 March.
1959	Sept. 12	*Lunik 2	U.S.S.R.	Landed on the Moon, 13 September.
1959	Oct. 4	*Lunik 3	U.S.S.R.	Went round the Moon and photographed the far side.
1959	Nov. 26	Able 4	U.S.A.	Failure soon after take-off.
1960	Oct. 25	Able 5A	U.S.A.	Total failure.
1960	Dec. 15	Able 5B	U.S.A.	Exploded 70 sec. after take-off.
1961	Aug. 23	Ranger 1	U.S.A.	Failed to go anywhere near the Moon.
1961	Nov. 18	Ranger 2	U.S.A.	Total failure.
1962	Jan. 26	Ranger 3	U.S.A.	Missed the Moon by 23,000 miles (28 January).
1962	Apr. 23	Ranger 4	U.S.A.	Instruments and guidance failure; probably landed on the night side of the Moon on 26 April.
1962	Oct. 18	Ranger 5	U.S.A.	Missed the Moon by over 400 miles.

Pioneer 4
37,300 miles
(now orbiting the Sun
in 398 days, aphelion
106 million miles from Sun)

Pioneer 1   70,840 miles
Pioneer 3   66,220 miles

Pioneer 2   963 miles
Burn-up
in Atmosphere

ORBITS OF THE PIONEER PROBES OF 1958-9. Nos. 1 and 3 reached altitudes of over 65,000 miles before falling back to the ground; No. 2 was a failure and No. 4 passed within 37,000 miles of the Moon, after which it entered an orbit round the Sun and became a tiny "artificial planet".

1963	Apr.	2	Lunik 4	U.S.S.R.	Missed the Moon by over 5,200 miles.
1964	Jan.	30	Ranger 6	U.S.A.	Hit the Moon on 2 February, but the cameras failed.
1964	July	28	*Ranger 7	U.S.A.	Hit the Moon on 31 July; sent back 4,308 photographs.
1965	Feb.	17	*Ranger 8	U.S.A.	Hit the Moon on 20 February; sent back 7,137 photographs.
1965	Mar.	21	*Ranger 9	U.S.A.	Hit the Moon on 24 March; sent back 5,814 photographs.
1965	May	9	Luna 5	U.S.S.R.	Crash-landed on the Moon on 12 May; soft landing failure.
1965	June	8	Luna 6	U.S.S.R.	Missed the Moon by 100,000 miles (11 June).
1965	July	18	*Zond 3	U.S.S.R.	Photographed far side of the Moon; entered solar orbit.
1965	Oct.	4	Luna 7	U.S.S.R.	Soft-landing failure; crashed on the Moon.
1965	Dec.	3	Luna 8	U.S.S.R.	Soft-landing failure; crashed on the Moon.
1966	Jan	31	*Luna 9	U.S.S.R.	Soft landing; photographs sent back from the Moon.
1966	Mar.	31	*Luna 10	U.S.S.R.	Entered orbit round the Moon; data sent back.
1966	May	30	*Surveyor 1	U.S.A.	Soft landing; 11,150 photographs sent back.
1966	Aug.	10	*Orbiter 1	U.S.A.	Entered orbit round the Moon; photographs sent back.
1966	Aug.	24	*Luna 11	U.S.S.R.	Entered orbit round the Moon; data sent back.
1966	Sept.	20	Surveyor 2	U.S.A.	Guidance failure; crash-landed on the Moon.
1966	Oct.	22	*Luna 12	U.S.S.R.	Entered orbit round the Moon; data sent back.
1966	Nov.	7	*Orbiter 2	U.S.A.	Entered orbit round the Moon; photographs sent back.
1966	Dec.	21	*Luna 13	U.S.S.R.	Soft landing; photographs and data sent back.

From this list I have excluded an anonymous Russian launching of 4 January 1963, which may have been a lunar probe, but about which no information has been given. I have also excluded Cosmos 3, of 1 March 1966, which has been regarded as a lunar probe possibility, but which was much more probably an ordinary Earth satellite of the long Cosmos series. Even so, it is an impressive list; over thirty launchings, of which most of the later attempts have been partially or completely successful. There was no definite 'pause' at the end of 1966, as with the manned launchings, and the next American Orbiter went up to continue the general programme on 4 February 1967, while Surveyor 3 was launched on April 17 and made a successful soft landing.

Sending a rocket from the Earth to the Moon is not merely a question of taking aim and then pushing the starting-button at the right moment. Both Earth and Moon are in motion; the rocket has to take off gradually, just as with satellite launchings; and there are all manner of complications to be taken into account. The first American attempts were undertaken in the days when the propellant power was very limited, judged by modern standards, and it is not surprising that they failed. Pioneer 1 did hold out some hopes, and for a time it was thought that the Moon might be reached, but then it became only too painfully clear that the vehicle was off-course. There had been a slight error in the angle of trajectory, and the final velocity was only 23,454 m.p.h. instead

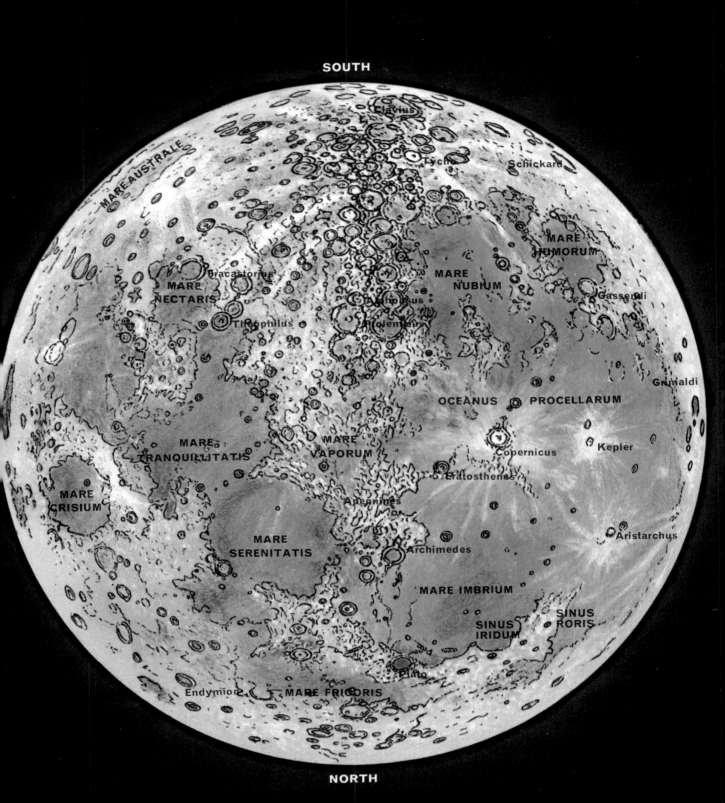

MAP OF THE MOON, showing the main features of the visible hemisphere. South is at the top, as is the usual astronomical practice.

SOUTH

NORTH

Clavius

Tycho

Schickard

MARE AUSTRALE

MARE HUMORUM

Fracastorius

MARE NECTARIS

MARE NUBIUM

Gassendi

Alphonsus

Theophilus

Ptolemaus

OCEANUS   PROCELLARUM

Grimaldi

Copernicus

Kepler

MARE TRANQUILLITATIS

MARE VAPORUM

Eratosthenes

Apennines

Aristarchus

MARE CRISIUM

MARE SERENITATIS

Archimedes

MARE IMBRIUM

SINUS RORIS

SINUS IRIDUM

Plato

Endymion   MARE FRIGORIS

of the calculated 24,034 m.p.h. A deficiency of less than 600 m.p.h. may not seem much when we are dealing with very high speeds, but it was enough to wreck the experiment. An extra 100 m.p.h. was gained by firing the eight rockets in the final stage of the vehicle, but even this was not enough, and on the late evening of 12 October Pioneer fell back to Earth, presumably burning out and depositing its remains somewhere in the Pacific.

The next Pioneers were no better. No. 2 reached less than 1,000 miles, because the third stage of its launcher failed to ignite at all; No. 3 reached more than 66,000 miles, but the rocket motor in the first stage of the launcher cut out $3\frac{3}{4}$ seconds too early, giving a final velocity of 23,606 m.p.h. instead of the required 24,486. Pioneer 4 was delayed until 3 March 1959, and was rather more encouraging; admittedly it missed the Moon by more than 37,000 miles, but it did not return to Earth, and entered an orbit round the Sun, so becoming a tiny artificial planet. At the present moment it is probably following a path which takes it round the Sun in a period of 392 days, with a distance ranging between 90,500,000 and 105,500,000 miles. Certainly we shall never find it again; it was tracked out to 400,000 miles by means of radio, and set up a record for that time, but it has long since passed from our ken for ever.

Yet the Russians, with their greater 'brute force', were able to do better. Lunik 1, the first successful Moon probe, ushered in the year 1959, and passed within 4,660 miles of its target. It was a small body only 40 inches across, but it carried various instruments, including the inevitable cosmic-ray detectors. According to Moscow, it was not designed to hit the Moon; it was a 'fly-by', and it sent back some interesting information. In particular, it told us that the Moon has no appreciable magnetic field.

The Earth's magnetism is bound up with the heavy core of the globe, which is presumably made up largely of the highly magnetic element iron. The Moon has an average density less than that of the Earth, and presumably has no comparable core, in which case it would also lack an equivalent magnetic field. This is what Lunik 1 found.

I have put an asterisk against Lunik 1 in my list because within its limitations, it did all that had been asked of it. It even signalled its position in space by sending out a 60-mile cloud of sodium vapour when it reached a distance of 70,000 miles, and this cloud was photographed. Of course, there were radio signals too, picked up by the Jodrell Bank team as well as by the Russians.

Lunik's closest approach to the Moon was made on 4 January, 34 hours after launching. Signals from it were lost permanently on the following day, but by then its future orbit had been worked out; unless it has been dragged off course by the gravitational pull of an unknown body, or unless it has been destroyed by collision with a meteoroid, it is now moving in a 446-day path, with its distance from the Sun ranging between 91,000,000 and 122,000,000 miles. Incidentally, this would mean that it may approach the planet Mars to within 6,000,000 miles, though the chances of its being seen by Martian astronomers are unfortunately very slight!

It is rather intriguing to speculate about the eventual careers of 'artificial planets', of which Lunik 1 was the first and Pioneer 4 the second. There is nothing to destroy them apart from the unlikely mischance of an asteroid or meteoroid hit, and so they will remain permanent members of the Solar System. Should they be recovered in the distant future, they will look just the same as they did when first launched—apart, of course, from the wear and tear of bombardment by tiny particles and what we may call interplanetary dust.

The second Lunik followed in September 1959. This time there was a direct hit, probably in the area of the Moon not far from the prominent 50-mile crater Archimedes. There is not the slightest doubt about the time of impact; it was 21 hours 2 minutes 23 seconds G.M.T. on 13 September. The Soviet authorities had asked for co-operation from the Jodrell Bank team headed by Professor (now Sir) Bernard Lovell, and this had willingly been given. Signals from Lunik 2 were strong and clear right up to the critical moment, and ceased abruptly at the instant when the rocket crashed down on to the Moon and destroyed itself. As before, an artificial sodium-cloud had been released *en route*; also as before, instruments had been carried which indicated an absence of any strong lunar magnetism.

For the first time, direct contact with another world had been made. Goddard's then-ridiculed prediction of 1919 had come true, and the Earth was no longer completely isolated from the other members of the Solar System. Nowadays, a lunar probe does not cause any general excitement even among scientists, but the idea was refreshingly novel not so very long ago.

LUNIK 2, which hit the Moon on 13 September 1959, thereby becoming the first man-made vehicle to reach another world. The landing was uncontrolled, and undoubtedly the vehicle was destroyed on impact, but even so it represented a notable advance.

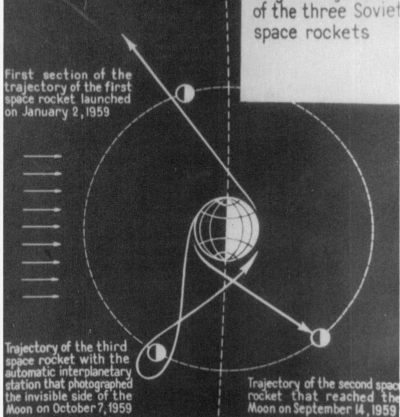

Flight trajectories of the three Soviet space rockets

First section of the trajectory of the first space rocket launched on January 2, 1959

Trajectory of the third space rocket with the automatic interplanetary station that photographed the invisible side of the Moon on October 7, 1959

Trajectory of the second space rocket that reached the Moon on September 14, 1959

ORBITS OF THE FIRST THREE LUNIKS. These Russian Moon probes were launched in 1959. No. 1 by-passed the Moon, No. 2 landed on the surface, and No. 3 went right round the Moon, sending back the first photographs of the hidden side.

Chapter 22

Round the Moon

The Moon is so close to us, astronomically speaking, that its surface can be mapped in great detail. Even before the first successful rocket probes were sent up, we knew more about the topography of, say, the Mare Imbrium than we do about the central parts of Antarctica. Yet strangely enough, our knowledge of 41 per cent. of the lunar surface was a complete blank, because this part of the Moon is always turned away from us.

The Moon, as we have seen, goes round the Earth (or, more accurately, round the 'barycentre' or centre of gravity of the Earth-Moon system) in 27.3 days. It takes exactly the same time to spin once on its axis. The result is that the same hemisphere is always presented to us, just as a man who walks round a chair, turning slowly as he goes, can keep his face turned toward the chair all the time.

There is no mystery about this behaviour. In very ancient times, before the Earth and Moon were properly solid, it is likely that the rate of spin was much quicker; but the Earth raised huge tides in the body of the Moon, and tended to keep a bulge pointing Earthward. As the Moon rotated, it had to fight against this tidal force,

THE LUNAR CRATER BAILLY, photographed by Commander H. R. Hatfield on 5 March 1966 with his 12in. reflector. Bailly is over 180 miles in diameter, and is the largest true crater-like structure on the visible hemisphere. Unfortunately it lies near the Moon's limb, and so is not very well placed for observation from the Earth. The illustration, right, indicates its size compared with the British Isles. The crater would cover much of England, and there are no comparable structures on the Earth.

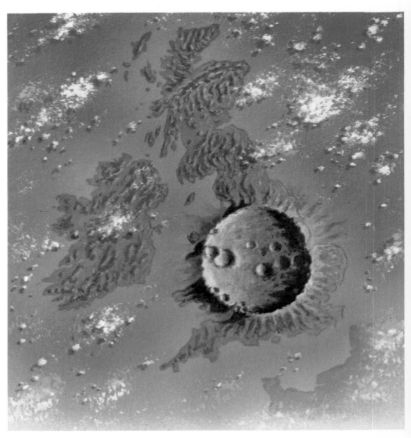

and so it was slowed down, until *relative to the Earth* the rotation had stopped altogether. Of course, the Moon's tidal force was tending to slow down the spin of the Earth in the same way, but the effect was not so marked, because the Moon has a much weaker pull. The Earth's day is still getting gradually longer because of lunar tides, but the increase amounts to a very small fraction of a second, and for practical purposes it can be ignored completely.

In the last paragraph I have put the words *relative to the Earth* in italics, because they are important. The Moon's rotation has not come to a halt relative to the Sun, and so day and night conditions on the 'other side' are just the same as on the side we can see.[1]

There are various effects known as 'librations' which make it possible for us to examine rather more than 50 per cent. of the lunar surface. The Moon spins on its axis at a steady rate, but it does not move in its orbit at a steady rate; the path round the Earth is elliptical, and so the Moon moves quickest when it is closest to us, obeying Kepler's Laws. The result is that the position in orbit and the amount of axial spin become periodically out of step, as it were, and we can see for some distance first round one limb and then round the other. This is called libration in longitude. There is also a libration in latitude, and a third sort of libration of much lesser extent. Altogether, we can examine 59 per cent. of the surface, though of course never more than 50 per cent. at any one particular moment. It is only the remaining 41 per cent. which is permanently out of view.

However, the situation is not so favourable as might be thought. Consider the well-formed sea called the Mare Crisium, or Sea of Crises. It measures 280 miles by 350 miles, and it is actually elongated in an east-west direction, though foreshortening means that it appears to be drawn out north-south. Very close to the limb, the foreshortening is tremendous; craters which are really circular look like long, narrow ellipses, very difficult to chart.

This sort of behaviour was infuriating to lunar students, but in the pre-rocket era nothing could be done about it. The last-century Danish astronomer Hansen went so far as to suggest that the Moon was lop-sided in mass, so that all the air and water had been drawn round to the far hemisphere—which might even be inhabited. Few people took Hansen's theory at all seriously, but there was no way of finding out what lay on the other side of the Moon.

This was the situation in 1959. Then on 4 October, exactly two years after Sputnik 1, the Russians achieved a really major triumph. Their new probe, Lunik 3, was sent on a trip round the Moon, and was able to send back photographs of the unknown regions.

Lunik 3 was a complex vehicle, launched by a step-arrangement in the usual way. Without fuel, the upper stage of the rocket weighed about $1\frac{1}{2}$ tons, while the actual probe accounted for about 9 cwt. It was given a full research programme, but its main task was photographic.

All went well. By 4.30 G.M.T. on 7 October, the rocket had passed by the Moon, and lay well beyond it, some 35,000 miles

[1] This still seems to confuse some people. Only a few days ago I read through an encyclopædia published in London by a well-known firm, and found a reference to a rocket which 'landed on the side of the Moon which is always dark'!

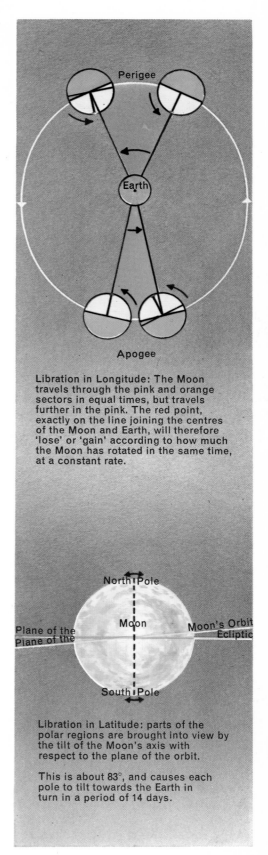

Libration in Longitude: The Moon travels through the pink and orange sectors in equal times, but travels further in the pink. The red point, exactly on the line joining the centres of the Moon and Earth, will therefore 'lose' or 'gain' according to how much the Moon has rotated in the same time, at a constant rate.

Libration in Latitude: parts of the polar regions are brought into view by the tilt of the Moon's axis with respect to the plane of the orbit.

This is about 83°, and causes each pole to tilt towards the Earth in turn in a period of 14 days.

from the surface. From Earth, the Moon was then almost new, so that the hemisphere facing Lunik 3 was in full sunlight. Then the cameras were switched on, by remote control, and for the next 40 minutes the pictures were taken; two cameras were used, giving photographs on different scales. After the programme had been finished, the films were automatically developed and fixed.

Lunik 3 was still moving away from the Earth. It reached apogee (292,000 miles) on 10 October, and then started to swing back, reaching perigee (29,000 miles) on 18 October. The pictures were then transmitted by complex television techniques, and were successfully received by the Russian operators on the ground. Six days later, they were released to the world. I shall always remember that I had the honour of being the first to show them in Britain, on a television programme over the B.B.C. that evening.

Very probably the Russians meant to keep in touch with the probe, and re-run the transmissions on the 'second time round', but contact was lost abruptly, and was never regained. It was suggested that the Lunik might have been hit by a meteoroid, and this is by no means impossible, though on the whole it is more likely that the instruments on board the vehicle developed some fault. In any case, Lunik 3 had done its work well.

Not all the averted hemisphere was covered by the pictures. This was intentional, since the Russians had deliberately included some of the Earth-turned regions so that the positions of the newly-

LUNIK 3, launched on 4 October 1959, which went round the Moon and photographed the hidden side. This was undoubtedly the most successful of the early lunar probes.

POSITION OF LUNIK 3 during the photography of the Moon's far side. The direction of the sunlight is shown by the arrows. Lunik 3 was over 30,000 miles from the Moon, on the far side from the Earth. The pictures were taken more or less under the equivalent of full-moon illumination, and there were no shadows, which was one important reason for the lack of fine detail shown.

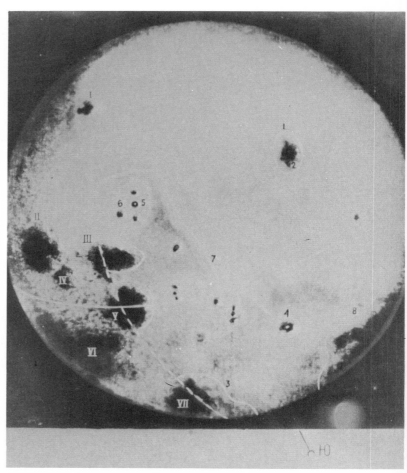

FIRST PHOTOGRAPHS OF THE MOON'S FAR SIDE, sent back from Lunik III in October 1959. Though very blurred by later standards, these photographs were rightly regarded, at the time, as a major technical triumph.

charted areas could be fixed accurately. Also, the photographs were taken under high light, so that they were less spectacular than some people had expected. But they were immensely informative, and they showed that the hidden side of the Moon is of the same basic nature as the side we have always known. There are fewer of the dark Mare-areas, but there are many craters, mountains, ridges and valleys. It is hardly necessary to add that there is no sign of life.

I had fully expected the Russians would follow up their success, but for some years they did not, while at this period the American lunar probe projects were still floundering. It was not until 1964 that the next real advances came, and these, the U.S. Ranger rockets, concerned the Earth-facing hemisphere of the Moon, so that discussion of them must be postponed until Chapter 23.

Then, in 1965, the Russians produced a new probe, Zond 3, which also went past the Moon and sent back photographs which were much clearer than those of Lunik 3. Zond never came back to the region of the Earth; after it had completed its lunar photography, and transmitted its pictures, it continued its journey, and at the moment it must still be going round the Sun, though all contact with it has long since been lost.

Obviously, it would be useful to have a rocket orbiting the Moon in the same way that an artificial satellite goes round the Earth. This is by no means a simple matter. The probe has to be sent close to the Moon, and then given a course alteration to put it

DETAILS OF LUNA 10. (1) Radio apparatus. (2) The upper stage which was sent into a path round the moon. (3) System for detaching the lunar probe. (4) Orientation System. (5) Power Unit.

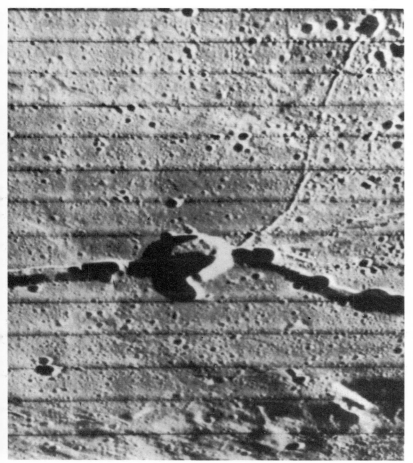

THE HYGINUS CLEFT ON THE MOON, photographed from the U.S. probe Orbiter 2. This great cleft is visible in a small telescope, but its detailed structure was not revealed until Orbiter 2 secured close-range pictures of it. The main crater, Hyginus, is clearly shown; the cleft is in part a crater-chain, and is presumably a collapse feature.

Photograph of the Moon's surface obtained on 20 July 1965 by the Russian vehicle Zond 3. At the time, the probe was about 10,000 kilometres above the Moon.

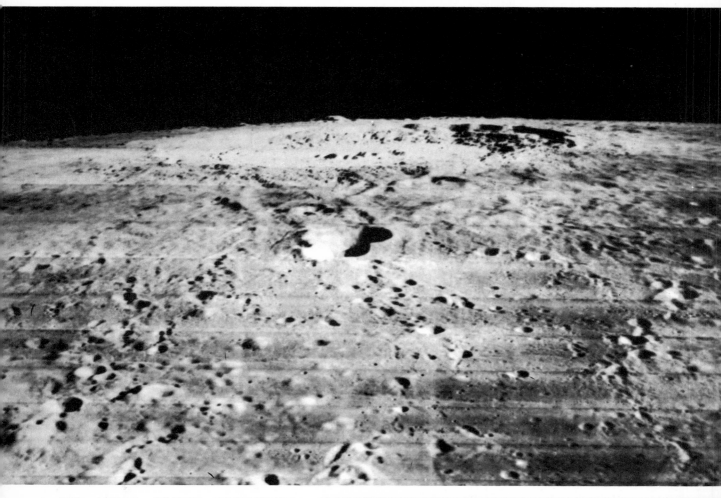

THE LUNAR CRATER COPERNICUS,
photographed from Orbiter 2 on 23 November 1966 with the telephoto camera lens. Copernicus is just on the horizon; the double crater in the foreground is named Fauth.

THE EARTH AS SEEN FROM THE MOON.
A colour reconstruction, obtained on 30 April, 1967 from the probe Surveyor 3.

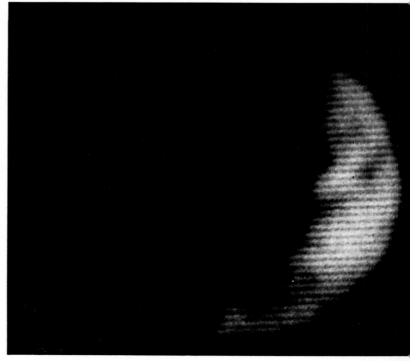

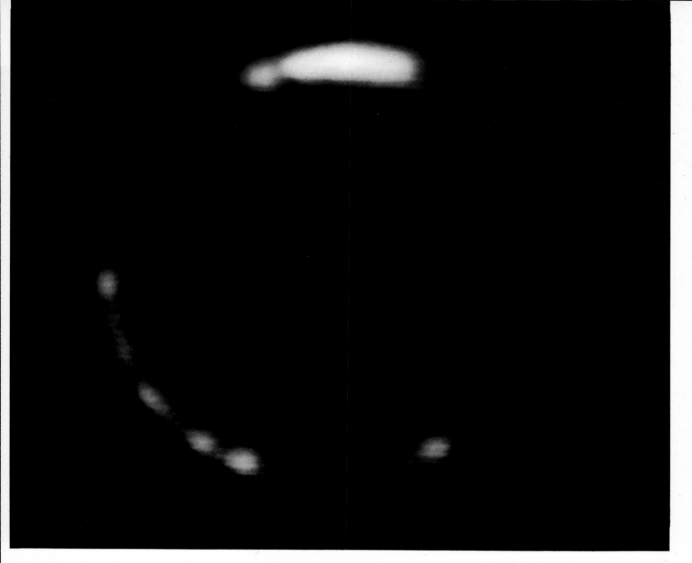

AN ECLIPSE OF THE SUN AS SEEN FROM THE MOON; photograph from Surveyor 3 on 24 April 1967. The Sun is being eclipsed by the Earth. The brightest portion of the lighted ring round the Earth appears in the north polar regions. The negatives were made through three colour filters in the space-craft's camera system.

THE LUNAR CRATER KEPLER, photographed in February 1967 from Orbiter 3. The wide-angle lens was used. Kepler, the most prominent crater shown, is over 20 miles in diameter and over 1 mile deep. The smaller, almost perfectly-formed crater to the right is the 9-mile Kepler A.

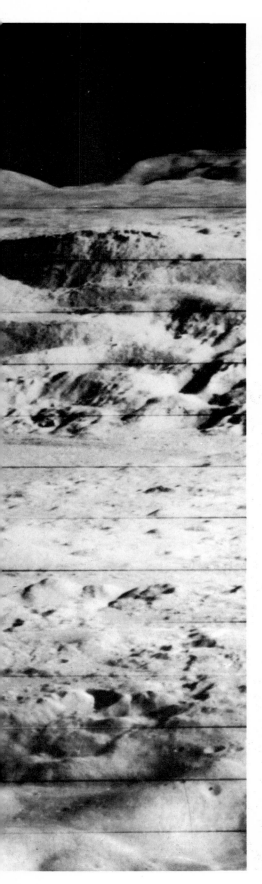

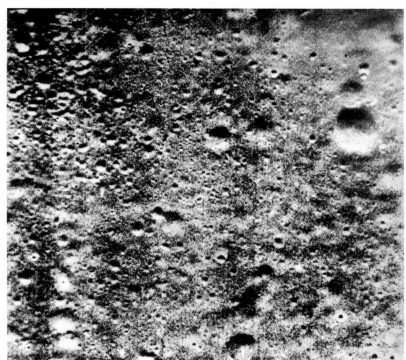

The Moon as photographed in October 1966 from Luna 12, a Russian vehicle which entered a circum-lunar orbit. The area shown is south-east of the brilliant crater Aristarchus, and covers about 25 square kilometres; the smallest craters shown are about 15 metres in diameter.

into a circum-lunar orbit. The Russians, as so often, led the way, and Luna 10, launched on 31 March 1966, became the first 'satellite of a satellite', though apparently it sent back no pictures, and was concerned chiefly with measurements of radiation level and micro-meteorite impacts. The same was true of Luna 11 and Luna 12, sent up later in 1966. But superb pictures were obtained in late 1966 by the first two United States Orbiters, and the photograph of Copernicus, from Orbiter 2, was justifiably hailed as 'the picture of the century'—or perhaps of any century.

Orbiter 1, incidentally, met with a sad fate. When its programme had been completed, it was given a final command to crash itself to destruction somewhere on the averted hemisphere, which it duly did.

The Orbiter programme was continued throughout 1967, with spectacular results. Numbers 3 (February), 4 (May) and 5 (August) were all successful, and the whole of the Moon was photographed in amazing detail. I well remember that at the meeting of the International Astronomical Union held in Prague, during August, a 'lunar mosaic' was displayed on the floor of a large room reserved for the purpose. It was remarkably impressive, and stressed that lunar mapping from Earth observatories had become very much out of date. There were no Russian launchings toward the Moon during 1967, but on 7 April 1968 the Soviet team sent up Lunar 14 to continue the programme.

COPERNICUS. The "Picture of the Century", taken in 1966 from Orbiter 2. Copernicus, 56 miles in diameter, is one of the Moon's great craters, but never before had it been seen in such remarkable detail. The central peaks are well shown. The cape in the background (upper left) lies near the small crater Gay-Lussac.

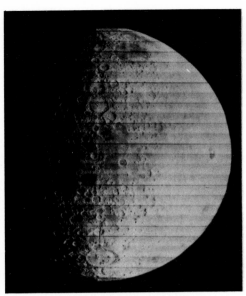

PART OF THE MOON'S HIDDEN SIDE,
photographed (wide-angle) from Orbiter 4 on
11 May 1967. At the time, Orbiter was about
3,000 kilometres above the Moon. The centre
of the photograph is approximately half-way
between the Moon's equator and pole.

By now we have a good working knowledge of almost the whole of the Moon's surface. There are definite differences between the two hemispheres with regard to the distribution of the craters and other features, but at least we may be sure that the general character is the same. The newly-mapped objects have been given names following the system introduced by Riccioli in 1651, and the Soviet authorities have been remarkably fair about it. There are many Russian names, of course, but there are also many craters and other features which have been named in honour of famous men from the Western countries. As we noted earlier, Jules Verne and H. G. Wells have been remembered. It is surely fitting, too, that an important crater should have been named after that great pioneer Konstantin Eduardovich Tsiolkovskii.

No doubt men will visit the far side of the Moon eventually, but not in the earliest days of lunar exploration. From the far side, remember, the Earth will never be seen, since it will remain below the horizon; therefore there can be no direct radio contact. Yet long before there is any question of an expedition there, the hidden hemisphere will have been mapped in great detail, so that the explorers will know just what to expect. This work was begun in 1959, with Lunik 3, and it ought to be finished well before the end of the nineteen-seventies.

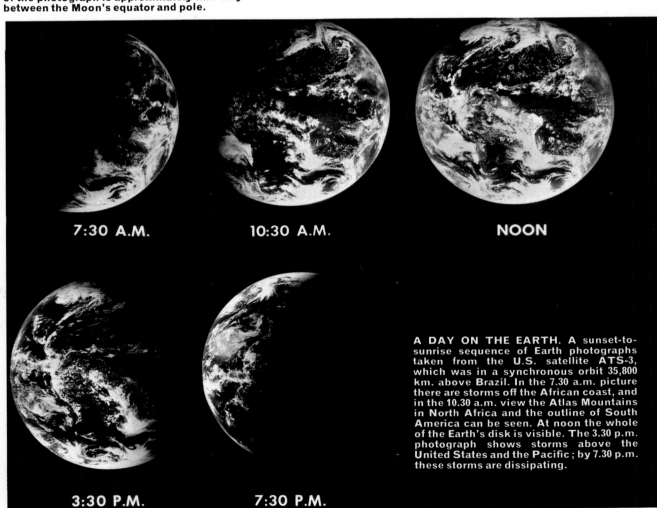

7:30 A.M.

10:30 A.M.

NOON

3:30 P.M.

7:30 P.M.

A DAY ON THE EARTH. A sunset-to-sunrise sequence of Earth photographs taken from the U.S. satellite ATS-3, which was in a synchronous orbit 35,800 km. above Brazil. In the 7.30 a.m. picture there are storms off the African coast, and in the 10.30 a.m. view the Atlas Mountains in North Africa and the outline of South America can be seen. At noon the whole of the Earth's disk is visible. The 3.30 p.m. photograph shows storms above the United States and the Pacific; by 7.30 p.m. these storms are dissipating.

Chapter 23

Touch-down on the Moon

The fact that the Moon has no appreciable atmosphere is, in many ways, a serious handicap to us. Not only does it mean that the lunar world must be lifeless, but it also makes controlled landings there much more difficult, because no form of air-braking can be used. A vehicle must depend solely upon rocket braking if it is not to crash down and destroy itself. Basically, the idea is to turn the vehicle until its engines are pointing moonward, after which the retro-rockets are fired, and the vehicle is brought to a halt just above the lunar surface before being allowed to settle down gently. This is usually called the soft-landing procedure.

Even in the early days, it was clear that a soft landing would be of the utmost value. Without it, it would be impossible to find out what the Moon is really like; and in America, though not in Russia, Gold's theory of deep dust-drifts was taken seriously.

The first step was not to achieve an actual soft landing, but to deposit an instrument package on the Moon. In 1961, therefore, the United States team began its programme with Ranger rockets —a programme which was to have many disappointments, but which was to end in triumph four years later.

RANGER 7; pre-launch photograph. Ranger hit the Moon on 31 July 1964. During the last few minutes of its flight it sent back over 4,300 photographs of the lunar surface from close range. It crash-landed in the area which has now been named the Mare Cognitum, or Known Sea.

DIAGRAM OF RANGER 7, launched on 28 July 1964; this was the first successful American lunar probe. (1) Omni antenna. (2) Camera aperature. (3) Television sub-system and shroud. (4) Solar panel latch. (5) Attitude control electronics. (6) High-gain antenna. (7) Batteries. (8) Attitude control gas-storage bottle. (9) Solar panel.

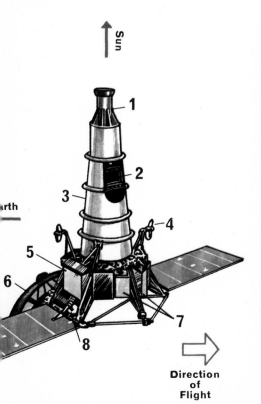

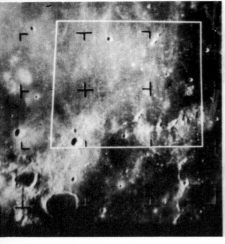
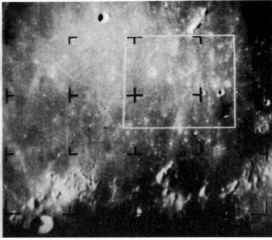
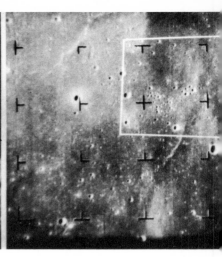

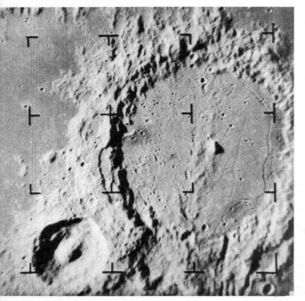

THE LUNAR CRATER ALPHONSUS, as photographed from Ranger 9 in March 1965. The photograph was taken at 258 miles above the Moon, 2 minutes 50 seconds before impact. Alphonsus fills the right half of the picture; Alpetragius is near the lower left, with its broad central peak. Davy A in the top left corner. Alphonsus has a floor with complex patterns of ridges and clefts, together with craterlets surrounded by dark patches. Alphonsus is particularly interesting, since mild volcanic outbreaks have been reported there—for instance, by N. A. Kozirev in 1958.

There were two preliminary launchings, Rangers 1 (23 August) and 2 (18 November). The main object was to test some new techniques, and in particular that of the 'parking orbit'. The launcher, made up of an Agena rocket mounted upon an Atlas rocket, was intended to put the probe into an orbit round the Earth; after a certain interval, a further burst of power would be given, and the Ranger itself would start to swing out on its long curve toward the Moon. The idea is quite sound, and has since been used many times by both the Russians and the Americans, but the initial launchings were unsuccessful. Ranger 1 failed to break free from the Earth's grip, and burned out in the atmosphere a week after being sent up, while No. 2 was a total failure. By the end of 1961 the United States team had sent up ten lunar probes altogether, but had achieved nothing of note with any of them.

Then, on 26 January 1962, came the third Ranger, which seemed to be much more promising. Both the Atlas and the Agena fired as planned; the Atlas exhausted its propellants when it had reached a height of 150 miles, 5 minutes after launching, and 30 seconds later the Agena motor came into action, giving a 2½-minute burst to clear the second stage of the vehicle from the Atlas. Unfortunately, it was found that the Atlas had been slightly too effective, and the Ranger achieved more than the planned velocity of 24,500 m.p.h. This was the cause of its failure to hit the Moon.

The flight plan was clear-cut. About 70,000 feet above the Moon and 8 seconds before impact, the instrument capsule would have been ejected, and would have landed gently enough to avoid destruction. The scientific equipment was packed in a cushioning cradle of balsa-wood and floated in oil, which would, it was hoped, provide protection against the inevitably severe jolt of landing. Twenty minutes later the instruments would have come into action sending back information about conditions on the Moon—temperature measurements, in particular.

Another project was to use cameras fitted to the Ranger, and obtain photographs taken from close range a few minutes before impact. It was claimed that very small craters, only a few feet in diameter, would be shown.

Originally all seemed to be well, but then it became clear that

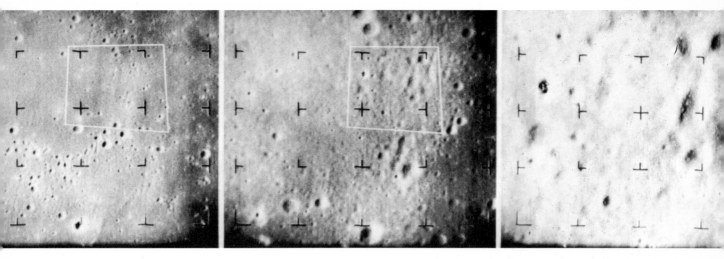

Ranger 3 was off course. Very little could be done to correct it. Hope was not dead; there was still a chance that the probe would pass within 25,000 miles of the Moon, so that pictures would be obtained even if the instrument capsule could not be 'dumped' upon the surface. Then, to the general regret, further faults developed inside the probe itself, and the entire project had to be written off as a failure. January 27 was certainly a discouraging day at Cape Canaveral, as it also marked the postponement of the planned orbital flight by John Glenn. (This delay, incidentally, was due to a power failure which stopped all the clocks in the ground control stations during the vital count-down.)

There is not much to be said about the next two Rangers, both of which had the same kinds of programmes and both of which were launched in 1962. No. 4 did at least hit the Moon, but the exact landing-point is not known, because guidance and communications had broken down. No. 5 missed the Moon by 450 miles, and entered an orbit round the Sun; presumably it is still roaming through the Solar System. For the moment, no more Rangers were dispatched. The only lunar probe of 1963 was a Russian one, Lunik 4, which may have been a first attempt at a soft landing, but which by-passed the Moon by thousands of miles and apparently sent back no information of any value.

All this was somewhat depressing, but setbacks were only to be expected, and the Ranger programme continued as steadily as possible. For the next (and last) four launchings, marked changes were made. The attempt to deposit an instrument package was given up, and it was accepted that the probes would crash-land so violently that they would be completely destroyed, whether they happened to come down in a dust-drift or on a layer of solid lava. Instead, it was hoped to make full use of the cameras during the last few minutes of flight.

By early 1964 Ranger 6 was ready, and was duly dispatched. As before, the lower stage of the launcher consisted of an Atlas rocket, which used up its power in the first part of the flight. The Agena then fired, and entered a parking orbit. When the Agena had 'coasted round' to a suitable position, a further burst was ordered, and the Ranger was started on the last lap – much the longest, though not necessarily the most difficult part of its journey. There

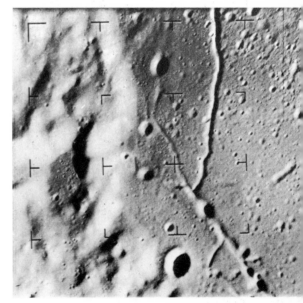

ANOTHER VIEW OF ALPHONSUS from Ranger 9, taken from 115 miles at 1 minute 17 seconds before impact. The photograph shows part of the floor of Alphonsus; the clefts are lined with dark-haloed craterlets. Part of the main wall of Alphonsus is also shown.

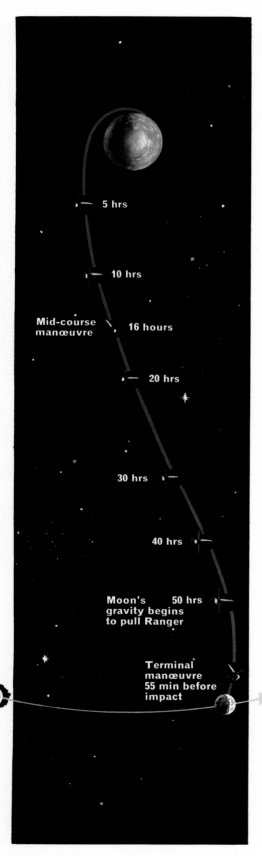

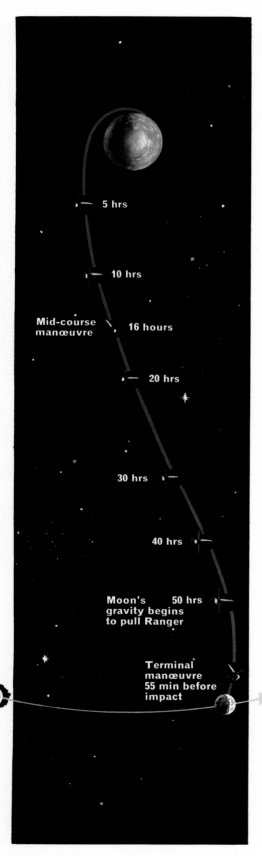

were special devices for keeping the probe on course, mainly by locking on to the Earth and the Sun. Also, it was possible to make a course correction about halfway between the Earth and the Moon.

Ranger 6 was partly successful, partly not. All the flight procedure was carried through perfectly, and the Ranger hit the Moon almost exactly in the planned spot, but the expected television pictures failed to come through, and it was later established that the photographic system had been accidentally turned on during the initial launch into a parking orbit, with the result that some vital circuits were put out of action.

It was a classic case of 'so near and yet so far', but better things were in store. Less than six months later, Ranger 7 landed in the Mare Nubium or Sea of Clouds, and performed all its tasks without a single hitch. It took 68½ hours to reach the Moon; it impacted at almost 5,000 m.p.h., and destroyed itself, but before then it had sent back more than 4,000 close-range photographs.

As the Ranger neared the Moon, on 31 July, tension in the control room at Cape Kennedy mounted. Though the vehicle weighed 'only' 804 pounds, it was so immensely complex that there were any number of things that might go wrong. Luckily, none did. At 13.07 G.M.T., the cameras were turned on, with the Ranger about 1,300 miles from the Moon, and almost at once the first picture came back; it showed the area of the ruined crater Guericke, a familiar object to all lunar observers. During the next quarter of an hour the photography went on, with the pictures becoming more and more detailed. Four cameras were used altogether, and all functioned faultlessly. The last photograph was transmitted only 0.19 second before impact, and showed a region of the Moon measuring about 105 feet by 150 feet, with craterpits down to a few inches in diameter.

The surface did not look in the least like soft dust, and from this point of view the outlook was encouraging. It was equally encouraging that the whole operation had been carried through so smoothly, and the outlook became even brighter when the last two Rangers, Nos. 8 and 9, repeated the success. No. 8 came down in the region of the grey plain of the Mare Tranquillitatis (Sea of Tranquillity), No. 9 in the middle of the crater Alphonsus—where a mild volcanic outbreak had been seen some years earlier by a Russian astronomer, N. A. Kozirev, working with a large telescope in the Crimea.

Undoubtedly the Alphonsus photographs from Ranger 9 were the most spectacular of all, and they were not surpassed until late 1966. One interesting point was that some of the clefts, or cracklike features inside the crater, proved to be not true clefts at all, but simply chains of small craters which could only be of volcanic origin. But to discuss all the findings of the successful Rangers would be beyond the scope of a general survey, and it is enough to repeat that the whole series represented a very major advance.

It was said at the time that the Ranger pictures had been taken at a total cost of over £70,000,000. There is some truth in this, though it must be added once more that much of the research would have been carried out in any case for military purposes.

When Ranger 9 hit the Moon, on 24 March 1965, the series came to an end. Meanwhile, the Russians had been having troubles

TRAJECTORY OF RANGER 7. The probe was launched on 28 July 1964, and landed on the Moon on 31 July. Unlike its six predecessors, it was completely successful—as were the last two Rangers, Numbers 8 and 9.

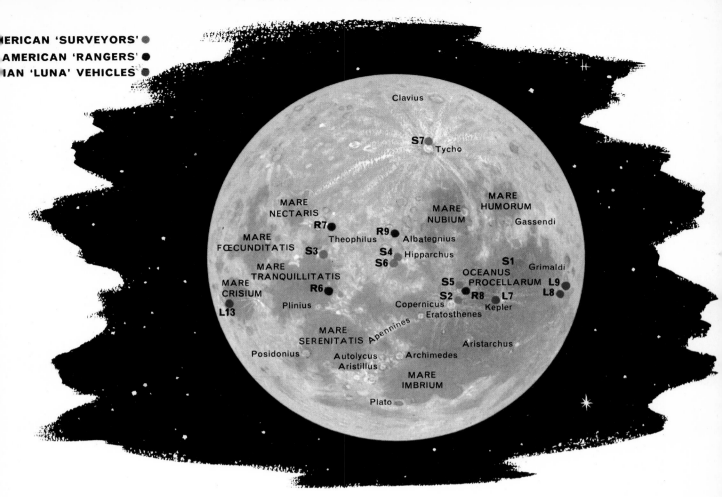

Clavius

S7 ● Tycho

MARE NECTARIS

MARE HUMORUM

MARE NUBIUM

Gassendi

R7 ●

R9 ●

Theophilus

Albategnius

MARE FŒCUNDITATIS

S3 ●

S4 ●

S6 ●

Hipparchus

MARE TRANQUILLITATIS

S1 ●

Grimaldi

OCEANUS PROCELLARUM

L9 ●

MARE CRISIUM

R6 ●

S5 ●

S2 ●

R8 ●

L7 ●

L8 ●

Plinius

Copernicus

Kepler

L13 ●

Eratosthenes

MARE SERENITATIS Apennines

Aristarchus

Posidonius

Autolycus
Aristillus

Archimedes

MARE IMBRIUM

Plato

IMPACTS OF LUNAR VEHICLES, 1959–1968.

of their own. So far as can be made out, they did not attempt close-range photography with a probe destined to crash on to the surface at high velocity; they were trying for a soft landing, and it is not surprising that they had several failures. The fifth, sixth, seventh and eighth Luna probes were all unsuccessful for various reasons. No. 6 missed the Moon by 100,000 miles, while the others came down with disastrous velocity instead of making gentle touch-downs. (For some reason, the term 'Lunik' seems to have been dropped after No. 4, to be replaced by the rather more attractive name 'Luna'.)

True, there was the Zond 3 success of 1965, referred to in the last chapter; but this was a fly-by, and was not intended to land. The troubles were due to faulty timing of the retro-rockets, but every failure provided new information, and it was no real surprise when the triumph came.

Luna 9 was launched on 31 January 1966. After a mid-course correction, the probe moved to a position rather more than 5,000 miles above the selected landing area, near the border of the Oceanus Procellarum or Ocean of Storms. It then began to drop. When the altitude above the Moon was between 40 and 50 miles, 48 seconds before impact, the braking system was switched on, and this time the calculations were perfect. Luna 9 came down relatively gently; the part containing the television system, the transmitter and the shock-absorbing system had been detached, and landed a short distance away. Within five minutes, the first signals

WIDE-ANGLE PHOTOGRAPH OF THE MOON'S FAR SIDE, from Orbiter 5 (7 August 1967). The smallest features shown are about 500 metres in diameter. North is at the top.

THE FIRST PHOTOGRAPH FROM THE MOON'S SURFACE. This was received from the Russian probe Luna 9, which was launched on 31 January 1966 and made a successful soft-landing. The general aspect of the Moon's surface in this area looks remarkably like a lava-field.

MODEL OF LUNA 9, the first probe to make a successful soft landing on the Moon. This photograph was taken in 1966, at the Exhibition of National Economic Achievements in Moscow. The real Luna 9 is still lying on the Moon's surface!

were being sent back direct from the surface of the Moon.

One important point was decided at once. Luna 9 did not sink into soft dust; it came down on perfectly firm ground, and a slight 'settling' of the terrain later on, between the second and third communications sessions with the probe, was very minor. Most astronomers who had hitherto clung to Gold's dust theory abandoned it immediately. Suggestions that this particular part of the Oceanus Procellarum might be exceptionally dust-free were highly unconvincing, because it was just in this sort of area that dust would be expected if it occurred anywhere in quantity.

Actually, the first pictures from Luna 9 were released for public showing not by the Russians, but from Jodrell Bank, where the radio astronomers picked up the transmissions quite independently. The question of priority is unimportant; the interest lay in the photographs themselves, which were of splendid quality. They showed a scene which was undeniably similar to a lava-field, with various rocks and boulders strewn about, and an impression of great roughness. One spectacular rock, casting a long shadow, caught the eye at once even though it can have been no more than 6 inches across. Certainly it could not be a meteorite which had hit the Moon; much more probably it was an object of the kind known as a volcanic bomb, thrown out during lunar vulcanism many hundreds of millions of years ago.

There were suggestions that Luna 9 might be moved about, or even brought back to Earth, but this was not attempted, and the signals stopped rather unexpectedly early. Yet the whole experi-

THE FIRST PHOTOGRAPH FROM SURVEYOR 1; 2 June 1966. The picture shows one of the craft's three landing legs left, an omnidirectional antenna boom at centre, and the helium container right. The disturbance of the lunar surface by the landing pad can also be seen.

ment was a first-class triumph, and astronomers from all countries were quick to give the Soviet team the credit that was due. Today, Luna 9 is still standing where it landed, on the Oceanus Procellarum some way from the huge walled plain Grimaldi. It will stay there until someone collects it and removes it to a museum, as will probably be done eventually.

As usual, a Russian advance was followed soon after by an American success on the same lines. This time the vehicle was Surveyor 1, which soft-landed about 500 miles from the site of Luna 9, still in the Oceanus Procellarum, and sent back more than 11,000 photographs; the probe even survived the cold of a lunar night, and began transmitting again when the Sun rose over it once more. All in all, the Surveyor photographs were probably even better than those from Luna 9, and there were many more of them. The general aspect of the surface was much the same, and indeed any marked difference would have come as a great surprise. In this run of successes, it came as an anti-climax when the second Surveyor, sent up in September, went out of control and crash-landed without providing any data; but, as one American scientist said, it would be conceited to expect that 'the jack-pot could be won every time'.

The year 1966 had been eventful, and it finished on an exciting note. On 21 December the Russians launched Luna 13, which made a soft landing in the favoured area of the Oceanus Procellarum. Photographs were sent back, as before, but this time there were other programmes as well; in particular, there were devices

PRE-LAUNCH PHOTOGRAPH OF SURVEYOR 1. The lunar probe is here shown under examination, prior to its launching on 30 May 1966. Surveyor 1 was a great success, and sent back more than 11,000 photographs of the Moon's surface.

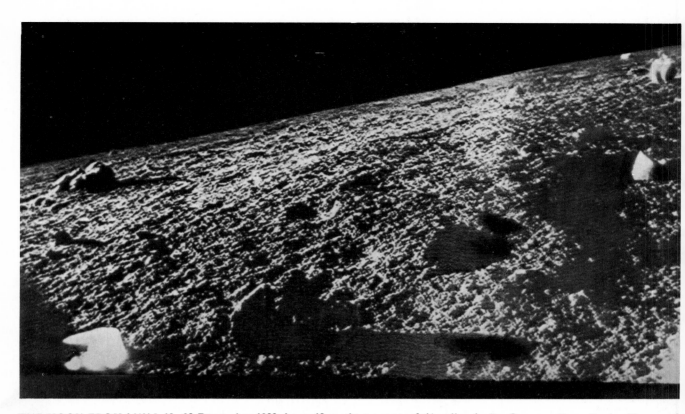

THE MOON FROM LUNA 13 : 26 December 1966. Luna 13 made a successful landing in the Oceanus Procellarum (Ocean of Storms) and sent back many valuable photographs and measurements.

SHADOW OF LUNA 13 **ON THE MOON.** The object to the upper left is a thrown-off part of the spacecraft's equipment.

170

IMPRESSION OF LUNA 13 ON THE SUR-FACE OF THE MOON. This drawing represents the landing site and the grounded space-craft. Key: (1) Mechanical soil meter. (2) Instrument positioning arms. (3) Petal antennæ. (4) Rod antennæ. (5) Television camera. (6) Radiation density meter. As well as sending back pictures, Luna 13 made actual measurements of the density and composition of the Moon's surface—the first time that this had been done.

to penetrate the ground in order to measure the temperatures and the degree of firmness below the outer surface of the Moon. These measures were still going on when 1966 came to an end, and it was clear even to the most hardened pessimists that the first manned flight to the lunar world was fast becoming a practical possibility.

To bring the story up to date, something should be said about the events of 1967—a year marked by good, steady progress. Surveyor 3 was dispatched on April 17, and just after midnight on the 20th it touched down on the Oceanus Procellarum, 230 miles from Copernicus and just over 70 miles from the well-marked crater Landsberg. There was a certain amount of 'bouncing', but the landing manoeuvre was carried through without a hitch. Unlike its predecessors, it carried a remote-control surface sampler to manipulate the lunar soil in full view of the television camera. This apparatus has been aptly described as a mechanical digger, and it worked successfully on the whole. Four separate trenches were scooped out, and several pebble-like objects were located and 'handled'. There were various interesting episodes. Once a partly-buried object, more reflective than its surroundings, was picked up and identified as a small rock. Unfortunately, it slipped out of the scoop, and was lost, before the tests were completed. In addition to these experiments, thousands of television pictures of the area were sent back, and excellent photographs were obtained of the Earth in the lunar sky. Moreover, during the lunar day, the Earth passed in front of the Sun, and the resulting eclipse was photographed

LUNAR LANDSCAPE FROM SURVEYOR 3, taken on 30 April 1967: looking north. The landing site was in the Oceanus Procellarum, near the crater Landsberg in the equatorial region. This picture is a mosaic, compiled from photographs taken with the narrow-angle lens.

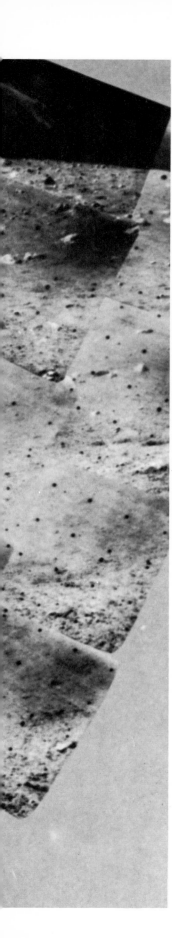

SURVEYOR I's SHADOW ON THE MOON, 13 June 1966, less than 24 hours before sunset over the area of the Oceanus Procellarum in which the spacecraft lay. After sunset the temperature dropped drastically, but Surveyor's instruments survived the cold of lunar night, and further photographs were received on the following lunar morning.

"CHEMICAL SET" ON THE MOON. This photograph, received on 11 September 1967 from Surveyor 5, shows the first "chemistry set" on the surface of the Moon. It is called an alpha-scattering instrument, and is making an analysis of the composition of the lunar surface layer. After Surveyor 5 made a successful soft landing in the Mare Tranquillitatis (Sea of Tranquillity), the device was lowered on to the Moon by a nylon line. The serpentine ribbon attached to the unit carried power to the instrument package, so that data could be sent back to the spacecraft's telemetry system.

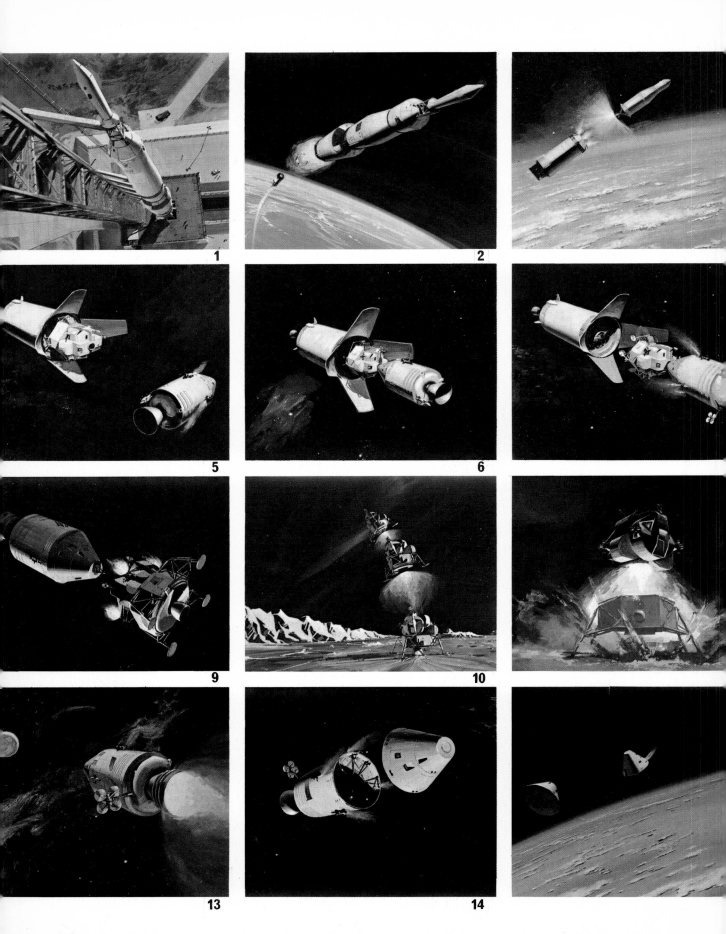

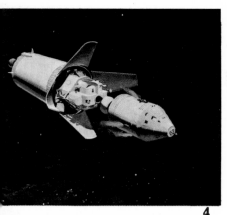

4

8

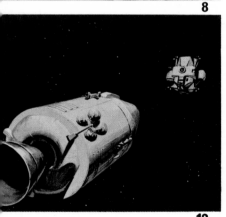

12

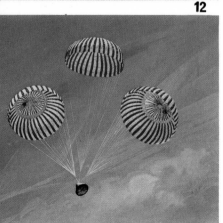

16

THE APOLLO MISSION TO THE MOON. A series of coloured drawings, showing the general plan of the projected flight to the Moon. (1) Pre-launch. The main vehicle is a Saturn rocket; when first successfully tested, in 1966, the Saturn was the most powerful rocket ever fired in the United States, and probably the most powerful ever fired anywhere. The five clustered engines of its 186-foot first stage burn 475 tons of propellant in 130 seconds, raising the speed to 6,000 m.p.h. (2) As the second stage separates and falls away, the third stage takes over; its single engine fires for 2 minutes, and the craft enters a parking orbit at 115 miles above the surface while the crew make final calculations, in consultation with Mission Control Center. (3) At a precisely-calculated moment the third stage engine is re-ignited, and operates for about 5 minutes, boosting the velocity to nearly 25,000 m.p.h. and driving the craft out of its parking orbit on the way to the Moon. (4) The actual lunar craft is separated from the third stage when the main journey Moonward is over, and the craft is now correctly assembled for the final trip to the Moon. Launching could not have been carried out this way; the astronauts had then to be in the top of the vehicle. (5) Separation is effected. The third stage of the launcher is jettisoned, and the astronauts remain in the actual Moon-craft. (6) As the craft enters a circum-lunar orbit, the L.E.M. or Lunar Excursion Module (often nicknamed 'the Bug') is separated; this is the vehicle which will carry the astronauts to the lunar surface. (7) Final separation of the L.E.M., with two astronauts aboard; the other members of the expedition remain in lunar orbit. (8) Moving away from the Command Module; the explorers have begun the last stage of their journey to the Moon. (9&10) The landing procedure; the L.E.M. comes down on the surface of the Moon. Everything must be carried out by rocket braking; parachutes and similar devices are of course useless on the Moon, where there is no atmosphere. The engines of the L.E.M. must be fired so as to bring the craft to a halt close above the lunar surface, so that the final drop to the ground is gentle enough to prevent damage either to the space-ship or to the crew. Exploration of the Moon can now begin. When this has been completed, the explorers return to the L.E.M. and begin preparations for blasting back into orbit. (11) Leaving the Moon. The astronauts detach the base portion of the L.E.M., which now becomes the launch pad. The ascent engine is relatively weak, but it has enough power to overcome the feeble lunar gravity and send the L.E.M. itself back into a circum-lunar orbit. (12) The L.E.M. reaches orbit, and makes a rendezvous with the waiting Command Module, which has been circling the Moon while the surface exploration has been in progress. (13) Leaving the neighbourhood of the Moon. The L.E.M., its work done, is left in lunar orbit. (14) Just before the craft re-enters the Earth's atmosphere, the Service Module section is jettisoned. Of the 364-foot vehicle that set out on the journey, only a small cone 13 feet in diameter at the blunt end is coming back. (15) Reaction control jets are fired to turn the Command Module round, so that its protective shield points toward the Earth and absorbs the fiery heat generated as the craft is slowed down by friction against the atmosphere. At about 70 miles above ground level the friction becomes very marked, and perfect control is needed to prevent the drop into the denser layers from being too steep and too rapid. Here we see three successive stages of the manœuvre. (16) The final descent. When rocket braking and friction have slowed the Command Module down, the parachutes are deployed, and bring the Module down to a gentle landing. The journey to the Moon and back is over; it began at Cape Kennedy, and ended, half a million miles later, in the Pacific Ocean near Hawaii. These are the plans that have been drawn up for the Apollo project; they should be carried out within the next few years—perhaps sooner than many people expect.

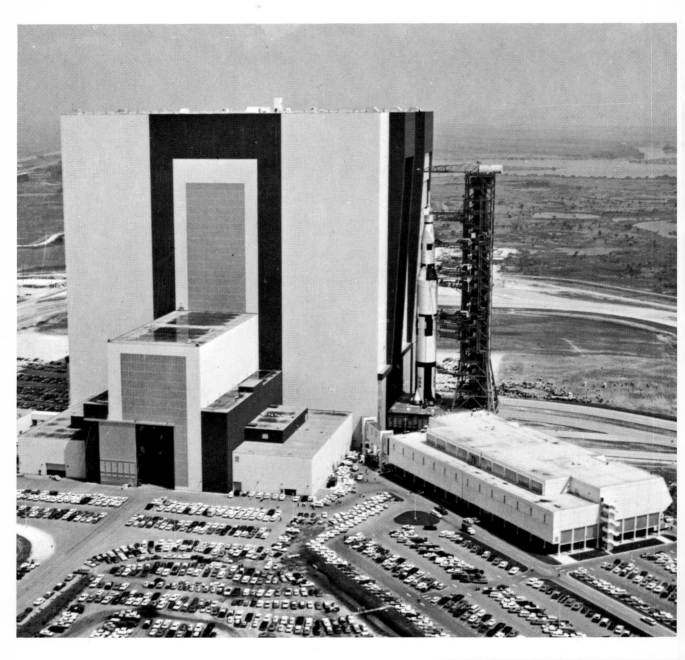

THE JOHN F. KENNEDY SPACE CENTER in Florida, photographed in May 1966. The picture shows the Saturn-5 rocket 500-foot facility vehicle en route from **NASA's** vehicle assembly building to the launch complex.

CROSS-SECTION OF THE APOLLO SPACECRAFT, designed to carry two American astronauts to the Moon. The crew of three will ride in the Command Module during the flight to and from the Moon; the actual landing on the Moon will be made by two of the astronauts in the L.E.M. or Lunar Module; after the two return to the Command Module, a rocket motor in the Service Module will be fired to power the flight back to Earth.

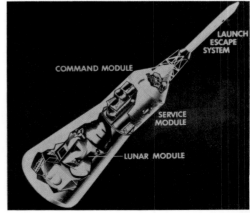

from Surveyor; Venus was also shown, though the stars refused to reveal themselves on the pictures.

Surveyor 4, sent up on July 14, was a failure. Control of it was lost, and it crash-landed without sending back any useful data (by now it seemed that the odd-number Surveyors were successful, and the even numbers were not!). But No. 5, launched on September 8, came down safely three days later on the south-west part of the Mare Tranquillitatis. It carried what may be described as a portable chemical laboratory, and confirmed that the Moon's surface layer was made up largely of a composition resembling basalt, a grey volcanic rock very common on Earth. By the beginning of October it had transmitted over 18,000 television pictures, and had done all that its makers had hoped of it.

The last two Surveyors continued the pattern—and the final member of the series sent back spectacular pictures of the almost incredibly rugged area just outside Tycho, the most conspicuous crater on the entire surface of the Moon. By the time that the Surveyor programme came to an end, much had been learned. Most important of all, from the manned-landing point of view, was the fact that the lunar surface seemed quite definitely strong enough to bear the weight of even a relatively massive vehicle.

And, of course, all this led on to the ambitious Apollo project, the aim of which was to send the first astronaut from the Earth to the Moon. There had been seemingly endless delays, almost all of which were concerned with the massive launchers—and, incidentally, finance entered into it; America was being drained by the muddled, profitless war in Vietnam, and scientific expenditure was being drastically cut down. A few failures would have set the entire programme back not by weeks or months, but probably by years. It was not surprising that the space-planners were anxious about the performance of the huge Saturn 5 rocket which was so essential to Project Apollo.

The first Saturn flew in early 1968. There was immense relief when it performed well, but optimism was somewhat dampened a short time later, when the second test resulted in the rocket entering the wrong orbit. No passengers were aboard, and the descent into the ocean was successfully controlled, but clearly there were still many problems to be faced before an astronaut could be dispatched Moonward, and it seemed that the first manned tests in orbital flight round the Earth would have to be postponed well beyond their original schedule of summer 1968.

Apollo is, of course, an immensely complex procedure. The general plan is shown in the series of drawings given here—and it will be seen that only the so-called command module returns to Earth; the lunar excursion module or L.E.M., used for landing on the Moon and returning to lunar orbit, is jettisoned before the return flight begins. Unfortunately, the failure of any one of the various stages in the operation would be disastrous, and it is no wonder that the planners are reluctant to try a full-scale experiment until they are satisfied that all potential troubles have been well and truly eliminated. Just when the Apollo project will reach its climax remains to be seen. It should not be very long now; but it is always dangerous to be over-optimistic.

Up to the time when I write these words (April 1968) the Russians have not given any clear-cut statement of their equiva-

TRAINING FOR THE APOLLO FLIGHT. Members of the scheduled crew practice water egress in the Gulf of Mexico. Sliding down the boilerplate capsule is Walter Schirra, the command pilot; seated in the life raft are two more astronauts, Donn Eisele and Walter Cunningham.

'CRATER CLIMBING' AT THE MANNED SPACECRAFT CENTER AT HOUSTON, TEXAS. J. B. Slight, a test engineer with NASA, is shown climbing out of a crater at the Lunar Topographical Simulation Area. The engineer wears an Apollo pressure suit, and carries a Jacob's staff to assist in walking. The simulator in which he is strapped produces the effect of lunar gravity, i.e. 1/6 of Earth gravity.

lent of Project Apollo, but there is every reason to believe that they too are determined to reach the Moon as soon as possible. One interesting fact to have emerged lately is that for some of their 'boosters' they are making use, at least in part, of solid fuels. It has often been said that solid fuels are as out of date as Noah's Ark, and certainly they have disadvantages, mainly because they cannot be controlled to the same extent as liquids. Yet they are extremely simple, and they have their uses. Generally speaking, the Russians prefer to make their space-craft as unsophisticated as possible, and their results show that there is much to be said for this point of view.

At the risk of being repetitious, let me say once more that a vast amount of time and money has been wasted because the Soviet and American programmes have been carried out in competition rather than in harmony. Had it not been so, Grissom, White, Chaffee and Komarov might not have died. It would be refreshing to believe that the first voyage from Earth to Moon might be carried out by a combined team. Unfortunately, there seems little chance of anything of the sort as yet. When the history of lunar expedition comes to be written, it will become clear that at least some of the hazards have been created by the failure of the great nations to work together. One can only hope that the situation will change for the better in the years to come.

FIRST STAGE OF THE SATURN 5 MOON ROCKET, to be used in the Apollo manned flight to the Moon. When first tested, in 1967, the Saturn 5 proved to be completely successful. Had it not been so, the entire Apollo project would have suffered a very major delay.

SATURN 5 ON THE PAD. This is a model of a Saturn 5 Moon-rocket on the Complex 39 launching pad at Cape Kennedy. In this night view, more than a hundred searchlights illuminate the vehicle, which is 111 metres tall. Following procedures which will be used in an actual launch, the Saturn was assembled on a mobile launcher in the Vertical Assembly Building, and was taken to the pad on a huge tracked crawler; the 5.5-km. trip over a reinforced roadway took almost 9 hours.

Chapter 24

Mariner to Venus

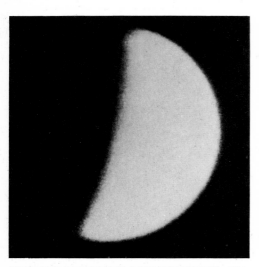

VENUS. This photograph was taken in 1965 by Henry Brinton with the 12in. reflector at his private observatory at Selsey. Like all photographs of Venus taken from Earth, it shows no surface detail, because Venus is permanently concealed by its dense, cloud-laden atmosphere.

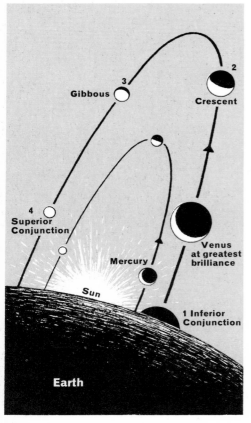

PHASES OF VENUS AND MERCURY. The phase depends upon how much of the planet's daylight side is turned toward us. When the planet is roughly between the Earth and the Sun, its night side faces us; the phase is 'new', and the planet cannot be seen. When on the far side of the Sun, the planet is 'full'.

Nobody—not even a lunar enthusiast such as myself—can claim that the Moon is a welcoming world. In every way it is just about as hostile as it can be, and it is the first target on our list merely because it happens to be our companion in space. We should like a Moon with atmosphere, water and a reasonably pleasant temperature. As it has none of these, we must accept it as Nature has left it, and start to look further afield.

A glance at the plan of the Solar System given on page 11 shows that there are only two planets within practicable range. These are Mars, further from the Sun than we are, and Venus, which is closer in. Both are much more remote than the Moon, and neither keeps company with us in our never-ending journey round the Sun, but at least they are not impossibly far off by modern standards.

A few years ago Venus was widely regarded as the more promising of the two, and it was also the first object beyond the Moon to be the subject of practical experiments. Keeping more or less to my chronological sequence, I propose therefore to deal with it first, even though it now seems to be much less of a prospect than Mars. But as a preliminary, something should be said about the general pattern of a planetary voyage.

Venus can come within 24,000,000 miles of the Earth when at its closest, but at such times it is difficult to observe. Like all the planets, it has no light of its own, and depends entirely upon light reflected from the Sun. Obviously, the Sun can make only half the planet shine at once, and the night side will be non-luminous. Venus goes round the Sun in 224.7 days, and so it must regularly pass what is called inferior conjunction (position 1 in the diagram), when it is approximately between the Sun and the Earth. Its night side then faces us, and Venus cannot be seen. Quite apart from anything else, it is practically in front of the Sun in the sky. (If the lining-up is perfect, then Venus appears in transit as a black disk against the Sun's brilliant surface, but these transits are rare, and the next will not occur until the year 2004). When at superior conjunction, on the far side of the Sun in position 3, Venus appears full, but is almost equally hard to see. At other times the planet shows up as a crescent, half or three-quarters disk; in fact, it shows phases similar to those of the Moon. When at its most brilliant, it may cast a definite shadow.

Since Venus at its closest is roughly 100 times as remote as the Moon, one might suppose that a journey there would take 100 times as long. Unfortunately, things are more complex than might be supposed. What we cannot do is to wait until Venus reaches its nearest point, and then fire a rocket straight across the 24,000,000-mile gap. This would be out of the question for many reasons; to give only one, it would mean using power all the way—and no rocket could possibly carry enough propellant.

What is done, in effect, is to put the probe into a parking orbit, using a launcher of the usual type. Then, at the correct moment, a further burst of power makes the probe leave the region of the Earth for good, and enter an independent orbit. This is so arranged that the probe moves away in the direction opposite to the Earth's movement round the Sun, so that broadly speaking the probe will be travelling round the Sun at a rate less than the Earth's own 66,000 m.p.h. ($18\frac{1}{2}$ miles per second). This means that it cannot follow the Earth round; it must start to swing inward, and if all goes well it will reach the orbit of Venus at the same time that Venus itself comes to the pre-arranged position. The diagram will show what is meant, and in principle there is nothing confusing about it, though the procedure is far from easy to carry out in practice! If there is no collision, the probe will eventually start to swing outward again, and will continue to move indefinitely in an elliptical path round the Sun.

A path of this kind, taking a probe from the orbit of one planet to that of another, is called a transfer orbit. The principle had been worked out long before the rocket had become a powerful piece of equipment, and some writers, notably the German scientist Walter Hohmann, had studied it in detail.

With Mars, the probe has to be speeded-up relative to the Earth, so that it will swing outward instead of inward; but let us defer a discussion of Mars for the moment.

Venus is about the same size as the Earth. Its diameter is about 7,700 miles as against the Earth's 7,926, and it has only slightly less mass, so that the surface gravity is much the same. One might expect, then, that it would be a world of the same basic type as our own. Its mean distance from the Sun is 67,000,000 miles, so that it receives more light and heat than the Earth, but it might be expected to be no more than rather uncomfortably warm. Incidentally, it has no known satellite.

Before the present decade, Venus had always been regarded as a planet of mystery. Its surface is never visible directly; there is a layer of dense atmosphere which defeats our telescopes with devastating completeness, and there is no chance of penetrating it optically. Vague shadings are visible at times, but are no more than what may be termed cloud effects. In 1957, when the Space Age began, nobody even knew the length of Venus' axial rotation period or 'day', and estimates ranged between 224.7 Earth-days and less than 24 hours. The most favoured period was that derived by G. P. Kuiper in America, who gave the period as about four Earth weeks.

Speculations were not lacking. For instance, it sometimes happens that the dark or night side of Venus is seen to be shining dimly, and this Ashen Light caused a great deal of interest. There is no analogy with the earthshine seen on the Moon; as we have noted, Venus has no natural satellite. Rather over a century ago, Franz von Paula Gruithuisen, a German observer with a keen eye but a lively imagination, put forward the idea that the Ashen Light might be caused by vast forest fires lit upon the surface of Venus by the local inhabitants, possibly to celebrate the election of a new Government. Not many astronomers took this seriously, but the idea of intelligent life on Venus was certainly not ruled out.

The one useful line of attack was analysis of the atmosphere, and in the nineteen-thirties it was found that there was a considerable

CHECKING OUT MARINER 2, which was sent to Venus in 1962. In this photograph, taken at Cape Canaveral (now Cape Kennedy) the solar panels, which convert energy from the Sun into electrical power to operate the spacecraft's instruments, are folded in the launch position. The shroud to the left is placed over the spacecraft before mating to the Atlas-Agena B rocket.

CRESCENT VENUS, drawn on 20 September 1959, at 15h. 15m. GMT, by the author with the 28in. refractor at the Royal Greenwich Observatory, Herstmonceux; the magnification used was 600. As usual, no specific details can be seen on the planet.

VENUS, 13 June 1967, from a drawing made by the author at 13h. 20m. with a magnification of 360 on the 10in. refractor at Armagh Observatory. The cusp-cap to the south (top) is clearly shown, but is certainly an atmospheric feature rather than a true polar cap such as those of the Earth or Mars. Various vague cloudy dark areas are also seen on the disk.

quantity of carbon dioxide. This is the gas contained in soda-water, and there is a small percentage of it in the atmosphere of the Earth. Carbon dioxide is breathed out by animals, including men; in the remote past, the Earth's air must have contained more of it than is the case now, and the change is accounted for by the development of plants, which take in carbon dioxide and give off pure oxygen. It was thought possible, therefore, that Venus might lack vegetation, so that there would be nothing to purify the atmosphere.

On the other hand, all investigations were confined to the upper layers of cloud, and there was no definite information about conditions lower down. It was tempting to suppose that the bottom part of the atmosphere might be comparatively rich in oxygen, but against this was the fact that carbon dioxide, a heavy gas, would be expected to sink rather than rise. As for the clouds themselves, suggestions ranged from a somewhat unprepossessing compound named formaldehyde (Rupert Wildt, of the United States) to ordinary H_2O (F. L. Whipple and D. H. Menzel, also of the United States).

In 1957 there were two schools of thought about Venus. The old, attractive picture of a world with lush vegetation, and creatures of what we would term the prehistoric variety, had been given up; instead it was thought possible that Venus might be a desert world, without a trace of moisture and with a very high surface temperature. However, the Whipple-Menzel Venus was supposed to be completely covered with ocean. If this were so, then there seemed no valid reason why primitive marine life might not exist there; after all, life on Earth began in the sea, when there was much more carbon dioxide in the atmosphere than there is now.

The best argument in favour of a very hot surface was that carbon dioxide gas tends to produce a 'greenhouse effect', and shut in the Sun's heat. At that time it was assumed that the atmosphere of Venus contained more carbon dioxide than anything else, and so the argument was eminently reasonable. On the other hand, instruments sent aloft in balloons, above the thickest part of the

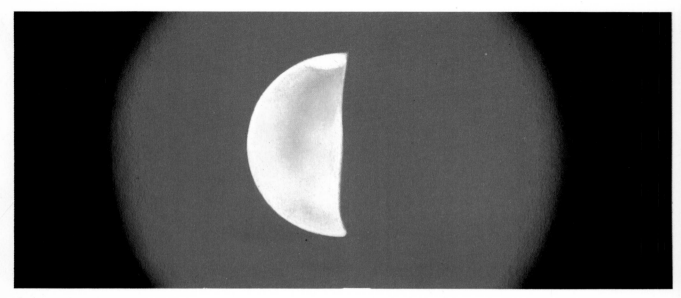

Earth's air, were used to photograph the spectrum of Venus, and showed distinct signs of water-vapour in the upper cloud layer. It was all very puzzling.

The only way to solve the problem was to send a probe on a fact-finding expedition, and the first step was (as usual) taken by the Russians. At this point it may be helpful to list the various Venus probes dispatched between 1961 and 1967, though as a matter of fact only Mariner 2 was a success:

The first Russian probe, that of 1961, was a complex affair, and at first it seemed to be highly promising. The Soviet Luniks were still fresh in mind, and there was no obvious reason to doubt that what had been done for the Moon could also be done for Venus, particularly as from all accounts the launching was carried through faultlessly by means of the step-arrangement and the parking orbit technique. Unfortunately, one major weakness in the Russian programme then showed itself for the first time. In the early years, the Soviet workers found it impossible to keep in touch with vehicles at great distances, and in fact they had still not properly overcome these difficulties by the beginning of 1967. In this field of research the United States techniques have always been much the better, and there is here, surely, an extra argument for combining the two programmes instead of proceeding separately.

Contact with Venus 1 was lost within a few weeks. It was never regained, and so what happened to the probe is not known, though there is every chance that it went within 65,000 miles of its target in the following May and then continued in orbit round the Sun. The best that could be said of it was that the launching had been encouraging. From all reports, there was no intention of hitting Venus; the idea was to obtain information from close range, and send back the results to be decoded in comfort.

In the following year the Mariner project was started from Cape Canaveral (still, then, called Canaveral and not Kennedy; the tragic assassination had yet to come). Mariner 1 was a prompt and total failure, but the second vehicle, sent up on 27 August, proved to be a very different matter.

As usual, the lower stage of the launcher was an Atlas rocket,

Date of Launch		Probe	Country	Remarks
1961	Feb. 12	Venus 1	U.S.S.R.	Contact los early. Probably passed within 65,00 miles of Venus in May 1961.
1962	July 22	Mariner 1	U.S.A.	Total failur
1962	Aug. 17	Mariner 2	U.S.A.	Passed 21,6 miles from Venus on 1 December 1962. Successful results transmitted back.
1964	Apr. 2	Zond 1	U.S.S.R.	Passed abo 70,000 miles from Venus in July 1964 Contact los
1965	Nov. 12	Venus 2	U.S.S.R.	Passed 15,(miles from Venus on 2 February 1966. Conta lost.
1965	Nov. 16	Venus 3	U.S.S.R.	Hit Venus 1 March 19(Contact los

The Ashen Light
of Venus
OBS. Patrick Moore
Mar. 31, 1953, 12½ in. Refl.
(Sun is to left of picture)

THE ASHEN LIGHT OF VENUS, from a drawing by the author made on 31 March 1953 with the 12½in. reflector at his old observatory at East Grinstead. The "night" side of Venus is shown shining faintly; this is the Ashen Light, which has been widely attributed to electrical effects in the planet's atmosphere, and may possibly be analogous to terrestrial auroræ—even though there is as yet no general agreement among astronomers as to its true nature.

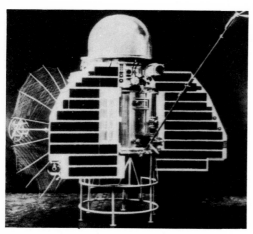

THE FIRST RUSSIAN VENUS PROBE of 1962. It was successfully launched, but radio communications broke down and were never restored, so that the vehicle must be regarded as a failure. Its final fate is unknown, but presumably it is still circling the Sun.

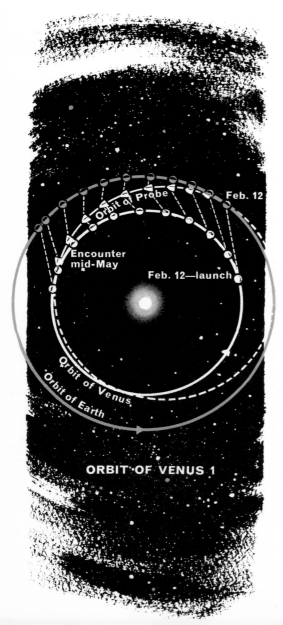

Orbit of Probe   Feb. 12

Encounter mid-May

Feb. 12—launch

Orbit of Venus

Orbit of Earth

ORBIT OF VENUS 1

which rose vertically from Cape Canaveral and then moved off in the general direction of South Africa. The second stage, an Agena rocket, then took over, and the Agena-Mariner combination was put into a parking orbit at a height of 115 miles, moving at the regulation 18,000 m.p.h. As it reached the African coast, the Agena fired once more, and the total velocity rose to 25,503 m.p.h., or about 850 m.p.h. more than the escape velocity for that height.

Remember that for a Venus probe, the direction of 'escape' has to be in the direction opposite to that in which the Earth is moving round the Sun. It was so on this occasion. As the Mariner moved away, it was slowed down by the Earth's pull of gravity, until at a distance of 600,000 miles the velocity relative to Earth had fallen to only 6,874 m.p.h. In other words, Mariner was moving round the Sun at a velocity of 6,874 m.p.h. less than that of the Earth—and it started to swing inwards toward the Sun, gathering speed as it went. Meanwhile, the Agena rocket had been separated from the Mariner, rotated through a wide angle and fired again, so that it was put into an entirely different orbit. Nobody knows what happened to it, and nobody cares; it had completed its task, and on the journey to Venus it would simply have been a nuisance. Henceforth, Mariner 2 was on its own.

This was only the beginning. Mariner was more or less in the right orbit, but it had to be kept there, and this was achieved by making it 'lock' on to the Earth and the Sun. The object of the flight was to send the probe past Venus at about 9,000 miles; when it reached Venus' orbit it was expected to have a velocity of 91,000 m.p.h., relative to the Sun, as against the 78,000 m.p.h. of Venus itself. This would make for a reasonably prolonged encounter.

It would have been over-optimistic to hope for complete success at what was to all intents and purposes the first attempt. (Mariner 1 can hardly be counted, as its flight lasted for only a few minutes.) A mid-course correction was made on 4 September, but even so the minimum distance from Venus was 21,594 miles instead of less than 10,000. Fortunately the instruments had been designed to operate over a considerable range, and the error was not ruinous.

The date of closest approach was 14 December. Contact was kept without difficulty, and a great deal of information was sent back. It took some time to analyze and interpret the results, but by February 1963 the American researchers were able to give some of the findings. To say that these findings were unexpected is to put it mildly. If Mariner 2 were to be trusted, then many long-cherished ideas about Venus would have to be swept away *in toto*.

First, and most important of all, was the matter of temperature. Instead of being merely warm, Venus seemed to have a surface at a temperature of something like 800° Fahrenheit, which at once disposed of the Whipple-Menzel ocean theory; liquid water could not exist under such conditions, as it would promptly turn into steam. Then there was the apparent absence of any measurable magnetic field, which was surprising inasmuch as Venus had always been regarded as strongly magnetic, with the baffling Ashen Light due perhaps to electrical effects of the same general type as our own auroræ. And the rotation period seemed to be very long, perhaps even longer than Venus' 'year' of 224¾ Earth-days.

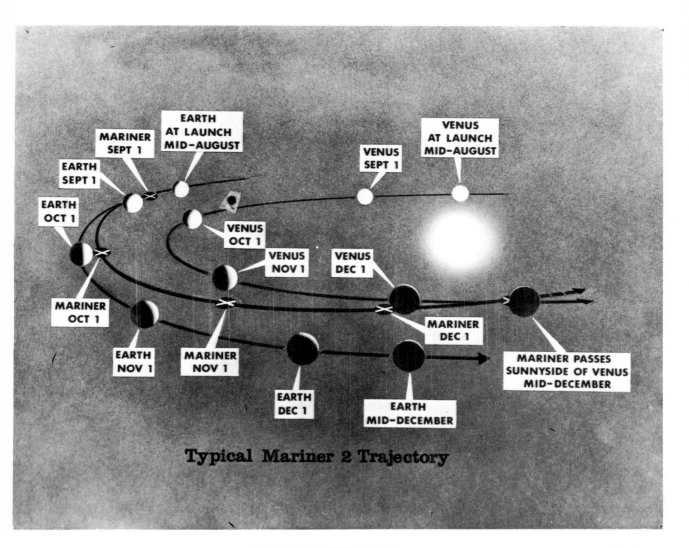

Typical Mariner 2 Trajectory

TRAJECTORY OF MARINER 2, 1962.

LISTENING IN ON VENUS. At the control centre in Jodrell Bank, Professor Sir Bernard Lovell, Professor John Davies and Robert Pritchard receive data from the Soviet probe Venus 4, which has made a gentle descent through Venus' atmosphere (18 October 1967).

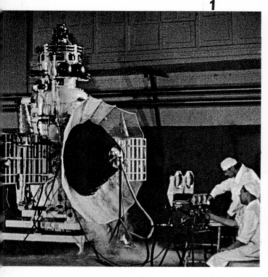
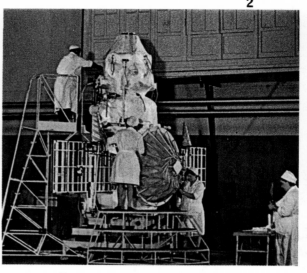

VENUS 4, the Russian probe which made a successful soft landing on Venus in October 1967. (1) Pre-launch; testing the various systems of Venus 4. (2) Detailed view of the probe, which was usually referred to by the Russians as 'a space-station'. (3) Preparations for centrifuge testing of the landing apparatus. (4) One of the final stages of flight preparation. (5) Preparing the thermo-regulation system for testing. All these photographs come from a colour film made by the Soviet authorities during trials of the Venus 4 probe.

It was true that the instruments had had to operate over a greater range than had been hoped, but there was no reason to suppose that the results were wildly wrong. Evidently Venus was just as hostile as the Moon, even if in a different way; the chances of finding life there were to all intents and purposes ruled out. Anyone who could stand on the surface would find himself in a gloomy, forbidding world, with the Sun hidden by the dense atmosphere and with strong winds tearing across the barren landscape. What living things could withstand a temperature of 800° coupled with a complete absence of water? The answer seemed to be, bluntly: 'None.'

Mariner 2 is still going round the Sun. Contact with it was finally lost on 4 January 1963, at 14 hours G.M.T., 130 days after the launching, at which time the distance from Earth amounted to as much as 54,000,000 miles. Certainly it had been a resounding success, even if its information had been unwelcome: certainly one result of the experiment was to relegate Venus to Target No. 3 in the space programme, and promote Mars above it in order of priority. In the pre-1967 period the Americans launched no more Venus probes, though the Russians attempted three.

Little need be said about Zond 1 of 1964, because it missed its target by a wide margin, and in any case it went out of contact before it had produced much of value. (Not so with Mariner 2, which sent back messages all through its outward flight; in particular, it provided some invaluable data about the solar wind.) Then, late in 1965, the Soviet workers sent up two Venus probes within a week. No. 2 passed by Venus at 15,000 miles or so in the following February, but it too went out of contact before the critical period, and is now, presumably, lost permanently. It was No. 3 which caused some excitement, and a great deal of controversy. Moscow reports gave out that on 1 March 1966, the probe actually landed on the surface of Venus.

The landing was not a controlled one, so that Venus 3 must have destroyed itself on impact. Contact with the probe was lost before the final descent through the planet's atmosphere, and so no scientific results were obtained. On balance, Venus 3, like Venus 2, must be classed as a failure.

This was a pity, but it could not be helped. The controversy

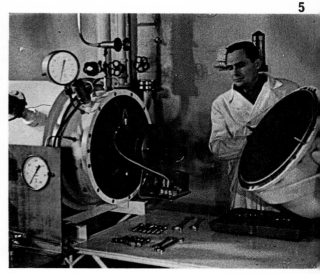

centred around the actual landing, since it was suggested that Earth contamination might have been taken to Venus, thereby ruining many important scientific investigations of the future.

We are virtually certain that Venus does not support advanced life-forms, and there has never been any serious suggestion that 'germs' carried from Earth might cause havoc among the local population (as, for instance, measles germs more or less wiped out the luckless Indians of Tierra del Fuego, who had never encountered measles until it was brought to the island by white men). But if Earth contamination were taken to Venus, it might easily spread, so that it would henceforth be impossible to tell which organisms belonged to the planet and which had been introduced from Earth. The problem of contamination affects every probe intended to land on another world, but it is not really serious for the airless Moon. It is only with planets surrounded by atmospheres that we must take the utmost care.

Naturally, all probes which are to be brought down elsewhere are sterilized as effectively as possible—and this applies even to the Moon vehicles, though more on principle than for any other reaon. There are various methods. For instance, the probe can be bombarded with the very short radiations known as gamma-rays, or it may be put into a gas chamber and exposed to the gas known as ethylene oxide, which is fatal to bacteria and viruses. Once a process of this kind has been carried out in the laboratory, great care must be taken not to expose the probe to any more contamination before it has been put into its launching-rocket and dispatched beyond the atmosphere. Probably the sterilization used today is more than 90 per cent. effective, but it is not foolproof; contamination might possibly persist. And if so, it may already have been carried to Venus.

In saying this, I am not trying to make any strong criticism of the Soviet attitude. I have no doubt that they made Venus 3 as harmless as they could, and it is not likely that any damage has been done. Moreover, the problem must be put into perspective; to expect that a probe can ever be 100 per cent. sterilized is asking a great deal, and sooner or later a mistake will be made. The only safeguard is to avoid any landings at all, automatic or manned, which would mean giving up a particularly interesting and important part of the whole space research programme.

The next developments came in 1967. During June, the Russians launched their probe Venus 4, and the Americans followed it a few days later with Mariner 5. However, the aims were different. The Soviet vehicle reached Venus on October 18; it was parachuted down through the planet's atmosphere, and made a successful soft landing—undoubtedly the greatest Russian triumph to date; communications were good, and signals were picked up both in the U.S.S.R. and at Jodrell Bank. The transmissions went on for more than an hour, though it is not clear whether they stopped just before or just after the landing was achieved. Venus 4, it must be admitted, had stolen the limelight from Mariner 5, which was a mere fly-by (even though a thoroughly successful one).

The information was quite definite. The surface temperature of Venus exceeded 500° Fahrenheit, and the atmosphere was extremely dense—perhaps 16 to 22 times as dense as that of the Earth at sea-level. This might well bend light-rays, and it was suggested that if an observer could stand on Venus and look straight ahead he would see the back of his neck. This may be an exaggeration, but that Venus is a weird world cannot be gainsaid. The rotation period, as derived from Earth-based radar, is now thought to be 243 Earth-days, retrograde; and we have to concede reluctantly, that instead of being a welcoming world, the Evening Star is a sort of Dantean inferno. It is certainly much less attractive than it looks.

Receiving signals from Venus 4, in the U.S.S.R. Each bowl of the radio equipment is 16 metres in diameter, and the instruments are fully steerable. Photograph by V. Konovalov, October 1967.

The Venus 4 probe, following a soft landing on Earth during its testing. Extensive tests had to be carried out, because nobody knew, originally, what the surface of Venus would be like.

Chapter 25

The Craters of Mars

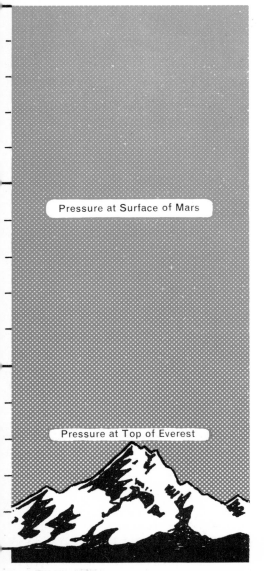

THE CANALS OF MARS, as drawn by Percival Lowell in 1894, and attributed by him to intelligent activity on the Martian surface.

Pressure at Surface of Mars

Pressure at Top of Everest

PRESSURE OF THE MARTIAN ATMOS-PHERE. The ground atmospheric pressure on Mars is very much less than that of the Earth's atmosphere on the top of Everest. It may be no more than the pressure over 90,000 feet above sea-level.

Sixty years ago it was thought quite likely that Mars, the Red Planet, was inhabited by advanced beings who had built up a brilliant civilization. More than one leading astronomer claimed that the so-called canals, straight features seen crossing the deserts of the planet, were artificial waterways—in which case we could actually observe the handiwork of Martian civilization. In 1906 Percival Lowell, founder of the famous observatory in Arizona which bears his name, went so far as to write: 'That Mars is inhabited by beings of some sort or other is as certain as it is uncercertain what these beings may be.'

At that time the idea of civilized Martians was not unreasonable, and certainly Mars appeared to be much more Earthlike than any other planet in the Solar System. It is further away from the Sun than we are, and moves at a mean distance of 141,500,000 miles, taking 687 Earth-days to complete one journey; its own 'day' amounts to 24 hours 37 minutes, and the tilt of the axis is much the same as that of the Earth, so that the seasons are of the same basic type even though they are much longer. It has a diameter of 4,200 miles, roughly intermediate between those of the Earth and Moon; the escape velocity is 3.1 miles per second. And Mars does, of course, possess an atmosphere.

Let us go into a little more detail about the all-important question of atmosphere. The Earth (escape velocity 7 miles per second) has a relatively dense air, while the Moon (escape velocity $1\frac{1}{2}$ miles per second) has virtually no atmosphere at all. Mars, with its value of just over 3 miles per second, might therefore be expected to have a rather thin atmosphere, and this is in full agreement with the observations. Before the Space Age, it was thought that the atmospheric pressure on the surface of Mars must be about the same as that of the Earth's atmosphere at a height of about 55,000 feet above sea-level.

This was reasonably encouraging, but no more, and there was never any serious suggestion that future space-travellers would be able to go to Mars and walk about unprotected. Climbers who go up to the top of our Mount Everest, which is less than 30,000 feet high, have to wear oxygen masks; the atmosphere of Mars was known to be much thinner than the Everest air, and in any case it did not contain much oxygen. Before the rocket probes went up, it was considered that the Martian atmosphere was made chiefly of nitrogen gas, with some carbon dioxide and a very little water vapour. At least this mixture would be non-toxic; our own air is 78 per cent nitrogen.

Studying Mars is much easier than trying to unravel the secrets of Venus. The Martian atmosphere is to all intents and purposes transparent to visible light, and the surface features can be seen without any difficulty, though it is true that for serious researches a powerful telescope is needed. There are whitish caps over the planet's poles, thought to be due to a thin layer of some icy or frosty deposit; there are prominent dark areas, and there are wide

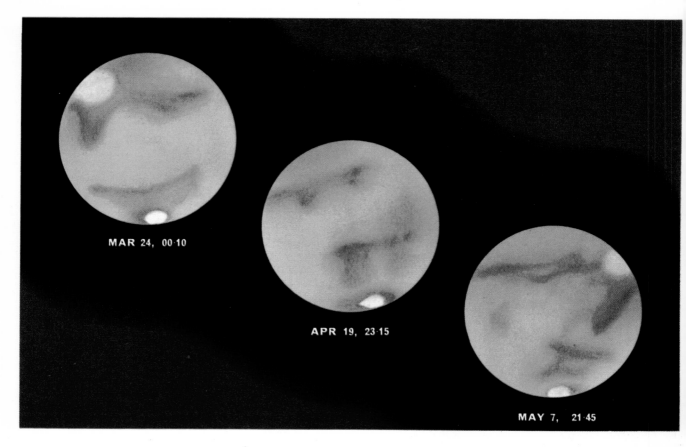

MAR 24, 00·10

APR 19, 23·15

MAY 7, 21·45

MARS IN 1967; from drawings made by the author on March 24 (00.10 hours GMT), April 19 (23.15 hours) and May 7 (21.45 hours), using x 500 on the 10in. refractor at Armagh Oservatory. Note the brilliant white area Hellas, and the north polar cap. The rather wedge-shaped feature shown in the first and third drawings is the Syrtis Major; the feature in the northern (lower) hemisphere, shown in the centre drawing, is the Mare Acidalium.

reddish-ochre tracts which are commonly termed 'deserts' even though they are totally unlike the sandy wastes such as the Earth's Sahara. A Martian desert is likely to be covered with some reddish mineral, and of course it will be cold. At mid-day on the equator, in midsummer, a thermometer would register something like 70° Fahrenheit, but the temperature would drop well below freezing point in the afternoon, and a Martian night is much colder than a polar night on our own world.

Mars is very short of water. There are no oceans, and even small lakes seem to be unlikely. Whatever the dark areas may be, they are not sheets of open water. As recently as 1963 it was thought virtually certain that the dark areas were covered with living organisms—or 'vegetation', to use the term rather loosely—and this is still the most probable answer, though our confidence has been rather shaken of late. On an arid world, with little oxygen in its atmosphere, and with a very wide temperature-range between day and night, advanced plants such as trees and flowers could not be expected. The Martian 'vegetation' was not thought likely to be more advanced in type than our lichens or mosses, though this is not to say that it was likely to bear a close resemblance to lichens, mosses or any other vegetation-types found on Earth.

As for the canals. . . . These curious features had been first mapped in detail by an Italian astronomer, G. V. Schiaparelli, as early as 1877, and were widely interpreted as being artificial. Percival Lowell, who was nothing if not whole-hearted about the matter, supposed that the Martians had built a planet-wide irrigation system in a desperate attempt to salvage every scrap of

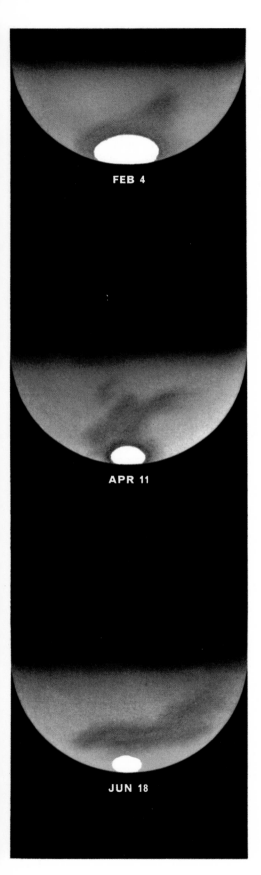

FEB 4

APR 11

JUN 18

water from the icy polar caps. On Lowell's theory, the water was pumped through the canals to the equatorial regions, and population centres were set up at the so-called oases, where two or more canals met.

It was an attractive theory, but from the outset it was regarded with grave suspicion, because there were some disquieting facts. Even before Lowell's death, in 1916, it was suggested that the polar caps must be too thin to provide enough water to supply a whole planet, canals or no canals. This has been amply borne out, and it now seems as though the polar caps cannot be more than a few inches deep at most. Moreover, Lowell and his followers certainly tended to exaggerate the straightness and regularity of the canals, and under good conditions the artificial aspect vanishes, leaving a 'canal' as nothing more than a rather broad, irregular streak. In any case, further studies have shown that Mars is simply not a world upon which advanced life-forms may be expected to flourish. Long before the start of the Space Age, the fascinating, brilliant-brained Martians had been handed over to the science-fiction writers, who made full use of them. Almost all scientists agreed that Mars must be uninhabitable.

I say 'almost all scientists', because there were a few exceptions. Most notable of these was (and is) the Russian astronomer I. Shklovsky, who has carried out pioneer theoretical investigations in stellar research, and whose reputation as an astrophysicist is second to none. Shklovsky considered the two tiny satellites of Mars, Phobos and Deimos, and came to the remarkable conclusion that they must be artificial space-stations, launched by the Martians for reasons of their own. His announcement caused a considerable stir when it was made a few years ago, though few people took it very seriously.

Admittedly, Phobos and Deimos are odd little worlds. Neither can be as much as a dozen miles in diameter, and both are close to Mars; Phobos moves round the planet in only $7\frac{1}{2}$ hours, at less than 4,000 miles above the surface. They seem to be quite unlike our own large Moon, and it is probable that they are captured minor planets instead of genuine Martian satellites. Yet I have the feeling that when space-travellers first pass them, they will find that Phobos and Deimos are natural bodies instead of Shklovsky's hollow space-stations!

Schiaparelli, mapper of the canals, was also responsible for the names of most of the Martian features. There is, for instance, the prominent V-shaped dark patch which was once known as the Kaiser Sea or the Hourglass Sea, but which Schiaparelli re-christened the Syrtis Major; it can be seen with a small telescope when Mars is well placed. In the northern hemisphere, there is a rather wedge-shaped area known as the Mare Acidalium, and so on. In general, the outlines of the dark regions are permanent, and have been so ever since Christiaan Huygens first glimpsed them as long ago as 1659; but changes in outline do occur, and sometimes a dark area will encroach on to a neighbouring 'desert', though it generally retreats again after a year or two.

Though Mars clearly could not support Earth-type animals, opinion in the pre-rocket era was almost unanimous in that life of a sort was to be found there. In particular, it was pointed out that there is a regular seasonal cycle bound up with the shrinking of the

THE SHRINKING POLAR CAPS OF MARS, from drawings made by the author in 1967 using x 500 on the Armagh Observatory 10in. refractor. The northern cap, shown here, is large in the upper drawing (Feb. 4), but shrinks in the centre drawing (Apr. 11) and the lower (June 18); by then, warmer weather had come to Mars' northern hemisphere. The polar caps are still thought to be due to a thin layer of icy or frosty deposit, though there is no complete agreement among astronomers.

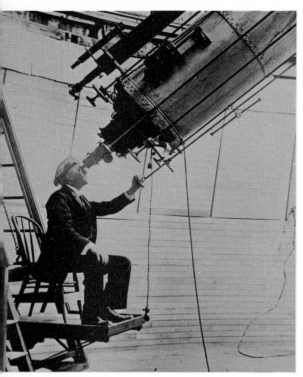

PERCIVAL LOWELL at the eyepiece of the great refractor at Flagstaff, where the Lowell Observatory was founded in 1895. Lowell is best remembered to-day for his theories about the canals of Mars, but he was also a brilliant mathematician, and it was his calculations that led to the discovery of the ninth planet, Pluto—though Pluto was not discovered during Lowell's lifetime. Lowell died in 1916; in 1930 Clyde Tombaugh, at the Lowell Observatory, identified Pluto almost exactly where Lowell had expected it to be.

polar caps. As a cap shrinks in the Martian spring and early summer, either by melting or by sublimation (i.e. changing direct from a solid into a gas), a certain amount of water vapour is released, and this is wafted toward the equator by the winds. As the moisture moves equatorward, it is picked up by the vegetation in the dark areas, which shows marked development; there is what has been called a 'wave of darkening', extending steadily from the pole toward the equator. I must admit that in my view, at least, the effect is much less striking than is usually supposed, but it does exist to some degree.

Let us, then, sum up the views about Mars which were held by most astronomers before the flight of Mariner 4, the American probe of 1965. It was said that:

1. Mars is a small, rather cold world, but not hopelessly frozen.
2. The atmosphere is thin, as might be expected from the escape velocity of only 3.1 miles per second; it is made up chiefly of nitrogen, so that at least it is not poisonous. The atmospheric ground pressure is about the same as that in the Earth's air at rather less than twice the height of Mount Everest.
3. The reddish-ochre deserts are made up of areas covered with a coloured mineral deposit, probably felsite or limonite.
4. The dark regions are likely to be covered with living organisms, which may be called 'vegetation'. The vegetation cannot be of advanced type; it is not likely to be of a higher order than terrestrial moss, though of course it may be quite unlike any vegetation to be found on Earth.
5. There are no oceans, but the thin polar caps are made up of some icy substance, and produce some atmospheric moisture even though they are only a few inches deep.
6. The famous canals have a basis of reality, but are not truly regular and artificial in aspect, so that thay must be surface features of natural origin.

Nowadays, conclusions 1, 3 and 6 are still valid; 4 and 5 are probably valid; 2 requires considerable modification, because the atmosphere is much less dense than was previously thought. Also, the idea of Mars as a smooth world, with gently undulating dust-plains and vegetation tracts, has been found to be very wide of the mark.

So long as observations had to be carried out solely from Earth, our knowledge could never be at all complete. Even with the world's largest telescopes, Mars can never be seen more clearly than the Moon shows up when viewed through ordinary binoculars; remember that the Moon is within a quarter of a million miles of us, whereas Mars can never approach closer than 34,000,000 miles—and to make things more difficult, its favourable approaches are not common, though it is reasonably well placed for a few months every alternate year.

Quite apart from all this, there was every reason for planning a rocket probe to Mars. There seemed to be a real chance of examining a world which is not dead, such as the Moon, but which contains life. Moreover only Mars and Venus, of the planets, are within practicable range, and Mariner 2 has shown that Venus is not suitable for manned landings on any large scale.

The first Mars rocket, a Russian one, was dispatched in late

1962. Since then there have been three more, though only one has been a success. A full list of the Mars probes launched before 1968 is as follows:

Date of Launch		Name	Country	Remarks
1962	Nov. 1	Mars 1	U.S.S.R.	Contact lost. Passed within 130,000 miles of Mars in June 1963.
1964	Nov. 5	Mariner 3	U.S.A.	Failure; loss of contact early on.
1964	Nov. 28	Mariner 4	U.S.A.	Complete success; photographed Mars from 6,300 miles on 15 July 1965. Now orbiting the Sun.
1964	Nov. 30	Zond 2	U.S.S.R.	Contact lost. Probably passed reasonably near Mars in August 1965.

With a Mars probe, the procedure is to 'speed it up' relative to the Earth, so that it starts to swing outwards and arrives at the Martian orbit to make a rendezvous with the planet. The Russians followed this procedure quite correctly with their 1962 probe, and at first all seemed to be well, but then contact was lost. Yet Mars 1 was not a total failure, as it did at least send back useful information, and was tracked out to 66,000,000 miles, which was a record at that time. In particular, it yielded data about solar wind and micro-meteoroid frequency before it 'went silent'. If it kept to its orbit—and there is no reason why it should have done anything else—it by-passed Mars in June 1963, but there was no close approach. It must still be travelling on around the Sun.

Then came the Mariners of 1964. No. 3 (Nos. 1 and 2 were, of course, the earlier Venus probes) went out of control early, and

THE RUSSIAN PROBE MARS 1, launched on 1 November 1962. The launching was successful, but unfortunately contact broke down when the probe had receded to 65,900,000 miles from Earth, and was never regained. However, Mars 1 was not a complete failure, since for some months it sent back valuable information about conditions in the space region between the orbits of the Earth and Mars.

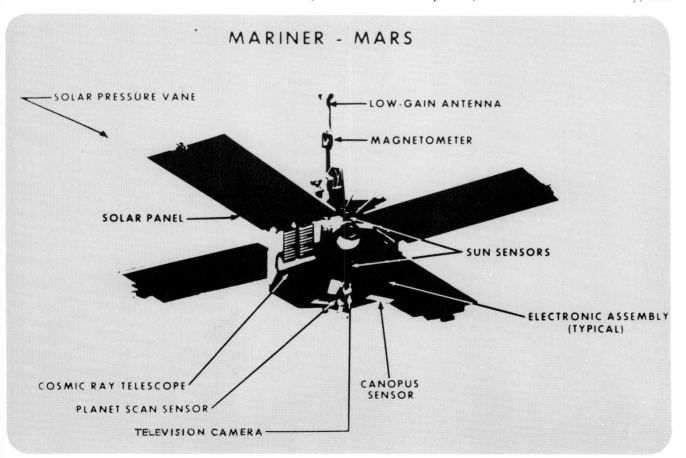

MARINER - MARS

SOLAR PRESSURE VANE

LOW-GAIN ANTENNA

MAGNETOMETER

SOLAR PANEL

SUN SENSORS

ELECTRONIC ASSEMBLY (TYPICAL)

COSMIC RAY TELESCOPE

CANOPUS SENSOR

PLANET SCAN SENSOR

TELEVISION CAMERA

MARINER 4, the successful Mars probe launched by the Americans on 28 November 1964. In the following July it by-passed Mars, and sent back photographs showing that the Martian surface is covered with craters. Here we see various pieces of equipment, including the 'Canopus sensor' which locked on to the brilliant southern star Canopus and was essential to the success of the operation.

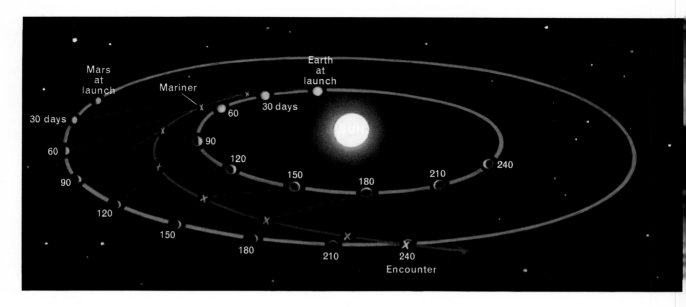

Earth at launch · Mars at launch · Mariner · 30 days · 60 · 90 · 120 · 150 · 180 · 210 · 240 · Encounter

TRAJECTORY OF MARINER 4, which by-passed Mars after a flight time of 240 days. Following its fly-by, Mariner 4 continued in a solar orbit, and radio contact with it was re-established after it had been right round the Sun. Undoubtedly Mariner 4 was the most successful of the planetary probes launched during the first decade of the Space Age.

sped off into space uncontrollable and uncontactable. But with No. 4, everything went well from the start. The launching, with parking orbit technique, was carried through without a hitch, and communications were good.

Two days later, the Russians made another attempt with their vehicle Zond 2, and there was the remarkable situation of two probes bound for Mars, one following the other. Needless to say, there was no suggestion of a race to Mars, but the position was an intriguing one, and there were many speculations as to which of the probes would prove to be the better. Actually, Zond 2 gave signs of trouble from the outset, and the transmitting power was much less than had been hoped. It was no surprise when, after some months, contact with it was lost, and all that can really be said about it is that it may have passed within reasonable range of Mars about August 1965. But by then, Mariner 4 had already claimed a major triumph, and had been responsible for what are often regarded as the most remarkable scientific photographs ever taken.

Mariner was not intended to land on Mars; like the other vehicles of its series it was a fly-by, and its main object was to take close-range pictures of the Martian surface. Yet it had other tasks as well, some of them to be carried out during the outward flight. It carried instruments to record the crossing of the shock-wave produced by the interaction of the solar wind and the Earth's magnetosphere, which has already been mentioned on page 106, and these measures were duly made without difficulty on the first day of the voyage. Magnetic fields in space were also studied, and the numbers of micro-meteorite hits were also recorded (nearly 100 of them during the first 3,500 flight-hours, though none caused any damage). Inevitably a few of the instruments failed, one loss being the Geiger counter to study cosmic rays, but in general everything seemed to be most satisfactory. On 5 December, a mid-course correction was made to the orbit. On 29 April 1965, on the 152nd day of travel, Mariner broke the 'communications record' of 66,000,000 miles that had been set up by the first Russian Mars probe. And on 14 July 1965 it passed by Mars at only 6,118

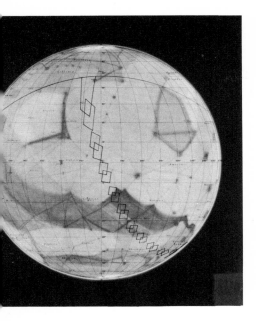

AREAS OF MARS PHOTOGRAPHED FROM MARINER 4. Bright 'desert' areas and dark regions were covered; both proved to be crater-scarred. At the time when the photographs were taken, on 14 July 1965, the probe and Mars were 134,000,000 miles from Earth.

THE FIRST PHOTOGRAPH OF MARS FROM MARINER 4. No craters are shown here, and the contrast is low, but the picture was immensely encouraging. Later photographs in the series were much clearer.

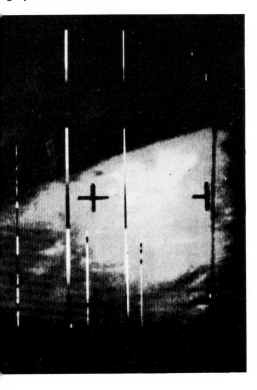

miles, and carried through its photographic programme with scarcely a fault. At that time it was 134,000,000 miles from the Earth. On the way to Mars, it had covered a total of 418,000,000 miles, so that it had certainly not moved along the shortest route; as we have noted, this would have been hopelessly uneconomical of fuel.

Since the programme was a 'first attempt', excluding the abortive flight of Mariner 3, the success was truly amazing. There were so many factors to be taken into account, and failure in any one of them would have involved failure in all. The guidance alone was extremely difficult, and it was also necessary to make sure that the Mariner was kept in the right 'attitude'—that is to say, pointing its equipment in the right direction. This was achieved by making use of the bright southern star Canopus, which is never visible from Europe, but which outshines all other stars with the exception of Sirius. The probe had to 'find' Canopus by means of its sensitive direction equipment, and then lock on to it. On one occasion it found the wrong star, and had to be given an order to unlock and start searching again.

Also, it was by no means easy to transmit the Mars photographs back to Earth even when they had been taken. Each one had to be sent back at a slow rate, and it took 8 hours 35 minutes to complete each photograph. Since 21 photographs were sent back altogether, the procedure was by no means a quick one.

When the pictures came through, they caused intense excitement. Instead of being flat, Mars turned out to be covered with craters remarkably like those of the Moon.

The idea of Martian craters was not entirely new; something of the sort had been forecast by the American astronomer R. B. Baldwin in 1949, and, slightly later, by E. J. Öpik in Ireland. But not many people had taken up the suggestion, and it came as a distinct shock to find that Mars was so lunar in aspect. Indications of craters were seen on the second photograph to be received, and more were shown up on the succeeding pictures—up to the finest of all, the eleventh. Some of the craters had central peaks, and the largest of them measured over 100 miles in diameter.

The best of the Mariner photographs is reproduced overleaf, and there is no need to emphasize the resemblance with lunar features. It is fairly clear that the two sets of craters must have been formed in the same way. If the Moon's craters are volcanic, then so are those of Mars; if the lunar craters were produced by meteorites hitting the surface, then the same must be true of Mars.

Mariner covered only a strip of the planet, but this included samples of both the dark areas and the reddish-ochre deserts, so that the strip may be regarded as representative. We have no reason to doubt that the rest of Mars, too, is crater-scarred, and on the whole it seems that the most likely force involved is volcanic activity. There may be active volcanoes on Mars even now, though personally I have serious doubts.

The photographs were so spectacular that they tended to steal all the limelight, but Mariner provided some other information as well – not all of it pleasant. The magnetic devices recorded no trace of a Van Allen type zone, which from an astronautical point of view was quite helpful; but then, about an hour after its closest

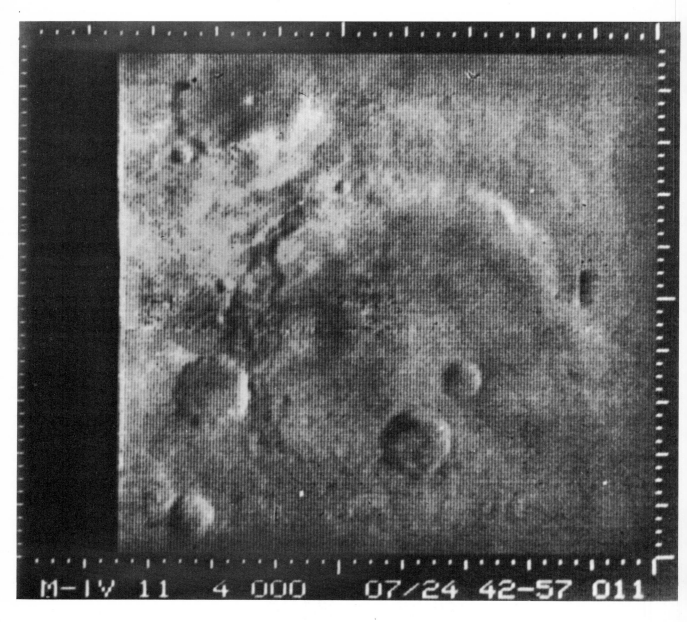

M-IV 11 4 000 07/24 42-57 011

THE CRATERS OF MARS, photographed by Mariner 4 on 14 July 1955 just before its closest approach to the planet. The slant range of the photograph is 7,800 miles. Area covered: east-west 170 miles, north-south 150 miles. Location lat.31 degrees S., long. 197 degrees E., in Atlantis between Mare Sirenum and Mare Cimmerium. A green filter was used. The Sun was 47 degrees from the zenith, from the north (top) of the photograph. This was the 11th picture in the Mariner series, and is generally regarded as the best.

approach to Mars, Mariner went behind the planet's edge as seen from Earth's reappearing on the opposite side an hour later. Just as it was being hidden or occulted, the probe sent back radio signals which came to us having passed through the Martian atmosphere; the same was done just as the Mariner emerged from occultation. Measures then made it possible to find out the electron density, i.e. the numbers of free electrons in the Martian ionosphere. From this, it became possible to calculate the total amount of atmosphere.

The result was discouraging. Previously, it had been thought that the ground pressure must be about equal to the Earth's air at some 55,000 feet. Mariner reduced this considerably, and it now seems that on the surface of Mars the atmospheric pressure is only between 1 and 2 per cent. of that of the Earth's air; that is to say, equal to the pressure at a height of between 93,000 and 100,000 feet above sea-level on Earth. Moreover, there is much more

MARTIAN EXPLORER; an artist's concept from the Boeing Aircraft Company. The Explorer would be constructed at a station orbiting the Earth, and dispatched toward Mars from this orbit. This design was completed in April 1960. Whether drastic modifications will be needed in the light of more recent research remains to be seen.

carbon dioxide than had been expected, and it is now thought that carbon dioxide accounts for at least 50 per cent. of the total mass of the Martian atmosphere, so that it is the major constituent.

This alters the overall situation very much for the worse. Instead of being reasonably dense, and an effective screen against harmful short-wave radiations as well as small meteoric particles, Mars has an atmosphere which is too thin to be of much use to future astronauts, even though it is considerably better than nothing at all. Our chances of finding liquid water below ground level are reduced, and we must take another look, too, at the favourite theory that the dark areas are due to something which lives and grows. It has been suggested recently that the dark regions may be due to 'dwarf hills' produced by frost phenomena, while the canals have been attributed to ridges or low ranges of hills.

Doubts, too, have been cast on the frost or ice theory of the polar caps, and there has been a marked revival of an earlier idea that they are due to solid carbon dioxide. Some astronomers consider that the temporary bright areas on the disk, formerly thought to be frost-covered elevations, are nothing more nor less than solid carbon dioxide concentrations in depressions; and there is a school of thought according to which the dark areas are higher than the deserts instead of *vice versa*. It seems that we now know rather less about Mars than we thought we did before the flight of Mariner 4!

On the whole, the most disquieting fact about the new findings is that the Martian atmosphere is not likely to be an effective screen against radiations. It has been claimed that the entire planet must be radiation-soaked, in which case life there cannot have gained a foothold. Before the flight of Mariner 4, it was regarded as more than probable that living organisms existed; nowadays we are not sure. There is a growing body of opinion that Mars is, and always has been completely sterile. Biologists, in particular, tend to take this point of view.

It is not likely that the problem will be solved before more probes have been sent to Mars. There are American plans for a Martian Orbiter, which will go round the planet and send back detailed photographs in the same manner as has already been done in the case of the Moon; presumably, too, there will be a soft landing on the lines of the Russian success with Venus. Until these experiments have been carried out, we cannot say for certain whether or not Mars is able to support any living thing.

In any case, nobody can deny that the Red Planet is more hostile than had been expected, and seems to be more lunar than terrestrial in type. If it still retains its position of priority in the space planners' thoughts, this is only because Venus, the only alternative target after the Moon, is even worse. Probably we must now wait until a probe can make a controlled landing on Mars and send back detailed information from the surface, as the Luna and Surveyor vehicles have done in the case of the Moon. No doubt this will be achieved before very long.

Even when it had completed its programme, Mariner 4 was still not 'dead'. In 1966, after it had been right round the Sun, it was contacted once more, and it still proved capable of obeying commands sent from Earth. Undoubtedly it was the most successful of all the probes sent up during the first ten years of the Space Age, and its place in history is assured.

Chapter 26

Exploring the Solar System

Within the first ten years of the Space Age, much had been achieved. The football-sized Sputnik 1 of 1957 had led, by 1967, to massive, complex artificial satellites; manned vehicles capable of staying in orbit for weeks if necessary; probes to the Moon, some of them landing gently and turning into what may be called lunar transmitting stations; messengers to Mars and Venus, and deep-space probes able to send back information about conditions tens of millions of miles away from the Earth.

This sounds impressive, and indeed it is. No doubt the second ten years of the new era will be equally productive, and perhaps even more spectacular. Certainly there is every chance of a manned landing on the Moon, which will in itself open up almost endless new fields for research.

Scientific forecasting is always a risky business, and more so in space research than in any other branch. There is, too always the chance of some totally unexpected difficulty which will hold up progress for a long time; and though this may be unlikely, it is not absolutely out of the question, particularly since we do not yet know as much as we would like about the long-term effects of zero gravity and potentially dangerous radiation. However, it

THE ECOSPHERE. In the Solar System, only the region within the so-called ecosphere (tinted red in the diagram) is at a temperature suitable for the existence of advanced life. Closer to the Sun, the temperature is too high; further out, the cold is too intense. Thus Mercury lies inside the ecosphere and Jupiter well outside. The only planets within the ecosphere are Venus, Earth and Mars—and only the Earth lies near the centre of the region.

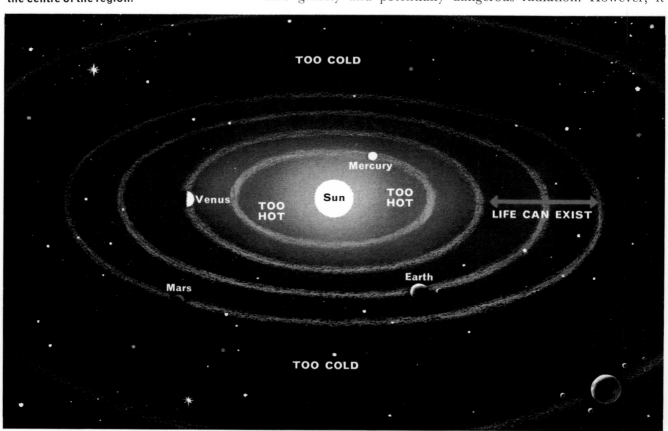

seems that nothing can hold up our exploration of the Solar System by unmanned vehicles (apart from political crises or the outbreak of another war, of course). Therefore, I propose to indulge in some mild speculation, though I realize that I may well be badly wrong, and I am strongly disinclined to attempt giving any hard and fast time-table.

So far as the Moon is concerned, unmanned probes can certainly continue the programmes which have already been started. They will take samples of the lunar ground, analyze these samples, and transmit back the information. Another possibility is that of a probe being sent to the Moon and then brought home again. The same sort of thing may be done with Mars, though not nearly so soon—and we must remember that any vehicle which returns from the Red Planet will have to be subjected to the most careful decontamination. The chances of its bringing back any harmful substance are very slight, but they do exist, and in a situation of this kind a single mistake would be one too many.

Of course, the question which has caused the most general discussion is: 'What are the chances of our finding life elsewhere in the Solar System?' I do not propose to say a great deal about this problem here, but a few general comments may be in order.

We do not know a great deal about the origin of life, but we have a good idea of the way in which living material is built up. There are only 92 elements which are known to occur in Nature, and these form a complete series, so that there is little or no chance of our having overlooked one. Of these, only one—carbon—is able to form the large, complex atom-groups needed for living matter. Its only rival is silicon, and we have no evidence that silicon-based life exists, though it cannot be completely ruled out.

It follows that life, wherever it may be, will be based on carbon. Consequently it will be basically similar to the life-forms known to us. It may have a completely different outward appearance, and I am quite prepared to believe in an alien astronomer with four heads and eight legs; but he (or she, or it) will still be carbon-based and will still need an environment with an equable temperature, a reasonably dense atmosphere containing oxygen, and an adequate supply of water. If these conditions are not met, then our alien creature will not be able to exist, any more than we could ourselves do.

In the Solar System, the only planet which meets all the requirements for advanced life is the Earth. On Mars there is too little atmosphere, and probably too little water, though we cannot be certain about this simply because we know nothing about possible underground supplies. Venus seems to be too hot. The Moon and the planet Mercury are virtually without atmosphere, and the remaining worlds in the Sun's family are too cold, quite apart from their numerous other disadvantages.

On balance, it seems that the chances of our finding advanced life elsewhere in the Solar System are vanishingly small. The most we can hope for is low-type 'vegetation' on Mars, and even with this we are rather less confident than we used to be before the flight of Mariner 4. The nearest civilizations to us must be many light-years away across the Galaxy, and totally beyond the reach of our rocket probes. However, the remaining planets in the Solar System will come within range eventually, provided that no un-

MERCURY, from a drawing made by the author on 26 May 1967, using a mangification of 500 on the Armagh 10in. refractor. A certain amount of detail can be seen, but Mercury is extremely difficult to study, and maps of its surface are still very arbitrary.

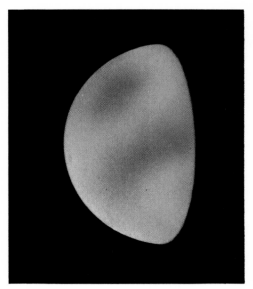

JUPITER, photographed on 10 March 1967 by Commander H. R. Hatfield with his 12in. reflector at Sevenoaks. The cloud belts are well shown, and there is a prominent white spot in the south temperate zone (left, above centre).

AN ORIGINAL FLYING SAUCER! The flying island of Laputa, from the classic book *Gulliver's Travels*, by Jonathan Swift. Dr. Gulliver observes the flying island as it prepares to land on Earth.

LAPUTAN ASTRONOMERS. In Swift's story, the astronomers of the flying island of Laputa were obsessed with the possibility of cosmic disaster. Here they are shown studying the sky with their telescopes. Both these illustrations come from an early illustrated edition of Swift's novel.

foreseen difficulties appear, and there is no harm in making some modest speculations as to the course of future events.

Following Mars and Venus, the most likely target is perhaps Mercury, the smallest of the principal planets and the nearest to the Sun. The problems of the actual journey are not much more troublesome than for Venus, although the distance is greater; Mercury never comes much within 50,000,000 miles of us, and it is not a great deal larger than the Moon, so that it is never conspicuous in our skies. With the naked eye, it can be seen when best placed shining down as a fairly bright star low in the west after sunset or low in the east before sunrise.

The Mercurian 'year' is 88 days. The rotation period is slow, and has been found to be $58\frac{1}{2}$ Earth-days, rather less than used to be thought. To an observer on the planet's surface, the interval between one sunrise and the next would be 176 Earth-days. Maps of Mercury are very rough, but some light regions and darker patches can be seen, and it is quite probable that there are craters of the same type as those on the Moon and Mars.

The surface temperatures are certainly uncomfortable. Mercury is a mere 36,000,000 miles from the Sun at its mean distance, and the maximum day-heat must be hundreds of degrees Fahrenheit, though the nights will be intensely cold. The escape velocity is $2\frac{1}{2}$ miles per second, and, predictably, the atmosphere is extremely thin—so thin, indeed, that some authorities dispute its existence, and in any case it is negligible by our standards.

The value of Mercury as a landing-site for an automatic probe would be mainly in that the planet is very close to the Sun, so that an unmanned solar observatory there would be of tremendous interest. Also, Mercurian fly-by probes would be valuable to students of Solar System dynamics. There is every reason to suppose that within the next decade or two, various vehicles will have been dispatched toward this strange, unfriendly little world, but a soft landing there will be delayed for much longer.

Then there are the minor planets or asteroids, most of which move round the Sun in the region between the orbits of Mars and Jupiter, but some of which have eccentric paths which swing them fairly close to the Earth. Such is Eros, which is an irregular body about 20 miles long and 5 wide; it can come within 15,000,000 miles of us, and will make its next close approach in 1975. The present holder of the 'approach record' is Hermes, no more than a mile across, which brushed past us in 1937 at less than twice the distance of the Moon. Perhaps the most interesting member of the whole swarm is Icarus, whose orbit carries it from beyond Mars in to the torrid regions of the Solar System; at perihelion it moves inside the orbit of Mercury. At its closest to the Earth, as in June 1968, it may come within 4,000,000 miles of us, but there is no fear of a collision on the line.

A minor planet of this type is so small that its gravitational pull is negligible, and an astronaut landing there would be to all intents and purposes weightless. Obviously, no trace of atmosphere or water can be expected even on the 427-mile Ceres, which is by far the largest member of the swarm and which keeps strictly to its stable orbit well beyond that of Mars.

There have been some suggestions that it would be a good idea to pull some of the small asteroids out of their paths, guide them suitably, and utilize them as space-stations or long-range probes. It can only be said, with regret, that the 'experts' who have written in this vein can have had not the slightest notion of the forces which would be needed. To alter the orbit of even a small asteroid is so completely out of the question that it is not worth discussing, except as an academic problem. On the other hand, it is quite true to say that studies of the compositions of minor planets would be of great value, and it may well be that a rendezvous will eventually be made between an Earth-launched probe and a suitable asteroid. More interesting still would be to land a transmitter upon Icarus or some such dwarf world, and keep in touch over a prolonged period. But this is not an imminent prospect, and whether it will ever be seriously considered remains to be seen. The same applies to the idea of sending up a probe to pass through a comet, and obtain measures of the make-up and nature of comets in general.

Far beyond Mars lie the giant planets Jupiter, Saturn, Uranus and Neptune. For astronautical purposes these four may be considered together, and it must be said at once that there is not the slightest prospect of landing a probe there, either now or in the foreseeable future. The escape velocities are very high (37 miles per second in the case of Jupiter), which would mean that a descending vehicle would be hard pressed to 'brake' sufficiently before being destroyed by friction against the outer atmosphere; if the escape velocity from a planet is high, then the gravitational pull must be strong, and an approaching probe will travel unpleasantly fast. But in any case, the giant planets have no visible solid surfaces. Their outer layers are made up of gas, chiefly hydrogen and hydrogen compounds, and we have no proof that properly solid surfaces exist, though near the centre of the globe of a giant planet the pressures and densities must be tremendous.

On the other hand, fly-by probes will eventually be dispatched, and will be most valuable. For instance, Jupiter is known to be a source of radio waves, and it seems probable that there is a powerful magnetic field. If so, then a probe capable of penetrating the Jovian magnetosphere and sending back its information would be extremely welcome, and this is not beyond the bounds of possibility.

A Jovian probe would have many additional uses. It would be able to transmit data about conditions in the outer parts of the Solar System (that is to say, the regions beyond the orbit of Mars), about which we know depressingly little as yet. We cannot tell much about the magnetic conditions, the density of the interplanetary material, or the numbers of meteoric particles, but these problems and many more could be studied by a probe to Jupiter, and such a vehicle would be worth launching even if it missed its main target. Unfortunately, the travel-time would amount to several years.

Of the Jovian satellites, two (Io and Europa) are roughly the size of our Moon, while two more (Ganymede and Callisto) are larger – perhaps equal in size, though not in mass, to the planet Mercury. Soft landings of automatic probes on these satellites may be considered in the future, though not yet awhile. There have been recent suggestions that the four satellites may have tenuous atmospheres, but there is no proof, and the temperatures are of course very low indeed. The remaining eight attendants of Jupiter are

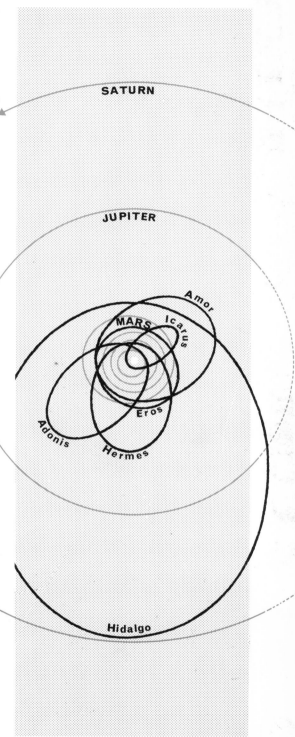

ORBITS OF SOME OF THE MINOR PLANETS; Icarus, which passes within the perihelion distance of Mercury, and which approached the Earth to a distance of 4,000,000 miles in June 1968; the 'earth-grazers' Amor, Adonis, Hermes; Eros, which came within 15,000,000 miles of us in 1931 and will do so again in 1975; and the exceptional Hidalgo, whose eccentric orbit carries it out almost as far as Saturn.

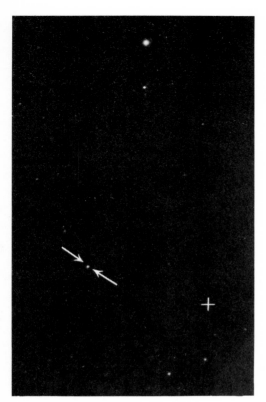

VESTA, photographed in 1965 by F. J. Acfield with the 10in. reflector at his private observatory at Forest Hall, Northumberland. The asteroid is shown between two arrows. The cross indicates Vesta's position 24 hours earlier.

SATURN, showing the ring system and the Cassini Division.

true dwarfs, and are probably captured asteroids rather than bona-fide satellites.

Most of the comments about Jupiter also apply to Saturn, though radio emissions from the Ringed Planet are less well established. The distance is much greater, and the conditions no less unfavourable, but there is at least one satellite with an atmosphere: Titan, which is a body of what we may term planetary size, and may be over 3,000 miles in diameter. (Estimates differ, but at least Titan is very large by satellite standards.) The atmosphere, detected by G. P. Kuiper as long ago as 1944, seems to be composed chiefly of the poisonous gas methane. Years ago, Arthur Clarke suggested that since methane can be used in rocket propellants, Titan might be reached before the system of Jupiter, but this is looking far ahead indeed, and I for one rather doubt whether chemically-fuelled rockets will ever take astronauts further than Mars. If we are to range further afield, nuclear propellants will have to be used.

We need spend no time in discussing the two outer giants, Uranus and Neptune; and Pluto, on the fringe of the Solar System, is a world about which we know very little, though it is not a giant, and appears to be about the same size as the Earth. To dispatch a probe to these far-away regions is beyond our present capabilities— or, more accurately, such a probe could not be tracked for more than the first part of its journey, so that there would be little point in launching it at all.

In looking at a plan of the Solar System, one tends to forget that the orbits of the planets beyond Mars are so widely spaced. Mars, as we have noted, can come within 35,000,000 miles of us. Jupiter never approaches us closer than 365,000,000 miles; over ten times as far. Saturn is more than twice as remote from us as Jupiter; Uranus, more than twice as far as Saturn; Neptune, not very much less than twice as far as Uranus. A probe bound for Neptune would have completed less than one-seventh of its journey by the time that it crossed the orbit of Jupiter. The Solar System is a large place, and our present-day chemically-fuelled rockets can take our scientific instruments only to the more accessible parts of it.

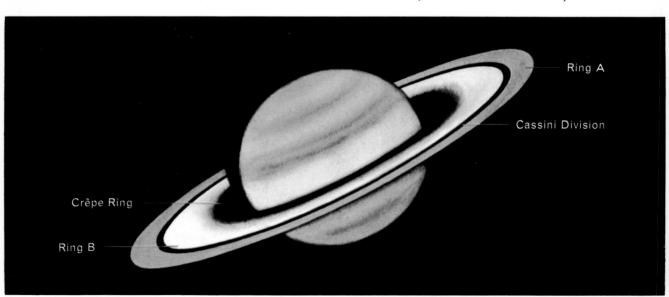

Ring A

Cassini Division

Crêpe Ring

Ring B

Lastly, something must be said about the future of manned exploration of the Solar System. Here it is necessary to be cautious, because a forecast made on Monday may be somewhat out of date by Tuesday, decidedly old-fashioned by Wednesday, and laughably outdated by the following Saturday. But if all goes well, research bases will be set up on the Moon in the reasonably near future—overground if possible (though it remains to be seen whether the attractive plastic-dome arrangement of the science-fiction writers will be practicable), underground if the surface conditions prove to be intolerable. Certainly there is every reason to establish a full-scale scientific laboratory on the Moon, because the conditions there cannot be duplicated on Earth. There is constant 'hard vacuum', reduced gravity, radiation and micro-meteoroid bombardment, and a sky free of clouds, turbulence and absorbing layers.

Yet although such bases are being planned, and will be set up unless there is some unforeseen complication, there is no chance of our turning the Moon into a second Earth. Life there will always be carried on under highly artificial conditions, and centres of population will be limited to a few research bases, which will—we hope—be international; any politician who dreams of 'claiming the Moon' for any particular country can only be regarded with a pitying smile.

There have been suggestions that in the future, surplus population from our fast-overcrowding Earth will be transported to the Moon, Mars or some other world. Actually, this is completely out of the question, because none of these bodies will ever be able to support more than a very limited number of people. Undoubtedly the over-population problem is looming up ahead of us, and every Government should even now be seeking methods not of maintaining the birth-rate, but of reducing it. However, this is a social problem, not an astronautical one—and astronauts cannot solve it.

If Venus has indeed a surface temperature of 500° Fahrenheit, bases there can be discounted for the moment at least. Mars is less mysterious, and at least it has an atmosphere of sorts, which makes it an improvement over the Moon; but the atmosphere has been shown to be disappointingly thin, so that the difference between a lunar and a Martian research base will not be nearly so marked as was expected before Mariner 4 sent back its findings. Much will depend upon whether the Martian atmosphere is reasonably efficient as a radiation and meteor screen, and whether there are any underground water supplies. Unmanned probes of the next decade should be able to tell us; meanwhile, the whole design of a future Martian base must be left in abeyance.

I wonder whether any copies of this book will still exist in, say, the year 2070? Possibly there will be one or two in museum libraries. Should any reader of that time pick up the book and scan through it, he will certainly be amused at the pictures of our archaic Earth Satellites, and he will chuckle dryly at some of the speculations I have made in the last few pages. But when all is said and done, the first years of the Space Age have been years of amazing progress. Real achievement may belong to the future, but the foundations of it are being laid now.

Chapter 27

Interstellar Flight

Man has started to explore space. Unmanned rockets have been sent out and tracked to well over 100,000,000 miles from Earth; there is every prospect of a manned landing on the Moon before long, and it is very probable that within the next few centuries automatic probes will have been dispatched to the more remote parts of the Solar System. Therefore, it is quite reasonable to look further afield, and consider flight to the stars.

Interstellar flight has been discussed quite seriously of late, but various points must be made immediately. First, there is no prospect of landing a probe on any star. A star is a sun, with an intensely hot gaseous surface, and so cannot be approached. If there are to be any target worlds beyond the Solar System, they must take the form of extra-solar planets; that is to say, planets moving round other stars.

Secondly, the flight-time would be immensely long. Even the nearest star beyond the Sun lies at a distance of more than 4 light-years, which is roughly equal to 24,000,000,000,000 (24 million million) miles. A probe sent up at a speed we now regard as practicable would take a vast period to reach its objective—even if it could be tracked and guided, which of course it could not. If we are to launch interstellar probes, then we must make use of nuclear power.

Thirdly, our guidance and communications techniques will have to be improved beyond all recognition before any interstellar experiments are tried. Otherwise, the whole operation will be futile from the outset. It is pointless to send a probe toward a distant star if we know that it will go out of our range before it has completed more than the tiniest fraction of its journey.

For the moment, let us forget about trifles such as the difficulty of working up to sufficient velocity, and consider which star-systems are likely targets. We must naturally deal with a star which is likely to have a planet or planets moving round it, and our first difficulty is that we do not know just what the prospects are. Planets are relatively small, non-luminous bodies, and so cannot be detected visually over great distances. The photograph on this page shows many stars, each of which is a sun but each of which looks like nothing more than a tiny dot of light. Obviously, there is no chance of seeing a body millions of times fainter and very close to its parent sun.

However, there is another line of attack. If a relatively nearby star of low mass (low, that is to say, by stellar standards) has a massive planet moving round it, then the individual or 'proper' motion of the star may be affected. Instead of moving in a straight line against the background of more distant stars, it will seem to wobble. The effect is very slow and slight, and cannot be detected except by photographic measurements made over a period of years, but in several cases it has been detected. The most spectacular success has been with Barnard's Star, which is our nearest

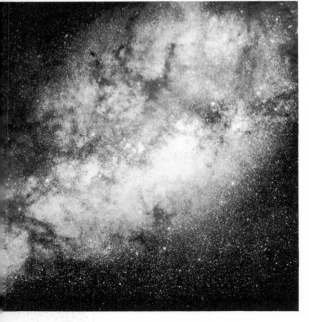

STAR-CLOUDS. Star-clouds in the Milky Way, photographed with the 60in. reflector at Mount Wilson Observatory, California.

stellar neighbour apart from Proxima and Alpha Centauri, and which is 6 light-years away. Researches by P. van de Kamp and his colleagues have proved that Barnard's Star is attended by an invisible body whose mass is only about $2\frac{1}{2}$ times that of Jupiter, and which is presumably a planet.

Incidentally, Barnard's Star has the greatest proper motion known, and travels across the sky by 10.27 seconds of arc per year. This is not very much, and it takes the star 180 years to cover a distance equal to the apparent diameter of the Sun or Moon, but it is easily measurable, and has led to the star being given the nickname of 'the Runaway'.

There are a few other cases, too, of stars known to be accompanied by invisible bodies, but it is perhaps dangerous to claim that these bodies are planets in the usually-accepted sense of the term. Moreover, it is hopeless to try to detect a planet of Earth mass. Only a giant planet, probably superior to Jupiter, will have a pull strong enough for it to produce a measurable wobble in the proper motion of even a lightweight star.

However, the evidence as it stands at present does indicate that planet-families are common, and there is a reasonable chance that several of the nearer stars are the centres of such families. But if we want to arrive on a planet which has any prospect of being inhabited, we must start by choosing the right sort of sun. The dim red dwarf stars are unsuitable candidates, and so are the very hot, massive stars; we need a star as much like our Sun as possible, and there are none of these in our immediate part of the Galaxy. Let us, then, list all the stars which lie within a radius of 14 light-years of us, omitting the red dwarfs (of which there are more than a dozen) and also the two exceptional objects of the type known as White Dwarfs, which are fascinating indeed but which need not concern us at the moment. The list is as follows:

STAR TRAILS. This photograph was taken by Peter Gill on 16 November 1966, and shows the constellation of Leo. The camera was fixed, so that the stars appear as trails. The exposure lasted for 10 minutes.

Star-clouds in the Andromeda Galaxy, photographed with the 100in. reflector also at Mount Wilson. It will be seen that the two are strictly comparable. The Andromeda Galaxy, at a distance of 2,200,000 light-years, is rather similar to our Galaxy, but is decidedly larger.

Star	Distance, light-years	Luminosity, Sun = 1		Remarks
Alpha Centauri	4.3	1.1	0.2	Binary system. Proxima, at 4.2 light-years, is a far-out member of the Alpha Centauri group.
Sirius	8.6	26		Hot white star with a faint White Dwarf companion.
Tau Ceti	10.2	0.35		Orange star.
Procyon	10.4	5.5		Yellow star with a very faint companion.
Epsilon Eridani	10.5	0.31		Orange star.
61 Cygni	11.2	0.06		Binary, made up of two faint red stars, one of which has an invisible companion which may be a massive planet.
Epsilon Indi	11.6	0.17		Orange star.

Of these, 61 Cygni is a red dwarf system, but seemed worth including because it is of special interest (it was also the first star to have its distance measured, by the German astronomer F. W. Bessel as long ago as 1838). However, the most 'sun-like' stars in the list are Tau Ceti and Epsilon Eridani, both of which are clearly visible to the naked eye. Were we able to launch an interstellar probe, then one of these two stars would be a probable target. Neither is known to have a planet associated with it, either Earth-

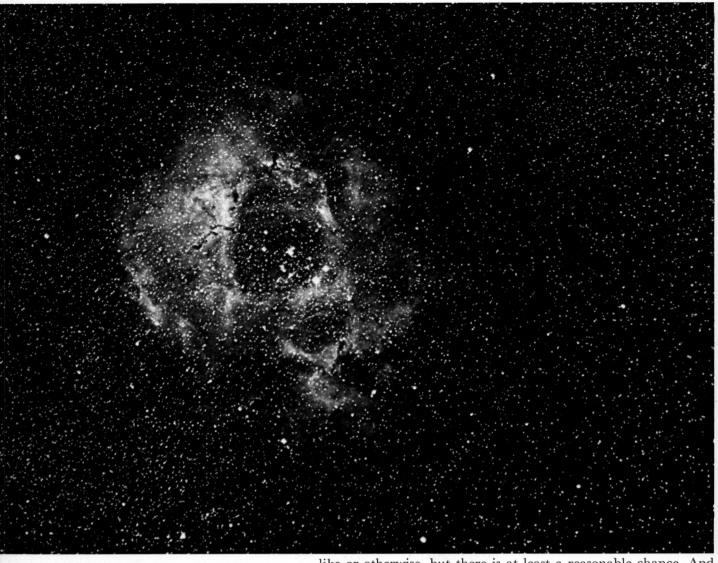

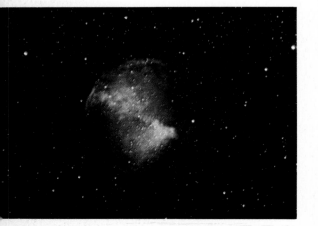

like or otherwise, but there is at least a reasonable chance. And yet . . . how can it be done?

The answer, so far as our present-day science is concerned, is that it cannot. Let us repeat that a chemically-fuelled vehicle would take much too long on the journey even if it could be tracked and guided. An alternative is to use the 'ion motor', which depends upon nuclear power, and which can – in theory – provide acceleration over a long period of time, so that the final velocity will be extremely high. But devices of this sort lie in the future so far as probes are concerned, and there is, in any case, an apparent limit to the velocity that can be reached.

According to modern theory, the greatest possible velocity is that of light: 186,000 miles per second. For a body travelling at near this so-called optic velocity, very strange situations begin to occur. because the time-scale is altered. By everyday standards, time slows down. Moreover, there is an increase in mass. Theoretically, for a body moving at optic velocity, time will stand still and mass will become infinite. This may or may not be confirmed by future research, and astronautically it is of academic interest only, because the effects are negligible until the velocity exceeds a major fraction of that of light; so far as our present-day probes are concerned, the effects are much too small to be measured at all.

Suppose, however, that we stretch several points and consider a vehicle moving at optic velocity and setting out on a voyage to Tau Ceti and back. It will take 10.2 years to arrive, and another 10.2 to return, so that a journey begun in 1970 would not end until after New Year's Day, 1990. And Tau Ceti is, as we have noted, one of the nearest of all the stars.

I do not propose to make many further comments, because it would take me into the realm of pure speculation, and there are many people better qualified in this respect than I shall ever be. Neither do I intend to spend any time in discussing the various 'dodges', such as space-arks (in which the original crew members do not expect to live long enough to see the end of their journey, but produce children *en route* and leave the eventual landing to their remote descendants) or the deep-freeze technique (in which the luckless voyagers are put into a state of suspended animation soon after blast-off, and are conveniently woken up as they arrive at their destination centuries later). Science-fiction writers are understandably fond of space-warps, time-warps, thought-travel machines and the like, but here too there is little that can be said for the moment.

I am not claiming that interstellar travel is impossible. All I am saying is that interstellar travel is out of the question *by our present-day methods*, which is a very different thing. If we are to achieve it, we must make use of principles about which we know little or nothing as yet; and this is a problem for scientists of the coming centuries.

Efforts have been made to pick up radio signals transmitted by beings living elsewhere in the Galaxy. In 1960 radio astronomers at Green Bank, West Virginia, initiated the famous Project Ozma, in which they listened-out for any signals which might be of artificial origin. The wavelength chosen was 21.1 centimetres, which is the wavelength of the radiation emitted by the clouds of hydrogen scattered through the Galaxy, and which would presumably be under study by radio astronomers wherever they might live; the stars selected for special attention were Tau Ceti and Epsilon Eridani, our two most likely candidates as nearby centres of planetary systems. Deliberate transmissions were also made at 21.1 centimetres during the Ozma series. Nothing came of it—and nobody seriously expected anything else; it is a measure of our changed attitude that the experiment was regarded as worth trying at all. Whether it will be repeated in the future remains to be seen.

There can never be any prospect of a rapid exchange of information between the Earth and beings living on an extra-solar planet. Quite apart from the difficulty of interpretation, radio signals travel at the same speed as light, and so would be years on their journey. The most that could ever be done would be to establish that other civilizations do exist—and if this were accomplished, then it might just be worth while attempting an unmanned, nuclear-powered interstellar probe vehicle. This sounds a wild scheme at the moment, but perhaps no wilder than the Luna and Surveyor projects would have sounded to George Washington or Horatio Nelson.

THE PLEIADES. This cluster is easily visible to the naked eye; it lies in Taurus (the Bull) and is known popularly as the 'Seven Sisters'. This photograph of it was taken with the 48in. Schmidt at Palomar Observatory. People with average eyesight can see at least 7 stars with the naked eye; people with keen eyes can see more—the record is said to be 19! This is the finest example of a loose or open cluster; it contains over 200 members and also a beautiful reflection nebula. The brightest star is Alcyone, of the 3rd magnitude. All the leading stars in the Pleiades are hot white stars of the Main Sequence.

Conclusion

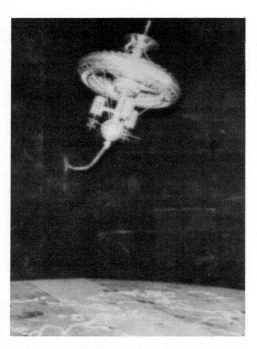

RUSSIAN SPACE-STATION DESIGN.
This pattern dates from 1959, when it was still thought that an orbital station, manned by a full crew, would be an essential preliminary to a Moon voyage. This is not now thought to be the case, and whether a permanent station of this sort will ever be constructed remains to be seen.

Fifty years ago, space research lay in the future; ideas of flight to the Moon were dismissed as idle dreams. Then came the first scientific rockets, feeble and unreliable, but good enough to hold out some hopes. Next, rockets soared to the upper part of the atmosphere; next they penetrated almost into 'space'. Artificial satellites were sent up, and manned orbital vehicles followed. Probes were dispatched Moonward, to Mars and Venus, and even beyond. The idea of a research base on the lunar surface became part of Government planning, and the Space Age had well and truly started.

The practical exploration of space is clearly of tremendous importance in itself, but there are other considerations to be borne in mind as well. We do not know nearly as much about the universe as we would like to do, and observations carried out from above the atmosphere will certainly provide us with a great deal of extra knowledge.

To show the extent of our limitations, let us consider two developments of the past decade. It has long been known that the objects once called 'starry nebulæ' are in fact external galaxies, in every way comparable with the Galaxy in which we live, but astronomers had thought that no entirely new classes of objects would be found. They were wrong. In 1963 some innocent-looking star-like images were found to be strong radio emitters, and to be immensely remote as well as almost inconceivably luminous. They were christened quasars, and remain very much of a mystery. If our present ideas are correct, then one quasar may shine as brilliantly as 200 whole galaxies put together. Just how it manages to produce this flood of energy is a problem which we simply cannot answer—yet.

Quasars were surprising enough, but they were rivalled in 1968 by the pulsars, which are rapidly-vibrating radio sources within a few hundreds of light-years of us. The first pulsars were found by the radio astronomers at Cambridge, and seemed so remarkable that for a few days the idea of intelligent transmission from beyond the Solar System was taken seriously. Pulsars have not proved to be as significant as that, as there is now no doubt that their signals are of natural origin; and yet—what *is* a pulsar? Again we have to confess that we do not know. Pulsars belong to our Galaxy, quasars are extragalactic; they are equally baffling, and it is worth noting that both were completely unsuspected as recently as the early nineteen-sixties.

If quasars and pulsars can arrive on the scene to take us so much by surprise, there may well be many other kinds of objects which are equally important but which we have not yet identified. This is where space research methods ought to help. They can free us from the restrictions imposed by our atmosphere, and they can lead us on to a better understanding of the universe.

Of one thing we may be sure; despite the tremendous advances made since the start of the Space Age, we are still only at the beginning. We cannot yet see what lies ahead; only time will tell.

The First Twenty-five Artificial Satellites

To list all the artificial satellites launched since 4 October 1957 would be pointless in a book of this kind, but it may be of historical interest to give the first few, and I have listed details of the original twenty-five. The Sputniks are Russian, while all the others are American.

An asterisk indicates that the satellite was still in orbit at the beginning of 1968, but will decay in the foreseeable future. A dash indicates that the satellite will stay aloft for a long time to come.

Date	Satellite	Lifetime	Date of descent	Weight, lb.	Initial height (miles)		Initial period minutes
					Perigee	Apogee	
1957							
Oct. 4	Sputnik 1	92 days	1958 Jan. 4	184	135	587	96
Nov. 3	Sputnik 2	162 days	1958 April 14	10,000 ?	134	1,034	104
1958							
Feb. 1	Explorer 1	± 10 years	*	31	224	1,585	115
Mar. 17	Vanguard 1	300 years	—	3	407	2,466	134
Mar. 26	Explorer 3	93 days	1958 June 28	31	119	1,741	116
May 15	Sputnik 3	692 days	1960 April 6	2,926	135	1,163	106
July 26	Explorer 4	454 days	1959 October 23	39	167	1,378	110
Dec. 18	Score	$33\frac{1}{2}$ days	1959 Jan. 21	8,700	118	924	101
1959							
Feb. 17	Vanguard 2	150 years	—	22	350	2,065	126
Feb. 28	Discoverer 1	About 5 days	1959 Mar. 5 ?	1,362	102 ?	608 ?	96 ?
April 13	Discoverer 2	13 days	1959 April 26	1,638	153	217	90
Aug. 7	Explorer 6	23 months ?	About 1961 July	142	160	26,400	765
Aug. 13	Discoverer 5	46 days	1959 Sept. 28	1,721	138	462	94
Aug. 19	Discoverer 6	62 days	1959 Oct. 20	1,726	133	532	95
Sept 18	Vanguard 3	±300 years	—	100	321	2,329	130
Oct. 13	Explorer 7	70 years	—	92	348	678	101
Nov. 7	Discoverer 7	19 days	1959 Nov. 26	1,750	103	527	95
Nov. 20	Discoverer 8	108 days	1960 March 8	1,753	118	1,046	104
1960							
April 1	Tiros 1	60 years	—	270	431	471	99
April 13	Transit 1B	$7\frac{1}{2}$ years	*	267	241	460	96
April 15	Discoverer 11	10.9 days	1960 April 26	1,750	107	369	92
May 15	Sputnik 4	$844\frac{1}{2}$ days	1962 Sept. 5	6,000	183	422	94
May 24	Midas 2	20 years	—	5,000	302	321	94
June 22	Transit 2A	150 years	—	223	392	655	102
June 22	Greb 1	80 years	—	42	385	662	102

Some Important Dates in The History of Rocketry and Space Research

BC
360 Flying Pigeon of Archytas.
250? Heron's aeolipile.

AD
150? Lucian's *True History* (first Moon-voyage story).
1232 Rockets used at the siege of Kai-fung-fu.
1405 Von Eichstädt writes about sky-rockets.
1420 Various rocket designs proposed by Fontana.
1591 Von Schmidlap's book about non-military rockets.
1634 Publication of Kepler's *Somnium*.
1638 Publication of Godwin's *Man in the Moone*.
1657 **Cyrano's** reference to 'fire-crackers' in his novel.
1668 Rocket experiments by Christoph von Geissler.
1781 Rockets used by Hyder Ali against the British forces in India.
1783 First manned balloons.
1792-99 Further use of military rockets against the British in India.
1801 Rocket experiments carried out by Congreve.
1806 First major rocket bombardment (Boulogne).
1807 Heavy rocket attack by the British on Copenhagen.
1813 British Rocket Corps formed, and in action near Leipzig.
1814 British Rocket bombardment of Fort McHenry, in the United States.
1865 Publication of Verne's novel *From the Earth to the Moon*.
1866 Austrian Rocket Corps routed by the Prussians, and disbanded in 1867.
1881 Last use of old-type military rockets, by the Russians in Turkestan.
1881 Early space-craft design by Kibaltchitch.
1891 Hermann Ganswindt delivers a public lecture about space-travel.
1895 Tsiolkovskii submits his first space-flight article.
1898 High-altitude meteorological balloon experiments by de Bort.
1903 Publication of Tsiolkovskii's first important article about rocketry.
1911 Further important articles by Tsiolkovskii published.
1916 Small French rocket weapons used against the German Zeppelins.
1919 Goddard's monograph *A Method of Reaching Extreme Altitudes*.

1922 Goddard carries out his first tests with liquid-fuel rocket motors.
1924 Publication of Oberth's classic book *The Rocket into Interplanetary Space*
1926 Goddard successfully launches his first liquid-propellant rocket.
1927 Formation of the VfR.
1929 Fiasco of the Oberth Rocket and the film *Frau im Mond*.
1930 Formation of the American Interplanetary Society (now the A.R.S.)
1931 Successful liquid-propellant rocket firing by Winkler in Germany.
1932 First rocket tests at Kummersdorf.
1933 Foundation of the British Interplanetary Society, by P. E. Cleator.
1937 First rocket tests at Peenemünde.
1942 Successful test of the A.4 (=V.2) rocket at Peenemünde.
1943 Peenemünde bombed and badly damaged by the R.A.F.
1944 First V.2 rockets launched against England.
1945 A.9 rocket from Peenemünde reaches 50 miles, and attains 2,700 m.p.h.
  Last V.2s fall upon England.
  Peenemünde captured by the Russians; leading German scientists taken by the Allies.
  White Sands Proving Ground established.
  Arthur Clarke's communications-satellite article in *Wireless World*.
1946 Captured V.2s taken to White Sands; first launching in June, to 67 miles.
1947 Woomera Rocket Range established.
1948 The Forrestal Report.
1949 First Viking launch from White Sands.
  V.2-WAC Corporal combination from White Sands reaches nearly 250 miles.
  V.2 from White Sands sent up to 132 miles.
  First tests at Woomera.
  Rocket testing ground established at Cape Canaveral.
1950 First rocket launching from Cape Canaveral.
1951 Viking 7, from White Sands, sent up to 135 miles.
1955 Announcement of the United States Vanguard project.
1957 OCTOBER 4. LAUNCHING OF SPUTNIK 1 BY THE U.S.S.R. BEGINNING OF THE SPACE AGE.
1957 Launching of massive vehicle Sputnik 2 (U.S.S.R.).

1957	Unsuccessful Vanguard firing in the U.S.A.
1958	First successful American satellite (Explorer 1).
	First successful Vanguard launching.
	Discovery of the Van Allen Zone.
	Tests with Pioneer rockets (pre-lunar probes).
1959	Russians launch Lunik 1 (first probe to go near the Moon).
	Lunik 2 (first crash-landing on the Moon).
	Far side of the Moon photographed with the probe Lunik 3.
1960	First television weather satellite (Tiros 1).
	Russians launch Sputnik 4, a dummy space-ship.
1961	First Venus probe launched by the Russians, but contact soon lost.
	First manned space-flight (Gagarin, U.S.S.R.)
	First manned American space-flight (Shepard, sub-orbital).
1962	First American orbital flight (Glenn).
	First British-built satellite (Ariel) launched from the U.S.A.
	Transatlantic television programmes relayed by the Telstar satellite.
	First active geodetic satellite (Anna 1B).
	Russians launch the first Mars probe, but contact lost.
	Venus probe Mariner 2 sends back close-range information about Venus.
1963	First manoeuvrable satellite (Polyot 1, U.S.S.R.).
	Two space-craft in orbit at the same time (Nikolayev and Popovich, U.S.S.R.).

1963	First space-woman (Valentina Tereshkova-Nikolayeva, U.S.S.R.).
1964	Close-range photographs of the Moon obtained from Ranger 7 (U.S.A.).
	First three-crew space-craft (Voskhod 1, U.S.S.R.).
1965	First 'space-walk' (Leonov, U.S.S.R.).
	First American 'space-walk' (White).
	Close-range photographs of Mars obtained from Mariner 4 (U.S.A.).
	Improved photographs of the Moon's far side obtained from Zond 3 (U.S.S.R.).
	Successful space-docking operation (Gemini 6 and 7, U.S.A.).
1966	First soft landing on the Moon, by Luna 9 (U.S.S.R.).
	Russian probe Venus 3 lands on Venus, though contact had been lost.
	First circum-lunar probe, Luna 10 (U.S.S.R.).
	First American soft-landing on the Moon (Surveyor 1)
	Improved close-range photographs of the Moon from the U.S. Orbiters.
1967	Disaster at Cape Kennedy, resulting in the deaths of three astronauts.
	Death of Colonel **Komarov** in Soyuz 1.
	First soft-landing on Venus (U.S.S.R.).
1968	Testing of the American Saturn 5 rocket (Project Apollo).
	First recovery of circum-lunar probe, Zond 5 (U.S.S.R.).

Photographic Illustrations

Acknowledgement has already been given, on page 7, to those who so generously gave of their time to obtain photographs with which to illustrate this work. The publishers and author wish to thank the following for the right to reproduce photographs (indicated here by page numbers and letters to show the position on the page where more than one photograph appears) of which they control the copyright:

F. J. Acfield: 202.

A. D. Andrews: 13B.

Associated Press: 195B.

Australia News and Information Service: 84A.

W. M. Baxter: 90, 109.

Boeing Co. of California: 197.

The British Broadcasting Corporation: 117A and B.

Henry Brinton: 19, 180.

The Trustees of the British Museum: 28A and 29.

Arthur C. Clarke: 82.

P. E. Cleator: 73A, 73B, 74.

F. Collard: 139C.

Crown Copyright: 101B.

Daily Express Newspapers: 93.

Peter Gill: 115A, 115B, 205A.

K. Gottlieb: 9B.

Cdr. H. R. Hatfield, R.N.: 18, 145, 154, 199.

The Hulton Picture Library: 58, 59.

The Trustees of the Imperial War Museum: 80, 81.

E. M. Lindsay: 15.

Dr. G. J. H. McCall: 149A, 149B.

The Mansell Collection: 16A, 16B.

Mount Wilson and Palomar Observatories: 204, 205B, 206A, 206B, 207.

The National Film Archives: 57.

The Trustees of the National Portrait Gallery: 57.

The New York Sun Newspapers: 67, 68.

Novosti News Agency: 60B, 62A, 64, 95A, 96A, 101A, 104, 108, 120-121, 124B, 128, 129A, 129B, 132B, 133A, 133B, 139B, 140A, 140B, 141, 144, 153A, 153B, 156A, 156B, 156C, 157B, 157C, 161, 168A, 168B, 186-187, 188A, 188B, 193A, 208.

Prof. H. Oberth: 71.

James Paton: 107.

H. B. Ridley: 13A.

The Royal Aircraft Establishment: 121B.

Tass: 96B, 125D, 132A.

Umschau Verlag: 75A, 75B, 76.

United States Information Service: Endpaper, Title Page, 8, 40-41, 48, 51, 54, 55, 60A, 65, 66, 69, 70, 84B, 85, 86, 92, 113, 114, 116A, 116B, 120, 121A, 122, 123, 124A, 125A, 125B, 125C, 126A, 126B, 126D, 127E, 128B, 130A, 131A, 134A, 134-135B, 134-135C, 136A, 136B, 137, 138, 139A, 142A, 142B, 143, 147A, 147B, 152, 157A, 158A, 158B, 159A, 159B, 160, 162B, 163A, 163B, 164-165, 168C, 169, 173A, 173B, 174-175, 176A, 176B, 177A, 177B, 178, 185, 189, 193B, 195A, 196.

U.S.S.R. Academy of Sciences: 9A.

The remaining photographs were supplied by the author, but in some cases it has proved impossible to trace the copyright holder; in these instances the publishers offer their apologies should any rights be inadvertently infringed.

Index

A3, 77
A4, 78-9
A9, 81
Aerobee rockets, 84
Aldrin, E., 142
Alexandrian Library, 22
Alfvén, H., 105
Almagest, 22
Alphonsus (lunar crater), 164, 165, 166
American Rocket Society
   (=American Interplanetary Society), 76
Andromeda Spiral, 15, 205
Ångström unit, 45
Anna 1B, 115
Anti-gravity devices, 38
Apollo programme, 139, 174-5, 177
Aquarius, figure of, 17
Arab astronomy, 22-3
Ariel satellite, 123
Aristarchus, 23
Armstrong, N., 142
Artificial satellites, 87 ff
—decay in atmosphere, 89
—earliest, list of, 208-9
—eclipses of, 102
—manœuvrable, 123, 141-2
—orbits of, 88, 90-1
—principles of, 87-8
Ashen Light of Venus, 181, 184
Asteroids, *see* Minor Planets
Astrology, 22, 25
Astronauts, training of, 126-7, 128
Atmosphere, density of, 99, 113
—extent of, 23, 26, 42
—gases in, 41, 45-7
—of other planets, 41-2
—structure of, 44
Auroræ, 47, 109
Austrian Rocket Corps, 59

Bailly (lunar crater), 154
Baker-Nunn Camera, 101
Baldwin, R. B., 195
Balloons, 42-4
—scientific, 42, 49, 52
Barnard's Star, 204
Barometers, 42
Barwell Meteorite, 111
Beer, W., 32, 35, 148
Belyayev, P., 141
Bessel, F. W., 205
Birkeland, O., 107
Black Knight, 121
Blanchard, 42
Boulogne, bombardment of, 57-8
Bykovsky, V., 140

Callisto, 210
Canaveral, Cape, *see* Kennedy, Cape

Canopus, 195
Cassini, G. D., 25
Casualties in astronautics, 136-7, 142, **144**, **178**
Cavorite, 38
Chaffee, R., 137
Cherwell, Lord (F. A. Lindemann), 77
Chudakov, V., 104
Clarke, A. C., 82, 90, 117-8, 120, 202
Clarke orbits, 118-9
Cleator, P. E., 76, 117
Columbiad, 33-7, 88
Comets, 13, 17
—Arend-Roland, 15
—Biela's, 108
—Encke's, 108
—Halley's, 13, 108
—Ikeya-Seki, 13, 108
—tails of, 108-9
Communications satellites, 90, 117-21, **123**
Congreve rockets, 57-8
Conrad, C., 142-3
Contamination, dangers of, 187, 199
Cooper, G., 143
Copenhagen, bombardment of, 58
Copernicus, 23-4
Copernicus (lunar crater), 158
Cosmic rays, 103-5, 111
Cosmos satellites, 111, 123
Crater Lake,   149
Cunningham, W., 177

De Bort, T., 42, 44
Deimos, 191
Dornberger, W., 76, 77-80

Early Bird satellite, 100, 119
Earth, seen from Moon, 158
—shape of, 16, 115
—status of, 10
Echo satellites, 98, 99, 121, 123
Eclipses, lunar, 25
Eclipses, solar, seen from Moon, 159, 171
Ecosphere, 198
Eisele, D., 177
Eisenhower, General, 118
Electromagnetic spectrum, 47
Epsilon Eridani, 205
Eratosthenes, 16
Escape velocity, 36-7, 39, 54
Europa, 201
Explorer **1**, 103, 110, 111
—**2** and **3**, 104
—**6** (Paddle-Wheel), 121
—**18** (Imp-1), 123
—**29** (Geos A), 116
Eyraud, A., 61

"Fireflies", 135
Flat Earth Society, 85

Flying Saucers, 32
Fontana, J., de, 57
Forman, F., 130
Forrestal Report, 92
Fort McHenry, bombardment of, 58
French satellites, 123

Gagarin, Y., 9, 60, 124, 129, 131-3
Galaxy, shape of, 14
Galaxies, outer, 14-15
Galileo, 24-6
Gambier, Lord, 58
Gamma-rays, 187
Ganswindt, H., 61-3, 74
Ganymede, 201
Geiger counters, 103, 111, 194
Gemini programme, 137-44
Geodetic satellites, 115
Geos A (Explorer **29**), 116
Glenn, J., 128, 133, 135, 136, 165
Goddard, R. H., 64, 65-70, 71, 153
Godwin, Bishop, 27-30
Gordon, R., 142
Greek astronomy, 16-7
Grissom, V., 131, 133, 137
Gruithuisen, F., 181
Guericke (lunar crater), 166
Gusmão, Father, 42

Hale, W., 58
Halley's Comet, 13, 108
Hansen's theory, 37, 155
Harriot, T., 148
Heaviside, O., 45
Heraclitus, 16
Hermes, 200
Herschel, J., 31-2
Herschel, W., 31
Hewitt Camera, 101
Hipparchus, 16
Hitler, A., 69, 78
Hohmann Orbits, 181
Huygens, C., 191
Hyder Ali, 57
Hyginus Cleft, 157

I.A.F., 86
I.G.Y., 92
Icarus, 200-1
Icarus legend, 21
Imp-1 (Explorer **18**), 123
Indian rockets, 57
Interplanetary material, 47
Interstellar travel, 14, 204-7
Io, 201,
Ionosphere, 45-7

Japanese space programme, 123
Jeffries (balloonist), 42
Jesse, O., 47
Jodrell Bank, 95, 102, 153, 168, 185
Jupiter, 199, 200-1
—satellites of, 200-1

Kai-fung-fu, siege of, 56
Kennedy, Cape (Cape Canaveral), 85, 97, 103, 183
Kenelly-Heaviside Layer, 45

Kepler, J., 24-5, 26, 28-9
Kepler (lunar crater), 159
Kepler's Laws, 24-5, 155
King-Hele, D., 99
Kibaltchitch, N. I., 61
Komarov, V., 144
Kozirev, N., 166
Kryakutny, 42
Kuiper, G., 181, 202
Kummersdorf station, 77

LaPaz, L., 111
Laika, 96-7
Lang, F., 73
Leonov, A., 139, 141
Ley, W., 62, 73, 76
Librations, lunar, 155
Life, extraterrestrial, 199
Light-years, 14
Lilienthal, O., 60
Liquid fuels, 63
Locke, R., 31-2
Lovell, Sir B., 153, 185
Lowell, P., 189-92
Lucian, 17, 20-1
Luna **1**, 152
—**2**, 153
—**3**, 153, 155-6, 162
—**5** to **8**, 167
—**9**, 167-9
—**10**, 157, 161
—**12**, 161
—**13**, 169-70
—**14**, 161
Luniks, *see* Luna

Mädler, J. H., 32, 35, 148
Magdeburg Experiment, 76
Magnetic field of Earth (magnetosphere), 105-8, 123
Man in the Moon, 18
Mariner **1**, 183
—**2**, 181, 184-6
—**3**, 193
—**4**, 194-7
—**5**, 188
Mars, 12, 24, 42, 189-92
—atmosphere of, 189, 196-7, 203
—canals, 189-91
—craters on, 195-6
—description of, 189-92
—journeys to, 54
—life on ?, 189, 197, 199
—polar caps of, 191-2
—probes to, 181, 192-7
—probes to, list of, 193
Mars **1**, 193
Mass ratio, 67
Menzel, D.H., 182
Mercury, 199-200
Mercury, Project, 128
Meteor crater, 110, 148
Meteorites, 13, 111
Meteorology, 49, 113
Meteors, 13, 47, 111-2
Micrometeorites, 111-2
Minor Planets, 200-1

Mirak rockets, 74-75
Montgolfier Brothers, 42-3
Moon, 12
—atmosphere of, 39
—bases on, 203
—description of, 146-8
—dust on ?, 149, 163, 168
—far side of, 155-7
—Greek ideas about, 18-21
—probes to, 145 ff
—soft landings on, 163 ff
Moon Hoax, 31-2
Moonwatch, 101
MOUSE, 91-2

NASA, 128
Nebel, R., 73-4, 76, 77
Neptune, 202
'Neutral point', 35-7
Newton, Sir Isaac, 20, 24
New York Times, 65-8
Nikolayev, A., 139-40
Nimbus satellites, 115
Noctilucent clouds, 47, 51
Norton-Furnas Aerolite, 111

OSO, 120
Oberth, H., 64, 69, 71-4
Öpik, E., 195
Orbiter vehicles, 161
Ozma, Project, 207

Paddle-Wheel Satellite (Explorer 6), 121
Pageos, 116
Palomar reflector, 37
Peenemünde, 77-81, 82-3
Phobos, 191
Pioneer probes, 150, 152
Planets, 10-13
—extraterrestrial, 204-6
Pleiades, 207
Pliny, 17
Plutarch, 18-20
Pluto, 12, 192, 202
Poincaré, H., 105
Popovich, P., 139-40
Ptolemaic Theory, 17, 23
Ptolemy, 17, 22
Pulsars, 208

Radar tracking of satellites, 102
Radio waves, 45
Raketenflugplatz, the, 75-7
Ranger probes, 157, 164-5, 166-7
Re-entry problem, 123, 129
Repulsor rockets, 75
Riccioli, J., 148, 162
Rocket Brigade, 58
Rocket cars, 74
Rockets, Chinese, 56
—early military, 57-9
—Goddard's, 68-9
—marine, 59
—principle of, 52-4
—solid-fuel, modern, 178
—upper-atmosphere, 39, 64

Rosse reflector, 14
Ruggieri, 61

Satellites, artificial, *see* Artificial satellites
Saturn, 202
Saturn rocket, 177, 179
Schiaparelli, G. V., 190
Schmidlap, J., 57, 58
Score, 118
Scott, D., 142
Shepard, A., 124, 128, 133
Shershevsky, A., 73
Shklovsky, I., 191
Singer, S. F., 92
Slight, J. B., 177
Solar System, 10-11, 24
—exploration of, 198-203
—origin of, 40
Solar wind, 107-8
Soyuz 1, 144
Space-arks, 207
Space-guns, 33-7, 52
Space-stations, 109
Space-travel, early ideas about, 17-21
Sputnik 1, 9, 93-5, 110, 198
—2, 96
—3, 104, 112
—4, 129
—5, 123, 129
Stars, the, nature of, 13
—nearest, 205
—White Dwarf, 205
Step-rockets, 63, 84-5
Sterilization, method of, 187
Størmer, C., 105
Stratosphere, the, 44, 45
Sun, the, 10, 25, 90, 92, 109
Surveyor 1, 169
—2, 169
—3, 171
—4, 177
Syncom 1, 119

Tau Ceti, 205, 207
Telstar, 99, 100, 117, 119
Temperature, definition of, 44
Tereshkova, V., 140
Thiel, Dr., 80
Time-dilation effect, 206-7
Tippoo Sahib, 57
Tiros satellites, 84, 114-5
Titan, 202
Titov, H., 133
Transit 1B, 115
Transit 3A, 136
Troposphere, the, 44
Tsiolkovskii, K. E., 61-4, 71, 162
Tycho Brahe, 24
Tycho (lunar crater), 36

Uranus, 202

V.1, 80
V.2, 78-9, 80-1, 82-4
VfR, 73-6
Valier, M., 73, 74

Van Allen, J., 104
Van Allen Zone, 104-5, 107-9, 110, 121
Van de Kamp, P., 205
Vanguard, 86-7, 92, 97, 98
Vanguard **2**, 113, 115
Venus, 12, 42
—atmosphere of, 181-2, 188
—description of, 180
—from Moon, 177
—life on ?, 181, 199
—probes to, 180-8
—probes to, list of, 183
—temperature of, 184, 188, 203
Venus **1**, 183
—**2** and **3**, 186
—**4**, 188
Verne, J., 35-8, 52, 61, 85, 87-8, 162
Vernov, V., 104
Vesta, 201
Viking rockets, 85
Von Braun, W., 76-81, 83, 86, 97, 103, 105
Von Geissler, C., 57
Von Eichstädt, K., 57
Voskhod **1**, 141
Vostok **1**, 129, 132-3
—**2**, 133

WAC Corporal, 83-5

Wan-Hoo, 60-1
Wavelength, 45
Weather satellites, 113-5
Weightlessness, *see* Zero Gravity
Wellington, Duke of, 58
Wells, H. G., 38, 162
West Ford Experiment, 124
White, E., 134, 135, 137
White Sands, 83-5
Whipple, F. L., 182
Wildt, R., 182
Wilkins, Bishop, 29, 30
Wind tunnel, Tsiolkovskii's, 63
Winkler, J., 73, 75
Wolf Creek Crater, 149
Woomera range, 83, 84
Wright, O., 60, 68
Wright, W., 60

Yegorov, B., 141
Young, Astronaut, 141

Zeppelins, 61
Zero Gravity, 36-7, 62, 63, 128, 132, 135
Ziolkovsky, *see* Tsiolkovskii
Zond **1**, 186
—**2**, 194
—**3**, 157, 167